Fossil Insects

An introduction to palaeoentomology

David Penney & James E. Jepson

SIRI SCIENTIFIC PRESS

ISBN 978-0-9574530-6-7
Published by Siri Scientific Press, Manchester, UK
This and related titles are available directly from the publisher at:

http://www.siriscientificpress.co.uk

Cover image: Ground beetle (Coleoptera: Carabidae) from Enspel, Westerwald, Germany. An Upper Oligocene (24.7 Ma) oil shale deposit with abundant and diverse fossils insects. Photograph kindly provided by Markus Poschmann.

Printed and bound in the UK

Authors, if you would like to publish with us please email your
proposed titles (at any stage of preparation) to:
books@siriscientificpress.co.uk
or contact us via our website
(we specialize in high quality, rapid production and short print run
titles that would tend to be overlooked by larger publishers)

CONTENTS

Acknowledgements and image credits

We are grateful to all of our palaeo/entomological colleagues who have provided information, pdfs of their research publications or who have assisted us in any other way. Unfortunately, they are far too numerous to name individually and if we tried we would no doubt omit some by mistake. We also thank the institutions listed on the next page and the curators of their fossil insect collections. In particular, we would like to thank all those who provided images for use in this book. Special thanks go to Ron Blakey (http://cpgeosystems.com/paleomaps.html) for permission to use his palaeogeographic maps, to Richard Bizley (http://www.bizleyart.com) for his fabulous palaeoenvironmental reconstructions and to Marius Veta (http://www.ambertreasure4u.com [a great source of genuine Baltic amber fossils]) for excellent photographs of Baltic amber inclusions. Several other individuals were contacted about supplying images but they were either unable (due to institutional policy) or unwilling to do so. Others did not provide the images they said they would. Nonetheless, we believe we have managed to source a broad enough scope of fossil insect taxa from diverse deposits worldwide, in order to make this volume a useful introduction to the science of palaeoentomology. Of those who did provide images, a notable contribution was made by Professor Alex P. Rasnitsyn (Moscow), a true scholar and a gentleman. So, thanks again to all those who contributed. Special thanks also go to the Linnean Society of London and the Systematics Association for a grant to DP to part support production of this work.

Image credits (and special thanks)
S. Anderson: 40–42, 159, 169, 219; J. Ansorge: 39, 132; B. Archibald (and J. Howard): 82, 156; N. Barling: 25; G. Bechly: 95, 96; R. Bizley: 5, 7, 9, 11, 13, 15, 17; R. Blakey: 4, 6, 8, 10, 12, 16; A. Brødsgaard (and H. Madsen): 177; S. Butts: 71, 72, 104; R. Coram: 38, 176; P. Craig: 90, 158, 218, 225; A. Damgaard: 239; J. Dammer: 23; O. Gallego: 73–76; 134; L. Grauvogel-Stamm: 32, 33; D.I. Green: 18, 89, 93, 94, 111, 118, 126, 129, 181, 196–200, 205, 206, 208, 210, 217, 231–234; S.W. Heads: 229; C. & H. Hoffeins: 203; D. Huang: 195; J.-W. Janzen: 55, 110, 112, 123, 204; J. Jepson: 28–30, 34–36, 61–64, 77–81, 83, 84, 97, 103, 120, 133, 136, 139, 145, 151; E. Kaulfuss: 70; H. Kenwood: 236; D. Martill: 220, 221, 228; S. Martin: 65–69; A. McNeil: 20; E. Peñalver: 51, 52, 128; D. Penney: 3, 21, 37, 53, 54, 88, 101, 235, 237, 238; V. Perrichot: 22; G.O. Poinar Jr.: 190; M. Poschmann: 46–49; J. Prokop: 119; A.P. Rasnitsyn: 1, 56–60, 106–108, 113, 114, 124, 125, 137, 142, 148–150, 171, 173–175, 193, 194, 209, 226; A. Schmidt: 91; M. Veta: 2, 19, 26, 27, 92, 98, 109, 121, 127, 130, 131, 135, 138, 146, 147, 153–155, 157, 160–167, 170, 178–180, 182–188, 191, 192, 202, 207, 211–216, 222–224; Y. Wang: 122; S. Wedmann: 43–45, 227, 230; W. Weitschat: 201; J. Žalohar: 102; Florissant Fossil Beds National Monument: 85–87, 172; Creative Commons (Ghedohedo): 99, 100, 117, (H. Zell): 116; Creative Commons (see legend for source): 24, 31, 50, 105, 140, 141, 143, 144, 152, 168, 189, 240

Repository abbreviations

ADY: Archaeology Department, University of York, UK (specimen may be lost)
BCP: British Columbia Parks, British Columbia, Canada
BMMS: Bürgermeister Müller Museum Solnhofen, Germany
BSPGM: Bayerische Staatsammlung für Paläontologie und Geologie, Munich, Germany
CDM: Courtenay and District Museum, Courtenay, British Columbia, Canada
CNU: Capital Normal University, Beijing, China
CU: Collection unknown
CYNB: Chaoyang Bird Fossil National Geopark, Chaoyang City, Liaoning Province, China
FLFO: Florissant Fossil Beds National Monument, Colorado, USA
GDKE: Generaldirektion Kulturelles Erbe RLP, Referat Erdgeschichte, Mainz (part of the Landessammlung für Naturkunde RLP), Germany
GMCD: Geological Museum, Copenhagen, Denmark
GPIH: Geologisch-Paläontologisches Institut, University of Hamburg, Hamburg, Germany
GZG: Göttingen University Geoscience Centre, Göttingen, Germany
JM: Jura Museum, Eichstätt, Germany
KMNH: State Museum of Natural History, Karlsruhe, Germany
LGRF: Louis Grauvogel, Ringendorf, France
MCNAM: Museo de Ciencias Naturales y Antropológicas "Juan Cornelio Moyano", Mendoza, Argentina
MCZ: Museum of Comparative Zoology, Harvard, USA
MCSMB: Museo civico di Scienze Naturali di Bergamo, Italy
MfN: Museum für Naturkunde, Berlin, Germany
MGM: Museo Geominero, Madrid, Spain
MLF: Musée de Lodève, France
MMHN: Museo Municipal de Historia Natural de San Rafael, Mendoza, Argentina
MNEMG: Maidstone Museum & Bentlif Art Gallery, Maidstone, Kent, UK
MP ISEA: Natural History Museum of the Institute of Systematics and Evolution of Animals, Polish Academy of Science, Kraków, Poland
MVM: Museum of Victoria Invertebrate Paleontology collection, Melbourne, Australia
NHM: Natural History Museum, London, UK
NHMB: Naturhistorisches Museum, Basel, Switzerland
NHMS: Natural History Museum, Slovenia
NIGP: Nanjing Institute of Geology and Palaeontology, Nanjing, China
NMNH: National Museum of Natural History, Washington, USA
OU(GC): Otago University, Dunedin, New Zealand (geological collection)
PCAB: Private collection Alex Brødsgaard, Denmark
PCAD: Private collection Anders Damgaard, Denmark
PCCG: Private collection Carsten Gröhn, Germany
PCH: Private collection Christel and Hans Hoffeins, Germany (eventually to be deposited in the Senckenberg Deutsches Entomologisches Institut in Müncheberg [SDEI])
PCRC: Private collection Robert Coram, UK
PCYCT: Private collection Yap Choon Teck, Singapore
PCYW: Private collection Yinan Wang, USA
PIN: Paleontological Institute, Moscow, Russia
PMZU: Paleontological Museum, Zaragoza University, Zaragoza, Spain
PULR: Invertebrate Paleontological Collection, Universidad Nacional de La Rioja, La Rioja Province, Argentina
RCDP: Research collection David Penney, UK
RCJA: Research collection Jörg Ansorge, Germany
RCJN: Research collection John Nudds, UK
RCGP: Research collection George Poinar Jr., held at Oregon State University, Oregon, USA
SFNGM: Senckenberg Forschungsinstitut und Naturmuseum Forschungsstation Grube Messel, Messel, Germany
SMNK: Staatliches Museum für Naturkunde, Karlsruhe, Germany
SMNS: Staatliches Museum für Naturkunde, Stuttgart, Germany
WAM: Western Australian Museum, Perth, Australia
YPM: Peabody Museum of Natural History, Connecticut, USA

List of figures by order

Note added in proof: Two days before this work went to press Staniczek *et al.* (2014) erected the new fossil insect order Carbotriplurida for the enigmatic fossil *Carbotriplura kukalovae* from the Pennsylvanian of the Czech Republic. It is regarded as a possible transitional fossil link between Zygentoma and Pterygota and is considered as a putative fossil sister group of Pterygota.

List of figures by deposit

Introduction

Most people appreciate that insects are the dominant group on the planet today, in terms of both numbers of described species and numbers of individuals. Indeed, more than half of all described species are insects and they are probably more diverse now than they have been at any single point in their long geological history. They form an integral part of all terrestrial and freshwater ecosystems as pollinators, recyclers, detritivores, predators and as a food source for other animals. Some population and biomass estimates have proposed that ants alone account for 15% of the total biomass of tropical forests, weighing more than all vertebrates combined, and that termites recycle 50–100% of dead plant biomass in these habitats. However, such figures are based on rough calculations and are obviously very difficult to quantify with any degree of certainty. Nonetheless, these insects do tend to be super-abundant in the tropics. Some plants are dependent on just a single species of insect for pollination, without which they would become extinct. For example, different species of figs are pollinated by specific species of fig wasps. Other plants feed on insects. Some large mammals (e.g. anteaters) and many smaller mammal species (e.g. some bats) feed exclusively on insects. Indeed, the Earth's ecosystems as we know them, including the current lifeforms they sustain, would collapse without insects. Insects are also important as pest species of stored foods and crops, and plagues of locusts may result in dire economic and humanitarian consequences, especially in developing countries. Even in the developed world, certain species have the potential to cause staggering economic losses in the agricultural industry. Certain species (e.g. some mosquitoes and sandflies) are important vectors of debilitating or fatal diseases to both humans and livestock.

We do not know how many insect species exist on Earth at present. Estimates range from 2–100 million, with slightly more than one million formally described to date. As a result of ongoing tropical deforestation, many species of insect are going extinct before they have been discovered. Species that have already been described are also going extinct as a result of habitat loss, or are being out-competed or predated on by non-native, introduced or invasive species extending their geographical ranges as a result of climate change. Again, figures have been proposed for relatively recent insect extinctions, such as 44,000 species over the past 600 years; another proposes current extinctions at the rate of 100 species (for all groups of organsims) per day, or 36,500 species per year. Other figures for future predictions, that have appeared in the published scientific literature include 57,000 insect extinctions per million species on Earth over the next 50 years; and 100,000–500,000 insect species extinctions over the next 300 years. Most of these estimated figures are based on rates of known extinctions in better studied groups, such as birds and mammals, or extrapolations of numbers of threatened insect species from well studied faunas. However, there are many factors, such as small body size, number of individuals, short generation time, to name but a few, which may mean extinction rates of insects differ significantly from other groups, so the proposed figures need to be interpreted with caution. In reality, such unknowns are clearly very difficult to quantify, particularly as only approximately 70 cases of Recent insect species extinction have been formally documented, more than half of which relate to species of Lepidoptera. This extremely low number may seem rather bizzare given that the majority of extinctions estimated to have occurred in the geological or relatively recent past, and those predicted to occur in the future, are of insects. There are two situations in which insects may be at a higher risk of extinction than most other taxa: extinction of narrow habitat specialists and co-extinctions of parasites, specialist pollinators, etc. with the extinction of their animal or plant hosts. One recent co-extinction estimate predicted that 213,830–547,500 specialist plant-feeding insect species were committed to extinction via host extinction through habitat loss in biodiversity hotspots around the globe.

The total insect biodiversity on the planet today represents a mere 'snapshot' of their evolutionary history spanning approximately 400 million years. Thus, one thing we can be sure about is that more insect species have become extinct over geological time than exist at present. In other words, the total past insect diversity far exceeds that of the present, although for obvious reasons, most notably the long period of time and the incomplete fossil record, the number of extinct species is more difficult to estimate than that for living insects. We know that some groups (e.g. social insects) are of relatively recent origin, whereas others (e.g. Mecoptera = scorpionflies and their relatives) are relictual elements of groups that were much more diverse in the past. Even at the level of insect orders, many have become extinct over time and are known only from the fossil record. Indeed, new fossil and extant (living) insect orders are still being discovered or newly erected as a result of studying fossil insects. The extinct order Coxoplectoptera (primitive mayfly-like insects) was described in 2011 from the Cretaceous (approximately 115 million-years-old) Crato Formation of Brazil; Nakridletia was erected in 2010 for giant pterosaur parasites from the Upper Jurassic of Siberia (Fig. 1) and the Middle Jurassic of China (approximately 145–167 million-years-old), although species assigned to this order have recently been proposed to be basal aquatic Diptera of the

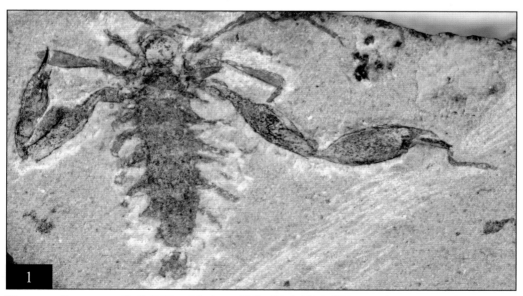

Pterosaur flea or aquatic fly? *Strashila incredibilis* ('Nakridletia'/Diptera: Strashilidae/Nymphomyiidae) in tuffaceous argillite from the Upper Jurassic, Bada Formation in the Khilok District near Mogzon, Russia. Holotype, PIN 3084-60

family Nymphomyiidae (Huang *et al.*, 2013), though not all palaeoentomologists are conviced about this. The extant suborder Mantophasmatodea (rock crawlers or gladiators) was first identified from fossils in Eocene (approximately 44–49 million-years-old) Baltic amber in 2002. Extant species were subsequently discovered in South Africa.

Given their small and fragile nature, insects do not preserve as readily as larger animals with internal, hard and bony skeletons or external, hard and calcareous shells. Hence, most people would be forgiven for expecting them to have a poor fossil record. However, amber deposits preserve insects in great abundance and with life-like fidelity (Fig. 2) and certain rock fossil localities yield exceptionally well preseved and diverse insect faunas. Together, these fossils provide tantalizing clues to the fluctuating fortunes of different insect groups since their origins in the Paleozoic, approximately 400 million years ago.

In this book we aim to provide a broadly accessible introduction to this remarkable and relatively poorly known (outside of academic circles) facet of insect biodiversity known as palaeoentomology, the scientific term for the study of fossil insects, and to illustrate the remarkable preservation of fossil insects from various deposits around the world. Those who wish to delve deeper into what the fossils can reveal, with regard to applied palaeoentomology, can do so via the more scholarly works cited throughout the text and listed at the end.

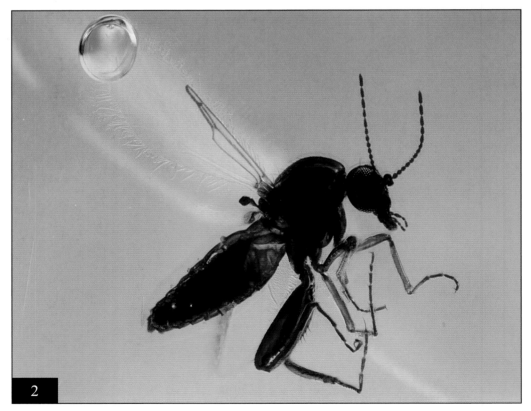

2

A biting midge *Serromyia polonica* (Diptera: Ceratopogonidae) in Eocene Baltic amber, demonstrating the truly remarkable preservational qualities of fossil resins. RCDP

A note on the geological timescale and the dating of insect fossils

Genuine fossils (as opposed to sub-fossils, see later) are usually too old to be dated using radiocarbon dating techniques, which are only effective on specimens up to approximately 60,000 years old. Usually it is the rock strata bearing the fossils, rather than the fossils themselves, that provide the means for absolute dating. The major biotic periods in the history of life on Earth are represented in the universally accepted geological timescale (Fig. 3). These periods have been defined through correlation of widespread and diverse fossils (usually marine), especially graptolites, ammonites, foraminiferans and pollen in layers of rock on a global scale. Dating of the various periods and epochs has been achieved using the known half-life (decay constant) of various different radioactive isotopes, e.g. uranium, lead, potassium, argon and carbon. An additional technique uses the geomagnetic polarity or orientation of iron oxide crystals with regard to the Earth's magnetic field when the rock was formed. However, the fossils themselves can provide clues for relative dating. For example, an assemblage with lots of extinct families can be expected to be older than one with mainly extant families.

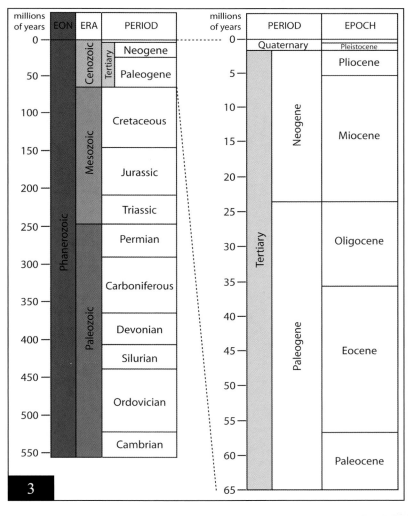

Summary of the Devonian Period

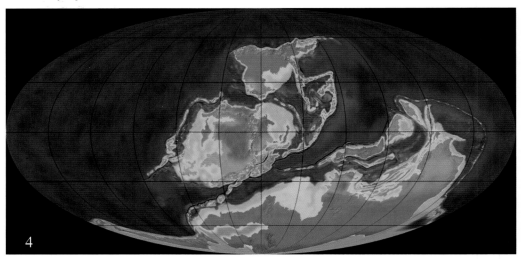

The Late Devonian, 370 MYA. © Dr Ron Blakey, used with permission

The Devonian Period was a time of much tectonic activity, including the formation of Euramerica, and the subsequent movement of Gondwana towards Euramerica on its collision course to form the supercontinent Pangaea. It witnessed the first significant terrestrial ecosystems, including seed-bearing plants and various arthropod groups in the Early Devonian, with the first land tetrapods appearing in the Late Devonian. This period ended *ca.* 359 million years ago, marked by an extinction event primarily affecting marine groups.

From a palaeoentomological perspective, the oldest fossil hexapod is an Early Devonian springtail from the Rhynie Chert of Scotland. In addition, bi-articulated mandibles, a feature only known in true insects such as silverfish (Zygentoma) and winged groups (Pterygota) have also been identified from the Rhynie deposits. The structure of the fossil mandibles bears greater resemblance to those of winged insects than silverfish, so despite the lack of direct fossil evidence, it is possible that flying insects existed as long as 400 million years ago and possibly much earlier. Additional Devonian localities with possible fossil insects include Gaspé Bay, Québec (some fragmentary samples, possibly from a bristletail (Archaeognatha), although it has been suggested this may have been contaminant material derived from an extant species) and Gilboa, New York (fragments of cuticle that may have come from bristletails or silverfish).

The painting opposite is a reconstruction of the *ca.* 410 million-years-old (Devonian) Rhynie Chert palaeohabitat from Aberdeenshire, Scotland, representing one of the earliest terrestrial ecosystems. It depicts some of the oldest hexapods (Collembola: *Rhyniella praecursor*), one of which is about to fall prey to *Palaeocharinus rhyniensis*, a member of the extinct arachnid order Trigonotarbia. The plant illustrated is *Horneophyton lignieri* (Horneophytopsida), which was an early colonizer of the hot sping sediments or sinter. The chert was formed when silica-rich water from hot springs rose rapidly, flooding the surrounding areas and permeating into the soil. © Richard Bizley

Summary of the Carboniferous Period

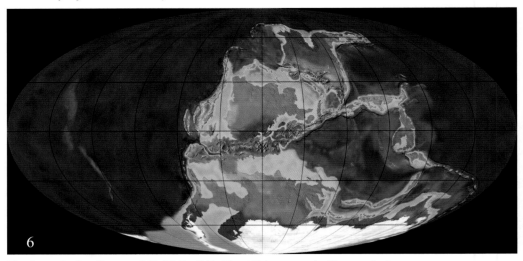

6

The Late Carboniferous, 300 MYA. © Dr Ron Blakey, used with permission

The Carboniferous Period spans approximately 61 million years. In some schemes, it is considered as two different periods: Mississippian (= Early Carboniferous) and Pennsylvanian (= Late Carboniferous). The name reflects the fact that many coal beds were formed globally during this time, deriving from the vast swathes of lowland swamp forests that covered the land, and which ultimately collapsed due to cooling and drying of the climate. It was a time of active orogenesis or mountain-building as Pangaea started to come together. Southern Gondwanaland was glaciated throughout this period due to a drop in south polar temperatures.

There is a 55 million year hiatus of palaeoentomological data from the Mid Devonian until the Early/Late Carboniferous boundary, at which point there is a sudden appearance of diverse and taxonomically informative fossil insects. The fauna was dominated by palaeopterous and 'orthopteroid' groups, supplemented by apterygotes, primitive hemipteroids and rare basal holometabolous groups. The higher oxygen content of the atmosphere (compared to the present) allowed Carboniferous insects to grow much larger than they do today. Hence, the large griffinflies (large dragonfly-like insects) often depicted in artistic reconstructions of the Carboniferous. There was a modest decrease in insect diversity at the end of this period.

The painting opposite is a reconstruction of a European Coal Measures swamp forest palaeohabitat. The vegetation consists of *Lepidodendron* trees and *Calamites* horsetails. The flying insects illustrated are giant griffinflies *Meganeura* sp. (Protodonata: Meganeuridae), and above is a member of the family Homoiopteridae (Palaeodictyoptera), which were characterized by long tails, a long beak, and flap-like pronotal paranota. A primitive roachoid *Manoblatta* sp. (Archimylacrididae) with a long ovipositor (absent in extant cockroaches) for laying eggs is resting on a *Calamites* stem. In the foreground is a primitive mesothele spider at the entrance of its burrow and in the background an amphibian has just emerged from the water. © Richard Bizley

Summary of the Permian Period

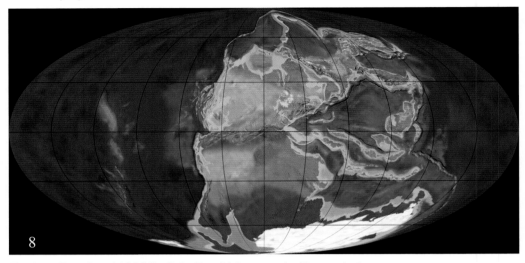

8

The Late Permian, 260 MYA. © Dr Ron Blakey, used with permission

The Permian was the last period of the Paleozoic Era and lasted for approximately 58 million years. The land consisted mainly of the supercontinent Pangaea and as the period progressed, the climate shifted from one of relictual glaciation to become hot and dry with large deserts a typical feature of the landscape. There was a change in vegetation from fern-like groups to seed-bearing gymnosperms. This period terminated with the largest extinction event in the history of life on Earth, the cause of which is hotly debated, but was probably caused by a combination of factors including volcanic eruptions of the Siberian Traps, the largest volcanic field in Earth history (MacLeod, 2013; Benton & Newell, 2014).

   From a palaeoentomological perspective, several important elements of insect evolution had been established by the end of the Paleozoic, such as flight, wing folding, complete and incomplete metamorphosis, and 60% of ecomorphological classes with regard to feeding strategies. Basal hemipteroid and holometabolous groups began to radiate in the Permian, but most of them did not survive into the Mesozoic. Some modern orders such as beetles (Coleoptera) first appear as fossils in the Permian. The end Permian mass extinction was the most important event in shaping insect diversity as we know it today. It decimated the existing entomofauna, with many groups e.g. monurans, paleodictyopteroids, protodonates, protelytropterans and caloneurodeans going extinct. However, some (e.g. the holometabolans) survived to initiate the transition from the Paleozoic insect faunas to the Mesozoic forms, resulting in the origination of many of the modern insect orders.

The painting opposite is a reconstruction of a Permian palaeohabitat from Russia. The flying insect is *Sylvohymen sibericus* (Megasecoptera: Bardohymenidae). The insect resting on the *Equisetum* horsetail is *Paleuthygramma tenuicornis* (Caloneurodea). On the rock in the foreground is the predatory arachnid *Permarachne novokshonovi* (Uraraneida: Permarachnidae). Also illustrated are two predatory synapsids, with their charateristic sail-fin backs. © Richard Bizley

Summary of the Triassic Period

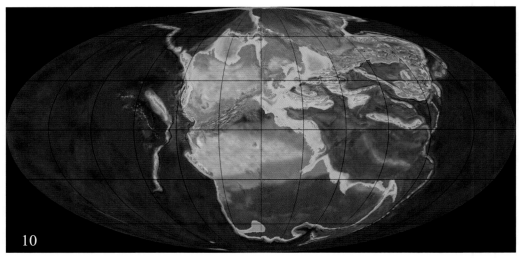

10

The Late Triassic, 220 MYA. © Dr Ron Blakey, used with permission

The Triassic Period represents the dawn of the Mesozoic and spans approximately 50 million years. From the Mid-Triassic onwards Pangaea began to rift apart forming two separate landmasses: Laurasia in the north and Gondwana in the south, although it did not split completely until the Late Triassic. The climate was mainly hot and dry, but became cooler and more moist as the two landmasses drifted apart; there is no evidence of any glaciation. The Early Triassic was very much a slow recovery phase following the end Permian extinction. This period witnessed the first frogs, true mammals and flying vertebrates (pterosaurs). It ended with an extinction event, the cause of which is not well understood, but once again probably involved a combination of factors, such as a fall in sea-level over an extended time period followed by the Central Atlantic Magmatic Province (CAMP) volcanism (MacLeod, 2013).

From a palaeoentomological perspective, the post-Permian extinction Triassic record is characterized by extremely depauperate faunas worldwide, prior to eventual rebound of taxa that are preserved in Middle and Late Triassic deposits. Very few fossil insect deposits are known from the Early Triassic. Most Triassic fossil insects belong to modern insect orders, with minimal carryover from Paleozoic lineages. Indeed, some of the first fossil records of extant plecopteran, orthopteran, dipteran, hymenopteran, coleopteran and heteropteran families derive from these deposits. Jarzembowski (2003) reviewed the entomological winners and losers with regard to the Triassic extinction.

The painting opposite is a reconstruction of a Triassic palaeohabitat from Australia. The insects in flight and in the bottom left foreground are *Clathrotitan scullyi* (Orthoptera: Clathrotitanidae). This was a large (30 cm wingspan) insect that stridulated by rubbing its wings together. Perched above to the right is a female scorpionfly *Choristopanorpa bifasciata* (Mecoptera: Parachoristidae), which was very similar to extant forms. Hanging from the vegetation (top left) is *Tillyardiptera prima* from the extinct tipulomorph-like fly family Tillyardipteridae, which is unique to the Triassic of Australia. The large herbivore is a dictynodont. © Richard Bizley

Summary of the Jurassic Period

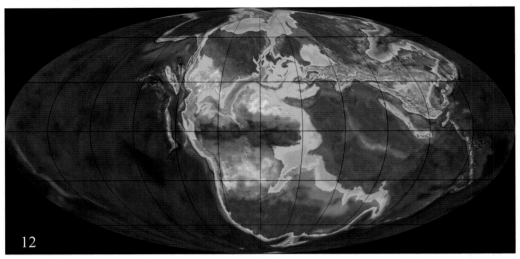

12

The Mid Jurassic, 170 MYA. © Dr Ron Blakey, used with permission

The Jurassic Period lasted for approximately 55 million years and is generally referred to as the age of reptiles. Laurasia and Gondwana existed as two distinctly separate landmasses. The Triassic deserts were replaced by rainforests and there is no evidence of any significant glaciation. Dinosaurs became the dominant large land animals. The first birds appeared in the Late Jurassic, although pterosaurs still ruled the skies. The Jurassic–Cretaceous transition is not marked by an extinction event, but rather by specific horizons from carefully selected locations.

From a palaeoentomological perspective, there appears to have been little differentiation of the insect faunas through the Triassic–Jurassic transition, with most fossil species belonging either to extinct families or stem groups of basal extant families. There is an abundance of excellent fossil insect deposits throughout Europe and Asia, including from Solnhofen, Germany, famous for its *Archaeopteryx* fossils (however, insect fossils tend to be complete, but poorly preserved), and there is a great wealth of new material being discovered in Asia, from China and Karatau, Kazakhstan. Interestingly, although amber deposits are known from the Jurassic no insect inclusions have been found to date. The Jurassic also yields the first record of many extant orders, including Lepidoptera, Raphidioptera and Notoptera.

The painting opposite is a reconstruction of a Jurassic palaeohabitat from China. The picture depicts the giant 'orb-web' spider *Mongolarachne jurassica* (Mongolarachnidae) catching a giant cicada *Palaeontinodes reshuitangensis* (Hemiptera: Auchenorrhyncha: Palaeontinidae) in its web. In the background are a pair of sauropods *Omeisaurus tianfuensis*. Drinking at the waters' edge is the earliest placental mammal *Juramaia sinensis*, whilst mayflies of the genus *Epicharmeropsis* (Ephemeroptera: Hexagenitidae) flit around above the surface. The large insect in the foreground is a large butterfly-like neuropteran *Limnogramma hani* of the extinct family Kalligrammatidae. © Richard Bizley

BIZLEY

13

Summary of the Cretaceous Period

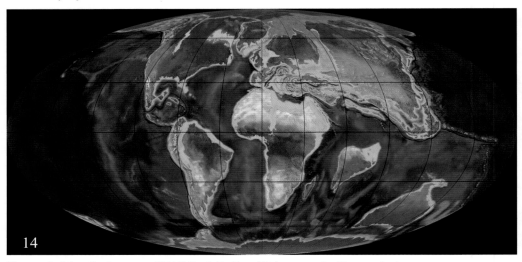

14

The end of the Cretaceous, 65 MYA. © Dr Ron Blakey, used with permission

The Cretaceous Period lasted approximately 80 million years, during which time the continents we recognize today were formed, although their positions were substantially different. The climate was relatively warm. Dinosaurs were still dominant, but new groups of mammals and birds appeared. Highly significant for this period are the origins and diversification of angiosperms or flowering plants. The Cretaceous ended with a mass extinction event famed for wiping out the dinosaurs. It is thought to have been initiated by a number of contributing events, including sea-level change, Deccan Trap volcanism and a bolide impact at Chicxulub on the Yucatán Peninsula (MacLeod, 2013).

From a palaeoentomological perspective, the fossil record is very rich, most notably as a result of Cretaceous amber deposits, but also as a result of important sedimentary deposits, such as the Crato Formation, Brazil, the Zaza Formation, Baissa (Siberia) and the Yixian Formation, China. The first eusocial bees, ants and termites first appear in the Cretaceous. Many small extant groups became much more diverse in the Cretaceous, such as Orthoptera, Neuroptera and Mecoptera, others (e.g. Coleoptera, Hymenoptera and Diptera) started increasing in diversity, prior to their rapid diversification in the Tertiary. On the whole, the insect fauna was essentially modern in terms of the orders and families represented, although there were some orders (e.g. Coxoplectoptera) and families that are now extinct.

The painting opposite is a reconstruction of the Cretaceous Crato semi-arid lagoonal palaeo-habitat from Brazil. The insects include a primitive 'mayfly' *Mickoleitia longimanus* (Coxoplectoptera: Mickoleitiidae), a pollinating wasp *Angarosphex* (*Cretosphex) parvus* (Hymenoptera: Angarosphecidae) visiting a magnolia-type flower, two antlions *Neurastenyx? cryptohymen* (Neuroptera: Myrmeleontidae), water striders *Chresmoda* sp. of the extinct order Chresmododea and a grasshopper *Cratolocustopsis* sp. (Orthoptera: Locustopsidae) about to be eaten by a sun spider *Cratosolpuga wunderlichi* (Solifugae: Ceromidae). Behind, a *Santanaraptor* looks out across the lagoon while two pterosaurs *Lacusovagus magnifens* fly overhead. © Richard Bizley

Summary of the 'Tertiary' Period

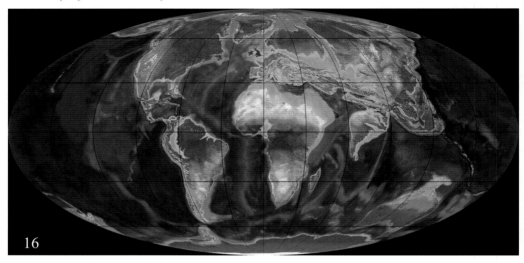

16

The Eocene, 50 MYA. © Dr Ron Blakey, used with permission

The 'Tertiary' (of traditional usage) Period is now usually spit and referred to as the Paleogene and Neogene Periods. The continents were close to their current configuration, though continental Europe consisted of an archipelago of islands. During this period sub-continental India shifted towards (and collided with) the Eurasian plate, resulting in orogenesis of the Tibetan Plateau and the Himalayas. The Paleocene–Eocene Thermal Maximum (PETM) was a time of rapid global warming (temperatures rose by about 6 °C over a period of approximately 20,000 years) and associated ecosystem change. Subsequently, the climate cooled leading to extensive glaciation at the start of the Quaternary.

From a palaeoentomological perspective, the Paleogene witnessed sustained evolutionary diversifications to fill the niches vacated by the Late Cretaceous extinctions. The modern evolutionary fauna underwent an exponential increase during this time. During the Eocene a huge sub-tropical forest ecosystem flourished througout Fennoscandia and probably extended further east and southwards (Weitschat & Wichard, 2010). This resulted in unprecedented, huge deposits of fossiliferous amber, from which more than 3500 species (mainly insects) have been described to date. Important sites in the rock record include the Green River Formation and Florrisant, USA, which have exceptionally preserved insects (including butterflies). Groups such as Lepidoptera, Diptera, Coleoptera and Hemiptera underwent great radiations throughout this period.

The painting opposite is a reconstruction of the Eocene Baltic amber forest palaeohabitat. Insects include a praying mantis (Mantodea) trapped in the fresh resin oozing from the tree, two damselflies (Odonata: Coenagrionoidea) and a rock crawler (Notoptera: Mantophasmatodea). Mayflies (Ephermeroptera) are flitting around over the water to the right and a swarm of midges (Diptera: Chironomidae) is close to the base of the tree on the left. Also on the trunk of this tree are a butterfly (Lepidoptera) and a true bug (Hemiptera). The larger animals are *Europolemur*, two *Propalaeotherium* and a flightless bird, *Diatryma*. © Richard Bizley

Insects and their fossilization

The fossil record of insects stems predominantly from lacustrine (lake) and fluvial (rivers and streams) sediments, but is supplemented in the Cretaceous and Tertiary by remarkably well preserved inclusions in amber. The oldest fossil hexapod is an Early Devonian (approximately 400 million-years-old) springtail *Rhyniella praecursor* (Collembola) from the Rhynie Chert of Scotland (Fig. 5), although confirmed evidence of the first flying insects did not appear in the known fossil record until the mid-Carboniferous. That said, bi-articulated mandibles, a feature of true insects such as silverfish (Zygentoma) and winged groups (Pterygota), have also been identified from the Rhynie Chert and described as *Rhyniognatha hirsti* (Engel & Grimaldi, 2004). Furthermore, the structure of the fossil mandibles bears greater resemblance to those of winged insects than silverfish, so despite the lack of direct fossil evidence it is possible that flying insects existed as far back as 400 million years ago. Additional Devonian localities with possible fossil insects include Gaspé Bay, Québec (some fragmentary samples, possibly from a bristletail, although it has been suggested this may have been contaminant material derived from an extant species) and Gilboa, New York (fragments of cuticle that may have come from bristletails or silverfish).

After the first 60 million years of their history, for which few fossils are known, the record is relatively rich when compared to other major terrestrial animal groups. It is not restricted to a few, easily preserved higher taxonomic groups, but consists of a wide range of extant and extinct orders. However, investigations of fossil insect diversity on a broad scale are notably few. The main reason for this is the lack of a suitable fossil species database; the last was published in 1908 by Handlirsch and recognized 5160 fossil insect species. A new database, which as of 2007 contained 23,200 fossil insect species records, is in preparation and can be found online at http://edna.palass-hosting.org, but is not yet complete enough to be useful for drawing reliable conclusions about fossil insect diversity. The completion and maintenance of this database should be deemed a priority in palaeoentomological research because it will facilitate fossil insect research at many different levels. It would permit more reliable conclusions on the changes in insect diversity throughout their long geological history and would form a basic reference point for new descriptive studies.

In addition to insects, other terrestrial arthropods such as arachnids (spiders and their relatives) (Penney & Selden, 2011; Dunlop & Penney, 2012), myriapods (centipedes and millipedes) and crustaceans (crabs, woodlice, etc) also appear in the fossil record, but tend to be less common and fall outside the remit of this book.

What are fossils and how are they preserved?
A fossil can be defined as the mineralized impression or cast of an organism (or its trace, e.g. footprints or feeding damage on leaves) from the geological past, preserved in the Earth's crust, either in rock or in amber. Insect fossils can be preserved in various different ways, each of which requires particular techniques of preparation, study and interpretation. Some insect fossils are simply preserved as flattened impressions in the rock, particularly in shales or limestones. Generally, the finer the grain of the stone, the better the quality of preservation. Such fossils tend to be rather two-dimensional, but

may retain some additional surface relief. A particular problem with shale fossils is that they can be prone to distortion, such as stretching or shearing. Hence, it is important to determine whether the appearance of a particular fossil insect might be due to tapho-nomic processes, which affected the shape of the organism during the preservation proc-ess. Other fossils may be discovered in concretions or nodules, where the animal has rotted away but has left a three dimensional impression of itself pressed into the inner walls of the nodule. This is commonly seen in specimens from the Carboniferous Coal Measures. With luck, when a nodule is split, it will reveal the upper surface of the insect in one half and its underside in the other. More unusual types of fossilization include the Early Devonian Rhynie Chert of Scotland, which includes the oldest known hexapods. Here, an entire ecosystem of plants and animals (Fig. 5) was silicified and the hard, translucent, almost glass-like chert preserves its contents in exquisite detail.

From the Cretaceous onwards, probably the richest and most important source of insect fossils is amber, as well as its younger precursor copal. Here, animals be-came trapped in sticky tree resin, which subsequently polymerized and hardened over hundreds to thousands or millions of years. Specimens trapped in amber are known as inclusions and are often very well preserved (Penney, 2010a; Penney & Green, 2011). In addition to copal, insects can also be found as sub-fossils in other localities. These specimens are usually only hundreds or thousands of years old and tend to occur in peat bogs or at archaeological sites. It is the original cuticle that remains and it is usually highly sclerotized parts (e.g. elytra) that are recovered under such circumstances. Evi-dence of insects also occurs as trace fossils in both the amber and rock fossil records.

As a very general rule of thumb, amber preserves mainly terrestrial organisms, whereas fossil insect faunas found in lithified sediments tend to be dominated by aquat-ic taxa, with the terrestrial fauna represented mainly by near-water species. As with all rules, there are exceptions. Indeed, Baltic amber contains a high proportion of aquatic species, including aquatic larvae (Wichard *et al.*, 2009).

Amber
Amber is the fossilized form of tree resin from long extinct sub/tropical forests (Fig. 17). Over millions of years the resin hardened through a progressive process of polym-erization of the original organic compounds. Any organisms, such as insects trapped in the resin became fossilized, providing us with a unique insight into prehistoric forest life (Poinar, 1992a; Poinar & Poinar, 1999; Penney, 2010a; Penney & Green, 2011). In some cases the fossil fauna is quite different to that in the region at present (e.g. Baltic amber), whereas in others (especially the younger deposits) it can be rather similar (e.g. Dominican amber). There are almost 200 known amber deposits around the world, some dating from as early as the Mid-Carboniferous (approximately 320 million years ago). Relatively few have produced abundant biological inclusions and those that do occur only in rocks of Tertiary or Cretaceous age (i.e. less than 135 million-years-old). A unique deposit of Triassic amber from Italy is known to contain tiny fossil arthropods, but only a few inclusions (one fly and several mites) have been found to date (Schmidt *et al.*, 2012). Many of the different ambers were produced by different tree families under somewhat different palaeoenvironmental conditions, yet due to the 'uniform trap-ping mechanism' of the tree resin, the different faunas they contain can be considered to

be broadly comparable in a palaeoecological context (Penney & Langan, 2006). Many insect supraspecific groups from older Cretaceous ambers are extinct, whereas many from the Tertiary still persist today.

Amber preserves insects with life-like fidelity and the degree of preservation is remarkable, in some cases including structures at the sub-cellular level, as revealed by studies using transmission electron microscopy (TEM). As a general rule, younger ambers usually exhibit a better degree of preservation than those from older deposits. Amber from the Miocene of the Dominican Republic has probably the best preservation of all (Fig. 18), although inclusions in the contemporaneous Mexican amber can sometimes be rather poorly preserved, presumably as a result of increased heat and pressure in the region resulting from tectonic activity. Inclusions in Eocene Baltic amber are also usually very well preserved, although a rather common problem with this deposit is Verlumung – a white coating that forms on the inclusion (Fig. 19), often obscuring important features of taxonomic interest. However, the relatively new application of

18

Head of a small (body length 4 mm) stingless bee *Proplebeia dominicana* (Hymenoptera: Apidae) in Miocene Dominican amber, showing the outstanding preservation of this fossil resin. PCYCT

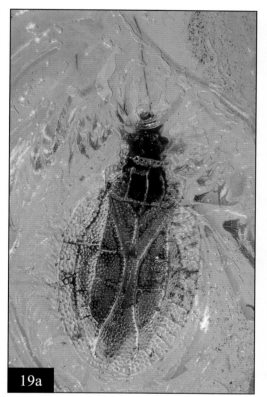 

Lace bug *Sinalda baltica* (Hemiptera: Heteroptera: Tingidae) in Eocene Baltic amber, showing the phenomenon termed Verlumung coating the underside of the specimen. RCDP

imaging techniques such as X-ray computed tomography (Fig. 20) and synchrotron scanning (Soriano *et al.*, 2010; Riedel *et al.*, 2012; Peris *et al.*, 2014; Sutton *et al.*, 2014) to amber fossils can easily overcome this problem.

Conservation of amber specimens is an issue of concern to private collectors and museum curators alike. Given the great antiquity of amber, one could be forgiven for expecting it to have achieved chemical stability and to be relatively inert. Unfortunately this is not the case and amber specimens do deteriorate over time. The major problem is oxidation of the amber, which is manifest as darkening and the formation of a crust on the surface. As degradation progresses, the surface develops cracks and fragments, a process that can be accelerated if specimens are kept in inappropriate conditions. Deterioration can be promoted by both high and low humidity levels (and especially fluctuations in humidty), and different ambers darken and craze at different rates when exposed to variations in temperature and humidity. Specimens are best kept in relatively constant anoxic conditions, although this is highly impractical for most collections. Keeping specimens in closed containers protected from exposure to light, high temperatures and fluctuating humidity lessens the rate of deterioration over time. Embedding amber samples in a high-grade epoxy (see Corral *et al.*, 1999; Nascimbene & Silverstein, 200; Hoffeins, 2001 for techniques) may be beneficial, but the long-term consequences of this are unknown (Bisulca *et al.*, 2012).

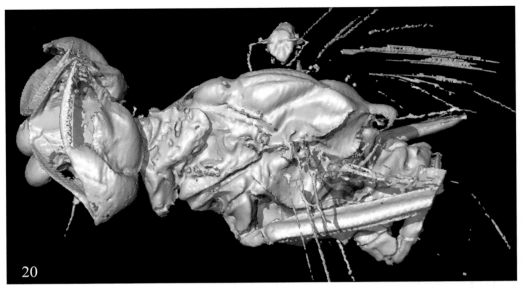

X-ray computed tomography reconstruction of the head and thorax of a mayfly (Ephemeroptera) in Miocene Dominican amber (note the phoretic springtail). RCDP

Work on the better known deposits, such as those from the Tertiary of the Dominican Republic and Baltic regions continues apace, with interesting new discoveries and ever increasing palaeontological 'data sets'. The diversity of insects preserved in amber is staggering. Even disease-vector associations are preserved, as in the microscopic trypanosomid parasites found *in situ* in their sand fly vector. The most common inclusions in amber are arthropods, especially insects. The commonest insect inclusions tend to be flies (Diptera), beetles (Coleoptera) and small wasps (Hymenoptera). Ants (Hymenoptera: Formicidae) are particularly abundant in some Tertiary ambers, but are considerably less common in Cretaceous deposits. Silverfish (Zygentoma), bristletails (Archaeognatha), true bugs (Hemiptera), termites ('Isoptera'), caddisflies (Trichoptera) and bark lice (Psocodea) are also reasonably common, although this does vary between deposits. For example, caddisflies are considerably more frequent in Baltic amber (approximately 2% of inclusions) than they are in Dominican amber (approximately 0.1% of inclusions). Lacewings (Neuroptera), crickets (Orthoptera), stoneflies (Plecoptera), mayflies (Ephemeroptera) and cockroaches (Blattodea) all have a reasonable number of species described from fossils in amber, but they are uncommon compared to the aforementioned groups.

The following orders are rarely encountered and are highly prized by collectors and scientists alike: twisted-winged parasites or stylopids (Strepsiptera), butterflies (Lepidoptera – micro-moths are more common), webspinners (Embiodea), zorapterans (Zoraptera), dragonflies and damselflies (Odonata), fleas (Siphonaptera), scorpionflies (Mecoptera) and alderflies etc. (Megaloptera). This pattern tends to hold true for most different ambers and many of these orders have not been recorded from smaller or less well studied deposits. Probably one of the most remarkable features of amber as a preservation medium is its ability to fossilize direct evidence of species interactions, described by some as frozen behaviours, and unlikely to be observed elsewhere in the fossil record (see later).

The discovery of new insect-bearing amber deposits continues. The new finds in recent years of fossiliferous Cretaceous amber deposits (including the first major deposits in Africa) have extended the known ranges of many living insect groups back to the Mesozoic. Newly discovered Tertiary deposits, including the first major deposits in Australia and India, will surely help us reconstruct major historical biogeographical processes.

Rock

Fossil insects are often found preserved in rock, with preservation varying from poorly preserved isolated wings or body parts, to exceptional preservation in which the insect is completely preserved in three-dimensions and with very fine detail retained. In contrast to amber, where all the inclusions are preserved in three dimensions, most rock compression fossils are usually visible only in two dimensions, sometimes with some surface relief. When a rock is split apart to reveal a fossil it usually results in a part and counter-part impression, i.e. the matching halves of a fossil-bearing rock matrix (Fig. 21). When split along the natural grain or cleavage of the rock a fossil embedded in the sediment may then also split down the middle, with fossil remains visible on both surfaces, or the counter-part may simply show a negative impression or mould of the fossil. It is very important to keep such specimens together, because each piece may provide important clues as to the correct identity of the fossil. However, sometimes fossil dealers may sell such specimens separately in the hope of getting more for them, whether it be to private collectors or to museums. As a consequence, it is not unknown for part and counter-part of the same fossil to end up in museums on different continents and in some instances they may even be described as separate species.

The sediment type is very important with regard to the amount of detail preserved, with finer grained sediments being the best for detailed preservation. Also of importance is the distance that the insect has travelled post-mortem to the site of depo-

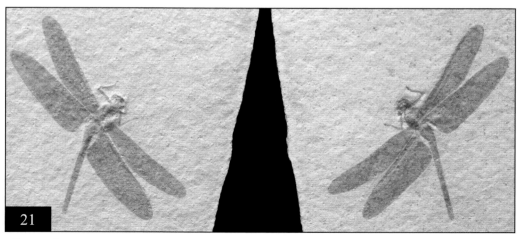

Part and counter-part slabs of a fossil dragonfly from the Jurassic of Solnhofen, Germany. CU

sition. For example, fragmentary wings in the Lower Cretaceous Purbeck and Wealden tell a story of post-mortem transport over long distances, whereas whole insects in the Crato Formation (Brazil) and Solnhofen (Germany) did not travel far, possibly being blown into the site of deposition or brought in from the bordering vegetation. Also, the environment at the site of deposition was very important. For example, the best preservation occurs in an environment which is devoid of predators, scavengers and organisms that will eat or decompose the dead insect. Therefore, an anoxic or hypersaline environment will preserve insects much better than an oxic environment. Rapid sedimentation will also preserve lots of detail. Martinez-Delclòs & Martinell (1993) conducted various experiments on extant insects to understand the taphonomy (preservation) of fossil insects, observing in experiments how insects broke surface tension on water, decayed on the water surface, decayed under the water surface and how they were affected by predation (see also the recent study by Wang et al., 2013). Experimental taphonomy studies of this nature can give us an insight into how insects became fossilized millions of years ago. The latter authors, for example, found that wing-folding behaviour and the relative size of the wings influenced the buoyancy times of dead insects on the surface of water, which was significantly correlated with the degree of preservation (Wang et al., 2013). As well as body fossils, insect trace fossils are known from the rock record, including borings into seeds, plants and dinosaur bones, leaf mining and feeding, galls and predation, and fossilized insect nests and larval cases. These trace fossils provide evidence of interactions between the insects and their environments and are covered in more detail later.

Why study fossil insects?
Fossil insects and their traces in amber and rock provide us with huge amounts of data (albeit it often fragmentary) concerning the evolution of insects, including their palaeoecology and palaeogeography (their past distributions) etc., from their first documented appearance in the Devonian through the entire geological record to the Quaternary. Nonetheless, we still do not fully understand the interrelationships of the extant orders (see Peters et al., 2014 and references therein), nor have scientists reached any concensus on the origins of insect flight or the complete metamorphosis life cycle (e.g. Toms, 2007), both of which represent major events in the evolutionary history of insects. Hence, despite the considerable progress that has been made in recent years in our understanding of evolutionary processes and patterns of insects (e.g. Mayhew, 2007; Bradley et al., 2009; Trautwein et al., 2012; Yeates et al., 2012), even very fundamental questions remain to be answered.

Many of the early palaeoentomological studies (and plenty of recent ones) were restricted to basic taxonomic descriptions. However, there is an increasing trend of researchers applying quantitative and analytical techniques (as used for extant faunas) to fossil assemblages in order to address interesting palaeobiological questions. Hence, palaeoentomology is moving into the 21st century, albeit rather slowly, alongside related branches of entomological research. The purpose of this book is primarily to introduce the reader to the great diversity of fossil insects around the world rather than to consider the finer details of applied fossil insect research. However, it would be remiss not to mention some of these briefly.

Identifying the closest relatives to the hexapods, and hence insights into their origins has been elusive. Traditional concepts based on morphological evidence include the Myriapoda, but recent molecular studies consistently indicate Crustacea, either in part or entirety (Grimaldi, 2010). The general picture of hexapod evolutionary history is of a Paleozoic fauna from the Early Devonian through to the Late Permian consisting of more primitive forms. Following the Permo–Triassic exctinction 251 million years ago, which was the most profound event in the history of insect evolution (Labandeira, 2005), a post-Paleozoic 'modern' fauna predominated. This consisted of more derived groups of odonates, orthopteroids and hemipteroids, but most significantly, there was a broad spectrum of holometabolous insects (Labandeira, 2005), i.e. those with a complete metamorphosis and which account for approximately 80% of current insect biodiversity. However, there was some overlap in these faunas and there is potential for adjustments of clades (e.g. orders) across this boundary through new fossil discoveries and as a result of taxon range extensions predicted from more refined evolutionary trees and through molecular clock dating estimates.

Unfortunately, there is a large gap in the early fossil record of apterygote insects of around 160 million years, leading up until their appearance as fossils in amber during the Early Cretaceous (Grimaldi, 2010). Nonetheless, a great deal of information with regard to the overall evolutionary history of insects can be extracted from the fossil record. This is best done by considering the relationships of fossils with their living relatives and calibrating these against the geological timescale based on the occurrence of known fossils. In very basic terms, a cladogram which shows the relationships between taxa gives only a relative indication for the timing of divergence events between groups. In order to get a better indication of absolute (minimum) dating for these events the cladograms need to be superimposed over geological time and calibrated using fossils to create an evolutionary tree. Such trees provide a useful tool for detecting gaps in the fossil record because (in theory) sister taxa should have identical origination dates. Thus, the presence of a fossil of one taxon at a certain point in time, also predicts the presence of the other at the same point in geological time, regardless of whether or not it has been identified from fossils of that age. Thus, fossils provide only minimum dates for the origin of particular insect groups. So-called super-trees can be generated by using several existing trees as their source of data input. Such a study by Davis *et al.* (2010) using the insect super-tree approach has recently shed additional light on important events in the evolutionary history of insects, such as radiations and mass extinction events.

Evolutionary trees for insects are frequently dated by applying a 'standard' mitochondrial DNA (mtDNA) clock constant (e.g. Papadopoulou *et al.*, 2010), which uses rates of molecular change (mtDNA substitution rates) and usually fossil constraints to determine at what point in the geological past particular groups diverged from one another. Given that different nucleotide sequences experience substitutions at different rates and that there appears to be variation within different insect lineages, the uncritical use of molecular clocks to calibrate insect evolutionary trees is fraught with pitfalls. Despite its rather common usage these days, no general consensus regarding reliable calibration points has been reached, and such studies frequently tend to over or underestimate origination and divergence times well beyond what can be confidently inferred from the fossil record. For example, recent research proposed that insects arose from a common ancestor with fairy shrimps (Anostraca) at around the Silurian–Ordovician boundary between 434–421 million years ago (Gaunt & Miles, 2002); another study (Pisani et al., 2004) dated their divergence from crustaceans at 666 million years ago! The oldest confirmed fossil hexapod is an Early Devonian springtail (approximately 400 million-years-old) from the Rhynie Chert of Scotland, so there is no fossil insect evidence to support the latter claim. The slightly younger Devonian Hunsrück Slate fossil *Devonohexapodus bocksbergensis* described by Haas et al. (2003) appears to have been misinterpreted and its hexapod affinities cannot be confirmed (Kühl & Rust, 2009). Similarly, the insect affinities of the Devonian fossil described as *Strudiella devonica* by Garrouste et al. (2012) have also been questioned (Hörnschemeyer et al., 2013).

Based on current evidence, the divergence of Hexapoda from their crustacean ancestors probably occurred in the Silurian, approximately 420–430 million years ago (Grimaldi, 2010). Wiegmann et al. (2009) proposed a Carboniferous (299–359 million years ago) origin for holometabolous insects, but noted that the first unequivocal fossils do not occur until the Permian (280–299 million years ago). This age has now been extended slightly by the description of the new fossil stem-group hymenopterid *Avioxyela gallica* (Avioxyelidae) and several other new species from the Carboniferous (Ghzelian: 299–303 Ma) of France by Nel et al. (2013).

Arthropod–primitive land plant interactions, inferred from the study of coprolites (fossil faeces), date back to Late Silurian to Mid-Devonian times (Labandeira, 2000; Hagstrom & Mehlqvist, 2012; Labandeira & Currano, 2013). However, the first evidence of insect–plant interactions does not occur until the interval spanning the Early Carboniferous to Late Permian, when primitive ancestral insects consumed spores, pre-pollen and pollen from ferns and seed plants (Labandeira, 2000). The early phase of the modern insect fauna and its association with non-angiosperm seed plants stems from the Early Triassic to the Mid-Cretaceous, during which time there was a relatively rapid change towards a dominance of modern insect taxa and angiosperm (flowering) plants (Labandeira, 2000). Fossil evidence exists for the presence of pollinating insects during the late Jurassic, their mutualisms may have been subsequently fine-tuned by the angiosperms (Labandeira, 2000). However, the major radiations of the obligate flower-associated insects probably occurred during the late Lower to Upper Cretaceous, because this period is consistent with the appearance of insect attracting features (entomophilous syndromes) in Cretaceous flowers (Grimaldi, 1999). However, 65–88% of the modern insect mouthpart classes were present by the Middle Jurassic (Labandeira & Sepkoski, 1993) and therefore, the great radiation of insects began at least 100 million years before the radiation of the angiosperms.

A number of mass extinction events have been recognized throughout the history of life on Earth. They vary from major catastrophes to less significant perturbations of the background extinction rate. The cause of some can be attributed to bolide impacts or massive volcanic eruptions producing so-called 'nuclear winters', which led to global environmental stress and extinction (Sharpton & Ward, 1990; MacLeod, 2013). The end-Cretaceous extinction event of 65 million years ago is the best studied and its catastrophic nature is generally accepted, but its causes are still hotly debated. Regardless of the causes, it is likely that mass extinctions have accounted for the demise of less than 5% of all extinct species (Erwin, 2001). Nevertheless, they created evolutionary opportunities for the survivors (e.g. Jarzembowski & Ross, 1996), which have had major effects on the history of life on Earth.

Insect family diversity was not drastically affected by the end-Cretaceous extinction, which so drastically affected many other life forms such as the dinosaurs (Labandeira & Sepkoski, 1993; Briggs, 1995; Ross et al., 2000). However, some specialist plant feeding insects disappeared along with the plants upon which they fed and failed to reappear subsequently (Labandeira et al., 2002). It is unclear whether the appearance and radiation of flowering plants in the Early Cretaceous had a major impact on insect family diversity, although when origination and extinction data are considered separately there appears to have been a high turnover of insect families around this time. The Tertiary insect fauna was essentially modern, though some of the higher taxa are now extinct. Also, the distribution patterns were sometimes significantly different to those to their extant descendants, for example, as a result of sub/tropical conditions in regions that now have more temperate climates.

As will be seen later, fossil insect sites are found across the world and on all continents. They generate important data for palaeobiogeographic studies, such as centres of endemism and dispersal through geological time. Although current insect distributions must represent some function of those of the past, the patterns observed in the fossil record are not always easy to interpret. Many of the insects found in Paleozoic rock deposits are now extinct, such as the large griffinflies and palaeodictyopterans, with most extant orders having evolved in or by the Mesozoic.

On more recent and localized scales, fossil insect assemblages (particularly from very diverse amber deposits) provide evidence of regional extinctions. With more than 3500 fossil arthropod species described, Baltic amber is by far the richest source of fossil insects. Whilst many of the orders, families and genera represented as inclusions in Baltic amber still persist in the Palaearctic and Holarctic today, there are others that have become extinct in these regions since the Eocene, or at the very least have their greatest affinities elsewhere, such as the Afrotropics, Neotropics, and also the Australian and Indo-Malayan regions. Some examples include *Priacma* and *Cupes* beetles (Cupedidae), Strepsiptera of the family Myrmecolacidae, the chrysidoid hymenopteran family Scolebythidae, the trichopteran family Stenopsychidae, flies of the families Diopsidae, Sciadoceridae and the Xylophagidae subfamily Rachicerinae, and mantophasmatodeans, to name just a few. The regional extinction of these Baltic amber faunas was probably due to significant global cooling at the end of the Eocene which created more distinct lattitudinal climatic zonation, with warmer regions towards the equator. Thus, the subtropical and tropical elements of the Baltic amber forests died out in the higher palaeolatitudes (Weitschat & Wichard, 2002).

Even for relatively young fossil assemblages that are considered very similar to the extant fauna of the region, past distributions do not always reflect those of the present, and vice versa. While the fossil fauna for most insect orders in 16 million-years-old Miocene Domincan amber is very similar to the extant fauna at family (and in large part genus) level (e.g. Pérez-Gelabert, 2008), there are some interesting differences. For example, certain extant lineages of Hymenoptera, Trichoptera, Coleoptera, Isoptera, Diptera, Lepidoptera, Neuroptera and Strepsiptera were present on Hispaniola in the Miocene but are absent from the island today (Wilson, 1985; Wichard, 2007;

Grimaldi, 1991; Nagel, 1997; Poinar, 1999a; Poinar & Poinar, 1999; Hall *et al.*, 2004; Engel & Grimaldi, 2007; Kogan & Poinar, 2010). It has been proposed that the demise of certain groups known from Dominican amber but absent from the Greater Antilles today resulted from a cool period associated with increased aridity during the Plio-Pleistocene (Poinar, 1999a). However, an alternative theory suggested that the insularization (movement further way from the mainland) of Hispaniola was probably a more important factor (Peñalver & Grimaldi, 2006).

Analyzing fossil insect data in palaeobiogeographic studies is not as easy as it sounds. For example, the conclusions of the 'classic' ant biogeographic study by Wilson (1985), based on fossils preserved in Dominican amber, were considered untenable by Baroni-Urbani (1995). There can be no doubt that understanding the multifaceted complexities of the palaeobiogeography of the multitude of extant and extinct clades and their bearing on the present day biota will be no easy feat. Indeed, the methodologies for investigating these issues are still in their infancy (Upchurch *et al.*, 2011). Methods widely used by biologists and ecologists for extant taxa need to be co-opted in a palaeobiogeographic context, in order to stimulate the future interaction of neo- and palaeobiogeographers within a framework for comparing the dynamics of extinct and extant taxa across multiple timescales. Nontheless, a recent analysis of the spider family Archaeidae, which included the Baltic amber fossil species alongside their extant relatives has demonstrated that informative results can be obtained (Wood *et al.*, 2012).

Given their incredible (often understated) palaeodiversity, there is no doubt that fossil insects can be highly informative in a palaeoecological context, just as extant insects are today. Unfortunately, very little research has focused specifically on quantitative palaeoecology, but the idea of behavioural fixity is often drawn on to make qualitative conclusions about palaeoecosystems from which fossil taxa derive. Such conclusions are based on the broad assumption that extinct species probably behaved in a similar way (and had similar tolerances) to their extant relatives. It is not that difficult to amass datasets of a sufficient size for quantitative investigations, particularly for amber faunas, but also for insects in rock, where even incomplete or disarticulated specimens can be useful for such studies (e.g. Smith & Moe-Hoffman, 2007; Archibald *et al.*, 2013a). There is great scope for co-opting neontological ecological analytical methods and applying these to fossil insect data (e.g. Penney & Langan, 2006), though care must be taken to make sure the available data meet the prerequisites of the technique to be employed.

How to study fossil insects

Insects in amber

These are exciting times for palaeoentomologists. As mentioned earlier, the application of new technological approaches, such as X-ray computed tomography and synchrotron scanning, to the study of amber is revolutionizing how we can image and study these fossils. Such approaches to virtual palaeontology (e.g. Sutton *et al.*, 2014) include three-dimensional modelling and digital dissection of insect fossils in totally opaque ambers (Fig. 22), even to the extent whereby their preserved internal morphology can be visualized. Phenomena such as 'Verlumung' (a covering of white emulsion formed from tiny air bubbles), common in Baltic amber, no longer need hinder the study of inclusions. Historical specimens in heavily darkened, oxidized amber can again be studied with relative ease, with the benefit of additional morphological details unavailable to the original workers (Dunlop *et al.*, 2011a). Recently, Dammer *et al.* (2013) applied more traditional X-ray techniques to insect inclusions in amber (Fig. 23). On a more accessible level, new freely available photomicroscopy image stacking software now permits the production of sharp, high resolution, in-focus images without the need for access to highly specialized equipment. This technique overcomes the short depth of field encountered when working with small fossils under high magnifications, by taking

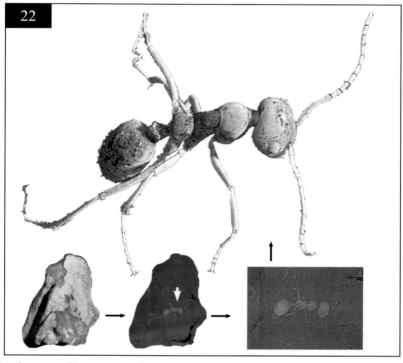

An example of opaque Charentes amber and phase contrast X-ray synchrotron imaging, following the sequence: A piece of fully opaque amber in normal optical view; microradiograph of the amber piece showing the presence of an ant inclusion (white arrow); 3D rendering of the sphecomyrmine ant (Formicidae) using phase contrast microtomography. Images by Paul Tafforeau and Malvina Lak (Université de Rennes 1), reproduced from Perrichot *et al.* (2010)

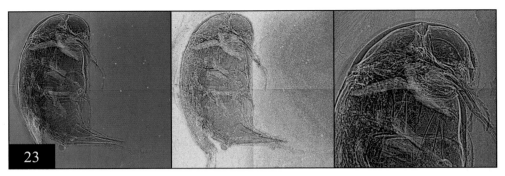

Tumbling flower beetle (Coleoptera: Mordellidae) in Eocene Baltic amber, X-ray images from a mammography X-ray unit (see Dammer *et al.*, 2013)

several photographs at different focal planes with different parts of the fossil in focus on different images. The software then automatically picks out all the in-focus parts of each separate image and merges them into a single image. Such photographs showing the amber inclusions preserved with life-like fidelity are used throughout this book. More traditional techniques for the study of amber insect fossils involve the use of a powerful hand lens or a dissecting microscope, once the specimen has been prepared for examination.

Once raw amber has been washed and cleaned, it is often possible to determine whether or not it contains inclusions by coating it with a thin smear of oil and holding it up to the light. The oil fills scratches and flaws on the surface of the amber, increasing the visibility of any inclusions present. If the external surface is particularly crusty, a 'window' will need to be ground and polished into the specimen. When something of interest is discovered, further preparation is usually required. This typically involves cutting or grinding and then polishing the amber. The first of these processes requires a circular trim saw (ideally a faceting saw) or a fine hand-held jeweller's saw with a thin diamond blade. Water is used as a coolant and lubricant to protect the specimen from overheating. Check the amber carefully for internal fractures before starting. The forces generated during cutting, grinding and polishing can cause specimens to break. In some cases they may be glued back together. It may then be possible to resume the preparation process without further damage to the specimen, but this is not always the case.

Once trimmed to size, the surface of the amber should be ground to remove saw marks and then polished. Amber is relatively soft and the best results are achieved by careful grinding by hand, or on a flat lap, using successively finer grades of good quality abrasive paper. Check the specimen regularly under a microscope to avoid grinding it too far and damaging the inclusion. Saw marks are easily removed using a medium 360-grade paper. Specimen and hands must be cleaned before transfer to 600, 1200 and 2500 grades. At each stage a careful inspection of the surface is required, even the tiniest scratches will not be removed by polishing. A fine napped polishing pad charged with a 1 micron diamond compound (14,000 mesh equivalent) or 200 nm alumina can be used to produce a highly polished surface. The polishing compound is made up as a paste in water which acts as a coolant to protect the amber and its inclusion from overheating.

The clarity of most Tertiary amber, in conjunction with the excellent preservation of the inclusions, means that cutting to an appropriate size followed by grinding and polishing is sufficient for most scientific study. More elaborate techniques using immersion fluids, embedding media of similar refractive index to amber and embedding in synthetic plastics have been developed by some researchers, especially for more brittle Cretaceous ambers (Nascimbene & Silverstein, 2000) or for tiny inclusions such as mites (Sidorchuk, 2013). Certain ambers will dissolve in some organic solvents, and articulated insect fragments, which retained their softness in a manner similar to freshly collected entomological material have been recovered (Azar, 2007; Mazur *et al.*, 2012; Penney *et al.*, 2013a [copal]), but this technique is rarely used and readers are cautioned that attempting to dissolve amber may lead to loss of both the amber and the inclusion!

Lighting is important when examining amber inclusions under a microscope. The more flexible the illumination system the better. Transmitted (from below) and incident light (from above) are required and the facility to produce dark ground illumination is a considerable advantage. Dark ground illumination produces an image of the object in scattered light and is useful when examining fine details such as hairs on the legs of insects. The use of polarized light has also proved useful for imaging amber fossils, including the production of 3D images (Haug *et al.*, 2013). Fibre optic light sources are commonly used to produce directional incident light. Transmitted (and dark ground) systems are usually built into the microscope base. Different specimens require different combinations of transmitted and incident light (or either on its own) to produce the best results. Different coloured backgrounds can radically alter the contrast and can have marked effects on the visibility of the inclusion and its finer features.

Insects in rock

Most rock fossil insects can simply be examined under a binocular microscope, although good illumination is essential, with low angle lighting helpful for bringing out surface relief. For shale fossils, depending on the way they are preserved, the use of polarized light or immersing the specimen in alcohol can reveal additional features. Oil immersion objective lenses can be particularly useful for resolving fine details in some modes of preservation. A fine coating of ammonium chloride to whiten the specimen is also sometimes helpful in shale or nodule-preserved fossils and again helps to define any surface relief. To remove excessive soft matrix, e.g. in Plattenkalk preservation and to clear kaolinite from ironstone nodules, a hypodermic needle attached by a tube to an air pump (see Selden, 2003) can be used, whilst viewing the specimen under a binocular microscope. The needle is used to dislodge debris, which the gentle flow of air blows clear from the working area. Gentle dissolution of excess calcite can be achieved with dilute hydrochloric acid, taking great care not damage the fossil.

Chert fossils need to be prepared by breaking the rock into manageable (translucent) fragments, or better still, making a series of thin sections which can be polished down to reveal objects of interest. The Rhynie Chert is an especially hard rock and requires a diamond saw to cut it effectively. Cuticle fragments in shales are usually macerated out by immersing the rock samples in hydrofluoric acid and then sorting through the resulting material that remains. Normally, specimens are mounted onto microscope slides for detailed study. Note that hydrofluoric acid (and other possible macerating agents) is very dangerous and this technique should only be carried out by trained staff in a properly equipped laboratory.

Drawing tubes (often refered to as a *camera lucida*) are available as an optional accessory for some stereomicroscopes (either built in to the body, as an optional add-on, or in some cases they slot into one of the sockets for the ocular lenses). They enable the researcher to look down the microscope and draw the specimen at the same time. Using a combination of angled mirrors, the user is able to see the tip of a pencil superimposed on the image of the specimen. It is then possible to trace its outline … or so the theory goes. In practice, using a drawing tube requires a degree of practice. Correct lighting is important in order to get the best results. Drawing tubes are only useful when trying to draw 'flat' specimens, i.e. the specimen must be fully in focus. Adjusting the focus will produce a misalignment on the drawing. Thus, they are more appropriate for insect fossils in rock rather than in amber.

In terms of imaging, photographic documentation forms the least subjective means of presenting 'data', i.e. the fossils, and so is crucial for palaeoentomological studies. Unfortunately, many fossils are notoriously difficult to photograph due to the lack of contrast, the lack of three-dimensional relief or a combination of both. In other cases, contrast and relief are very strong, making photographic documentation equally difficult. There are several 'tricks of the trade' and an excellent review of very simple methods and techniques to improve the quality of fossil photographic images can be found in Kerp & Bomfleur (2011).

Béthoux *et al.* (2004a) applied non-contact laser scanning to better resolve vein relief in fossil insect wings. They studied various Upper Carboniferous and Upper Permian insects from France and achieved high resolution 3D data visualization of the surface topography, resulting in high quality images. Interestingly, the authors noted that such digitization of fossil insect wings included in a 3D reconstruction of the whole insect could permit quantification of its flight performance via computer modelling approaches, in order to improve our knowledge of the origin and evolution of insect flight and its ecological significance (Béthoux *et al.*, 2004a).

Tomography techniques, as discussed above for amber inclusions, can also be applied to non-amber fossils (e.g. Garwood & Sutton, 2010; Garwood *et al.*, 2012), but given their (usually) poorer state of preservation the results are not so spectacular (Fig. 24). Synchrotron scanning has also been used to visualize the internal genitalia of 30 million-years-old clown beetle (Histeridae) fossils preserved in rock from Quercy, France (Schmied *et al.*, 2013). Image stacking software (as mentioned previously for amber) usually has limited applications to compression fossils as a result of their two-dimensional preservation. Nonetheless, it can still reveal a lot more morphological detail than would otherwise be available and it can be useful for superimposing images of part and counter-part fossils to generate a final image revealing more details than a single image of either specimen alone (e.g. Selden, 2010). Recently, Barling *et al.* (2013) used scanning electron microscopy (SEM) to describe a tiny new species of chalcidoid wasp from the Cretaceous Crato Formation of Brazil (Fig. 25). Another study (Compton *et al.*, 2010) used SEM to demonstrate the presence of pollen pockets in a tiny fig wasp '*Ponera*' *minuta* (Hymenoptera: Agaonidae) containing *Ficus* pollen from the Eocene, Insect Limestone of the Isle of Wight, England.

Computed tomography reconstruction of an aquatic insect nymph *Anebos phrixos* (order uncertain) from the Carboniferous of Montceau-les-Mines, France. Reproduced from Garwood *et al.* (2012) with permission. MNHN

Scanning electron micrograph of *Parviformosus wohlrabeae* (Hymenoptera: Chalcidoidea: Pteromalidae) from the Cretaceous Crato Formation, Brazil, described by Barling *et al.* (2013). Holotype, SMNS 70092

The palaeospecies concept

The biological species concept usually defines a species as *members of populations that actually or potentially interbreed in nature to produce fertile offspring*. Clearly, such a definition cannot be applied to fossils. Indeed, this definition is often problematic for extant species, especially with the new discoveries of cryptic insect species complexes using molecular methods (e.g. Eltz *et al.*, 2011), and the philosophical concepts that underpin biological classification also require very careful consideration (Zakharov, 2013). Identification of extinct species from the geological past relies solely on morphological features derived from fossils. Thus, a palaeospecies may be defined as *a group of similar fossils where the range of morphological variation does not exceed the range of variation as might be seen (or expected) in closely related extant species*. In some cases there are no similar extant forms and care must be taken to distinguish between genuine morphological variation and apparent morphological variation preserved as a result of taphonomic processes. There are of course additional problems of species identification in the fossil record, for example with regard to sexually dimorphic or highly polymorphic species, where distinctly different specimens will no doubt be described as separate species. It is also almost impossible to match larval and adult forms of the same species with any real degree of certainty.

Identification of fossil insect species

In an ideal world, fossil insect species taxonomy would be equivalent to that for extant species, thus permitting direct comparisons between the two faunas. However, due to the fragmentary nature of most fossil insects (in addition to their mode of preservation) this is usually impossible. For example, colour is often useful for the identification of extant butterflies and some beetles, but colour is not preserved in most fossils. Many extant insects require dissection of their internal genitalia in order to confirm species identification. Preservation of such structures in the fossil record is highly unusual, but occasionally insects are preserved with their genitalia extruded (Fig. 26). In some insects the important taxonomic aspects of the genital morphology are visible externally and these are often readily visible in well preserved amber fossils (Fig. 27). Indeed, the most complete preservation is seen in amber inclusions and X-ray computed tomography and synchrotron scanning are certainly bridging the taxonomic equivallency gap between palaeontology and neontology. Nonetheless, for the forseeable future fossils will always be taxonomically subequal to Recent forms.

In many instances fossil insect species are known only from isolated wings (Fig. 28). Hence, the study of wing venation patterns (horsimology) is particularly important in palaeoentomology. However, as noted by Gordh & Headrick (2011) horsimology is fraught with difficulties because of confusion regarding wing vein terminology. By convention, the veins are named from anterior to posterior and from proximal to distal. However, veins are identified from the wing base rather than their association with auxillary sclerites. Perfecting a system of homologous vein nomenclature has been difficult because of intraspecific variation and inconsistent published data from comparisons between different orders and families. Fig. 29 shows a generalized insect wing with its veins labelled.

Ross (2012) examined the forewing vein patterns of extant cockroach species and found considerable intraspecific variation in addition to differences between the left and right wings of individuals. He noted that such variation was probably able to occur in cockroaches because the forewings are not used actively during flight, so the positions of the veins are not so important for aerodynamics and flexing of the wing. Importantly, the results were considered in a palaeoentomological context, with Ross (2012) concluding that it can still be possible to describe new fossil cockroach species even from isolated and incomplete wings, but wing pigmentation patterns can also be very useful for differentiation of species. Cui et al. (2011) noted a wide range of intraspecific variation in the forewing venation in Late Carboniferous insects of the grylloblattidan insect family Sinonamuropteridae, considering nine previously described species to represent just a single species.

For further discussion of the importance of wing vein structure and terminology in the study of fossil insects see Béthoux (2008a and references therein). It is interesting to note that some researchers consider the wing vein homology discussion a rather unimportant and inconsequential pursuit, whereas others consider it to be of the utmost importance. Unfortunately, the fossil record does not provide too many clues to the evolutionary origins of wing venation patterns, because it 'suddenly' reveals well developed wings with complex venation in many different lineages.

Wing shape is another important feature, especially the relative proportions of the hind and forewings if both are preserved together (Fig. 28). In theory, it should be possible, at least for some specimens, to generate computer algorithms that will identify what group a particular fossil belongs to via its wing structure alone. Quantitative,

26

27

Anaspis sp. (Coleoptera: Scraptiidae) with genitalia extruded, in Eocene Baltic amber. RCDP

'*Pericoma*' sp. *sensu* Meunier (Diptera: Psychodidae) showing an example of external genitalia, in Eocene Baltic amber. RCDP

28

Giant cicada *Colossocossus bechlyi* (Hemiptera: Palaeontinidae) from the Cretaceous Crato Formation, Brazil. This specimen is more complete than the holotype, which consists only of an isolated forewing. The hindwing is also preserved in the specimen illustrated. RCDP

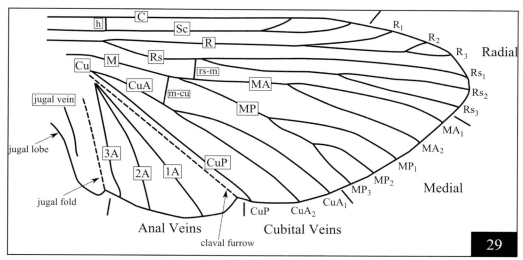

A generalized insect wing with veins labelled. Abbreviations: C, costa; Sc, sub-costa; R, radius; R1–3, first to third branches of radius; Rs, radial sector; Rs1–3, first to third branches of radial sector; M, media; MA, media anterior; MA1–3, first to third branches of media anterior; MP, media posterior; MP1–3, first to third branches of media posterior; Cu, cubitus; CuA, cubitus anterior; CuA1–3, first to third branches of cubitus anterior; CuP, cubitus posterior; 1–3A, first to third anal veins; h, humeral vein; rs-m, radial sector to media crossvein; m-cu, media to cubitus crossvein (after Comstock, 1918)

morphometric analyses can help to assign fossil specimens to modern groups, when a comprehensive database of modern specimen morphometric data are available for comparison. This is particularly useful for two-dimensional features, such as insect wings, which provide easily identifiable landmarks (e.g. wing vein intersections) that are not likely to be deformed in fossils. Studies applying this technique to fossil insects are few and far between, but a recent example involved fossil halictid bees (Hymenoptera) (De Meulemeester *et al.*, 2012). Although the authors were able to question the earlier systematic assignments of previously described fossil taxa at the level of tribe, they were rather limited as to how far they could identify a particular fossil taxon using this technique. This approach was taken further (Dewulf *et al.*, 2014), resulting in the transfer of a fossil bee species, preserved as a compression fossil from the Florissant shales of Colorado, USA, from the family Melittidae to Andrenidae. An earlier study claiming to assign fossils (spiders) to family level using this technique was found to be seriously flawed under closer scrutiny (see Penney & Langan, 2010).

Trace fossils (see later) are even more difficult to identify correctly because, by definition, the insect trace-maker is (usually) not preserved. Reassessment of such fossils or their descriptions can lead to competing ideas and ongoing (sometimes heated) debate. For example, the recent identification of the earliest (Carboniferous) trace fossil of a winged insect, which was considered to have been made by a mayfly by Knecht *et al.* (2011) has sparked such a discussion (Benner *et al.*, 2013; Marden, 2013ab), with the latter author suggesting plecopteran affinities for the trace maker.

How to formally describe new fossil insects

Descriptions of extant insects are based on a vast array of characters, including general body morphology, minute internal structures, genitalia and also more recently on molecular information. When dealing with fossils the number of characters available for diagnosing a species reduces dramatically. Occasionally, exceptional preservation (e.g. in amber) can provide more complete specimens and more useful characters; X-ray computed tomography has also enabled the virtual dissection of fossils, allowing internal structures to be observed. However, in many rock deposits the majority of specimens are preserved as isolated wings, crushed to a greater or lesser extent, with occasional body parts or more complete remains.

Using wing characters is the most common way of identifying fossil insects to families, genera and species. Each individual vein has a specific name (Fig. 29), with each order, family, genus and species having its own particular combination and arrangement of veins: some are multi-branched, some merged, some enclose 'cells', and some are reduced or absent. However, it is important to take into account intraspecific variation (the slight variation observed within a species, e.g. Ross, 2012) and also sexual dimorphism (the variation between the sexes), before erecting a new genus or species; knowledge of the variation that exists in extant insects is therefore necessary.

Descriptions of new fossil insect species in scientific publications are almost always accompanied by a photograph and a labelled drawing of the wing venation of the specimen on which the taxon is based (the holotype). The traditional (and still common) way of illustrating insects preserved in 2D (rather than the 3D preservation seen in amber) is by use of a drawing tube attached to a microscope, which superimposes the image of your drawing over the specimen, allowing you to literally trace over the fossil (see earlier). With improving technology, various software drawing packages are also being used to create illustrations of fossils. The process of digitally creating a wing venation drawing is shown in Fig. 30. The first step is to obtain a high resolution photograph of the fossil specimen, which is then imported into a drawing package, e.g. Adobe Illustrator. The image is then traced over on a new layer using the pen tool, followed by shading where necessary. The original photograph layer is then either deleted or hidden and the computer generated trace is labelled using the text function (see Coleman, 2003 for a more detailed method).

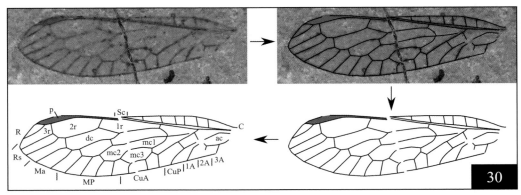

How illustrations of insect wings are created for publication

Significant fossil insect localities

Fossil insect deposits occur all over the world, with many new ones still being discovered on a reasonably regular basis. It is not unusual to find deposits of radically different ages in reasonably close proximity. For example, the UK boasts fossil hexapod/insect yielding deposits from the Devonian (Rhynie Chert), Jurassic (Lias of Dorset), Cretaceous (Purbeck Limestone Group and Wealden Supergroup) and the Tertiary (Bembridge Marls, Isle of Wight). The same is true for many other countries. For example, Spain has at least 41 fossil insect sites, but few of these have been thoroughly investigated (Peñalver *et al.*, 1999). Full coverage of all the known insect deposits is well beyond the scope of this introductory book, so only the most important or newly discovered fossil insect localities are briefly discussed below. For additional localities see Rasnitsyn & Quicke (2002), Schlüter (2003) and Grimaldi & Engel (2005).

Europe
NON-AMBER
Rhynie Chert, Scotland, UK. A Devonian (Pragian) site in Britain, which has evidence of the first definitive insect (*Rhyniognatha hirsti*) preserved as a pair of mandibles. Other hexapods such as springtails (*Rhyniella praecursor*) have been discovered (Whalley & Jarzembowski, 1981), as well as many plants and primitive arachnids (Fig. 5). This site is of global importance because it provides an insight into the very early colonization of land (Selden & Edwards, 1989). The fossils are silicified, being preserved in chert.

Commentry, France. This is a Carboniferous Coal Measure locality (Lower Pennsylvanian, Bashkirian) preserving fossils of the giant insects, the griffinflies (Protodonata). The site also has many fossils of early insects, such as palaeodictyopterans and protorthopterans (e.g. Brongniart, 1884, 1893; Bolton, 1917). Despite their age, the fossils are relatively well preserved. Similar Coal Measures deposits occur elsewhere in Europe, including the UK (Bolton, 1921; Jarzembowski, 1987; Ross, 2010) (Fig. 7).

Oboro, Czech Republic. An early Permian (Artinskian or Sakmarian) fossil insect locality and one of the most important diverse fossil insect sites of the Permian worldwide, with many described species (e.g. Kukalova, 1964; Kukalova-Peck & Willmann, 1990). The insects are preserved in fine-grained mudstone, representing a lacustrine palaeoenvironment.

Nierdermoschel, Germany. Approximately 900 insect fossils have been collected from this early Permian site in south-west Germany. Although relatively numerous, the fossils mainly belong to just a few very common taxa (Hörnschemeyer, 1999).

Lodève Basin, France. Fossil insects originate from the Middle Permian (Guadalupian) Salagou Formation. The Lodève entomofauna was diverse, but unfortunately the fossils consist mainly of isolated wings (Fig. 31), making identification difficult in some cases (Béthoux, 2008b; Prokop & Nel, 2011). Interestingly, beetles and other holometabolous orders are very scarce in the Lodève Basin, although they were already present in the

'Mayfly' wing (Syntonopterida: Syntonopteridae) from the Middle Permian Lodève Basin, France. Reproduced from Prokop & Nel (2011) with permission. MLF

Vosges fossil insects from the Triassic Grès à Voltzia Formation: (32) *Laurentiptera gallica* (Mecoptera: Liassophilidae), (33) *Triassomanthus parvulus* (Ephemeroptera: Triassomanthidae; considered Euephemeroptera *incertae sedis* by Kluge, 2013). LGRF

Lower Permian and dominate all the fossil entomofaunas after the Triassic of Vosges (Prokop & Nel, 2011).

Vosges, France. The Middle Triassic (early Anisian) Grès à Voltzia Formation has yielded a diverse insect fauna, with more than 11 orders known and hundreds of species described (Marchal-Papier, 1998) (Figs. 32, 33). The fauna is dominated by roaches (Papier *et al.*, 1994). It is one of the most significant Triassic insect localities in Europe and represents a model of the type of environment that may have acted as a refugium for terrestrial communities during the end-Permian mass extinction and its Triassic aftermath (Gall & Grauvogel-Stamm, 2005). The insects are preserved in clays and siltstone, representing a brackish palaeoenvironment (Gall, 1985).

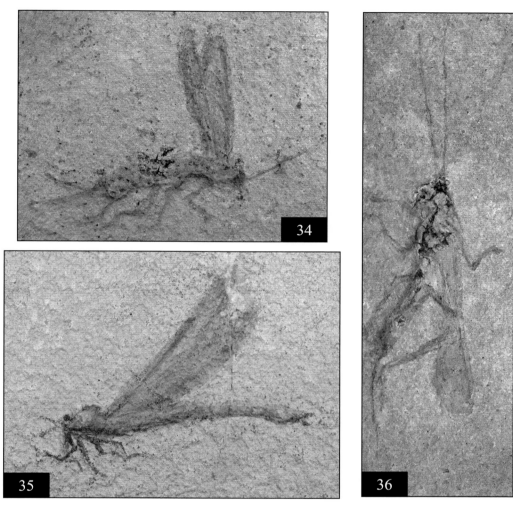

Solnhofen (Germany) fossil insects: (34) Mayfly (Ephemeroptera), (35) dragonfly (Odonata), (36) 'grasshopper' (Orthoptera). The images have been modified to enhance contrast. RCDP

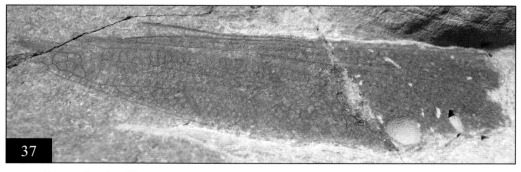

Dragonfly wing (Odonata) from the Lower Jurassic of Charmouth, Dorset, UK. CU

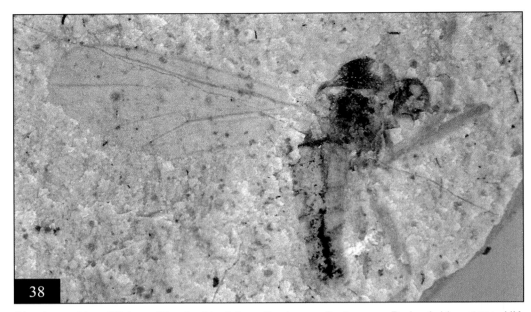

Phantom midge (Diptera: Chaoboridae) from the Lower Cretaceous Purbeck Limestone, UK. MNEMG 1998.25

Pałęgi clay-pit, Poland. A newly discovered Triassic (latest Olenekian–early Anisian) deposit in the Holy Cross Moutains (Żyła *et al.*, 2013). The assemblage is similar to that described from the Middle Triassic of France and Germany (e.g. Bashkuev *et al.*, 2012), but is dominated by the remains of conchostracans (Crustacea) and cockroaches, with grylloblattids and mecopterans also recorded. On the whole, the fossils are rather poorly preserved.

Solnhofen, Germany. A Jurassic fossil locality famous for the early bird *Archaeopteryx*. Fossil insects are known from this locality, including many dragonflies. Orders include Odonata (Figs. 21, 35, 100), Neuroptera, Ephemeroptera (Fig. 34), Hemiptera, Coleoptera (Fikáček *et al.*, 2014), Diptera, Orthoptera (Fig. 36), Chresmododea (Fig. 117) and Blattodea (Ponomarenko, 1985). The fossils are preserved in a fine-grained laminated limestone, which represents a very saline lagoonal environment. Although the fossil insects are often complete, they are rather poorly preserved.

Lias of Europe. These are Lower Jurassic (Rhaetian–Toarcian) deposits, the main locality and most studied is Charmouth, Dorset, UK. Here the insects are quite rare, although in excess of 400 specimens have been collected (Whalley, 1985) (Fig. 37). More than 11 orders and 66 species have been described to date, including the oldest lepidopteran. The fauna is dominated by Coleoptera and Orthoptera. The rocks represent a marine/ deltaic environment, so the insects here have been washed in from the surrounding land (i.e. they are allochthonous). A review of additional European localities can be found in Ansorge (2003).

Lower Cretaceous of southern England, UK. The two major deposits are the older **Purbeck Limestone Group** (Berriasian) and the younger **Wealden Supergroup** (Barremian–Hauterivian). Both deposits have yielded many thousands of specimens. The Purbeck has 17 insect orders recorded and more than 200 hundred species described (Coram & Jepson, 2012). The Wealden has 13 insect orders and more than 200 species described (Jarzembowski, 2011; Ross, 2011). The insects are predominantly preserved as isolated fragments, mainly wings (Fig. 176), however complete, articulated remains are occasionally found (Fig. 38).

El Montsec (and Las Hoyas), Spain. Like the Purbeck and Wealden, these are very important Lower Cretaceous insect sites (Barremian). More than 13 orders and 50 families of insects have been recorded from these lithographic limestones (see Ansorge, 1991; Szwedo & Ansorge, 2014 and references therein). Many aquatic insects are known, such as mayfly nymphs, water bugs and aquatic fly larvae. The rocks represent a hypersaline lagoonal palaeoenvironment, with complete insects common (Fig. 39), as well as disarticulated specimens. Beetles are the most common fossil insects, with more than 500 articulated individuals recovered (Soriano & Delclòs, 2006).

Mo Clay, Fur Formation, Denmark. A Palaeocene–Eocene deposit in Denmark, which has so far yielded more than 20,000 fossil insects (Rust, 1999). Representatives of many insect orders, including Odonata, Orthoptera, Hemiptera, Dermaptera (Fig. 42), Coleoptera, Lepidoptera (Fig. 169), Neuroptera (Fig. 40), Hymenoptera (Fig. 41), Mecoptera and Diptera (Fig. 159) have been recorded (Andersen in Bonde *et al.*, 2008). The fossils are preserved in diatomitic sediment, representing a marine palaeoenvironment.

39

March fly (Diptera: Bibionidae) from the Cretaceous La Cabrua outcrop of Montsech, Spain. RCJA

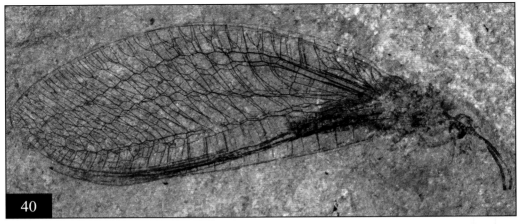

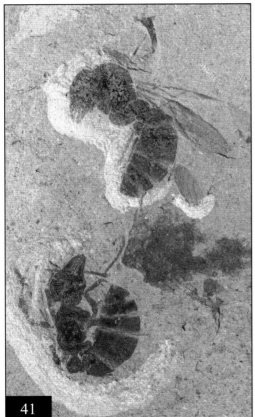

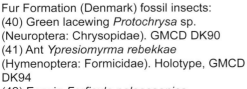

Fur Formation (Denmark) fossil insects:
(40) Green lacewing *Protochrysa* sp.
(Neuroptera: Chrysopidae). GMCD DK90
(41) Ant *Ypresiomyrma rebekkae*
(Hymenoptera: Formicidae). Holotype, GMCD
DK94
(42) Earwig *Forficula paleocaenica*
(Dermaptera: Forficulidae). GMCD

Messel, Germany. A world famous Eocene fossil site, known for its exceptional preservation of minute detail, including coloration (Figs. 44, 227). The insect fauna is very diverse, with the most notable fossils being the beetles and moths with iridescence preserved (e.g. McNamara *et al.*, 2012a; McNamara, 2013) and the only known fossil leaf insect (Fig. 230) (Wedmann *et al.*, 2007). Other insects include Blattodea (including Isoptera), Orthoptera, Plecoptera, Odonata, Hemiptera (Fig. 43), Hymenoptera (Fig. 45), Neuroptera, Diptera and even Strepsiptera. The fossils are preserved in an oil shale formed in a restricted lake basin palaeoenvironment (Wedmann *et al.*, 2007). The insect fauna of this deposit formed the basis of a taxonomic and palaeoecological study by Lutz (1990).

Eckfelder Maar, Germany. A Middle Eocene lacustrine deposit with around 4700 fossil insect specimens recovered, mostly well preserved. Terrestrial species predominate with 22 families of Coleoptera representing 84% of all specimens (Háva & Wappler, 2014). Other orders recorded include Odonata (very rare), Dermaptera, Blattodea (including Isoptera), Diptera, Plecoptera, Phthiraptera, Hemiptera, Trichoptera (larval cases only) and Hymenoptera. A palaeoentomological study of this fauna was conducted by Wappler (2003), who concluded that the insect assemblage was indicative of paratropical rainforest conditions.

Bembridge Marls (Insect Limestone Bed), England, UK. A highly fossiliferous locality on the Isle of Wight, England. The age of the deposit is Late Eocene. Hundreds of insect specimens have been collected and described. A thorough treatment of these fossil insects will shortly be published in two special volumes of the *Earth and Environmental Science Transactions of the Royal Society of Edinburgh*.

43

Cicada (Hemiptera: Auchenorrhyncha: Cicadidae) from Messel, Germany. SFNGM I1515

Messel (Germany) Eocene fossil insects:
(44) Stag beetle *Protognathinus spielbergi* (Coleoptera: Lucanidae). Holotype, SFNGM I1549-01
(45) Weaver ant *Oecophylla longiceps* (Hymenoptera: Formicidae). Holotype, SFNGM I03643-01

Jewel beetle (Coleoptera: Buprestidae) from Enspel (Germany), Upper Oligocene. GDKE

47

Ground beetle (Coleoptera: Carabidae) from the Upper Oligocene of Enspel, Germany. GDKE

Snout-nosed beetle (Coleoptera: Curculionoidea) from the Upper Oligocene of Enspel, Germany. GDKE

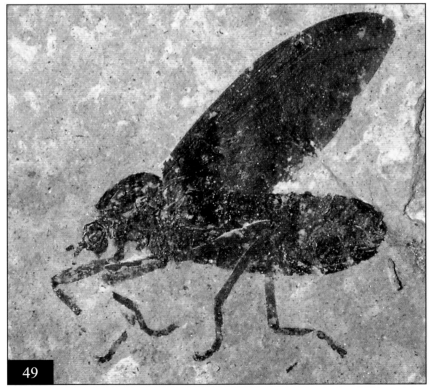

'March' fly (Diptera: Bibionidae) from the Upper Oligocene of Enspel, Germany. GDKE

Enspel, Westerwald, Germany. An Upper Oligocene (24.7 Ma) oil shale deposit with abundant and diverse fossils insects, sometimes with beautiful colour preservation (Figs. 46–48). More than 5000 specimens are known and were treated by Wedmann (2000). A more recent overview of the deposit (including a taxonomic checklist of known fossils) was given by Poschmann *et al.* (2010) and a summary of the insect fauna was provided by Wedmann *et al.* (2010). The mixed insect assemblage is dominated by weevils (Fig. 48), bibionid flies (Fig. 49) and ants, and is indicative of a warm-temperate palaeoclimate. Interestingly, the insect taphocoenosis comprises mainly terrestrial groups that inhabited the surroundings of the former lake, while aquatic insects that lived at least temporarily in the lake are very rare (Wedmann *et al.*, 2010).

Various Tertiary deposits, France. France has a rich fossil insect fauna originating from various Eocene/Oligocene deposits, including from localities such as Sannoisien du Gard, Sannoisien du Haut-Rhin, Camoins-les-Bains près Marseilles, Aix-en-Provence, Céreste (Fig. 116) and Auvergne. Their palaeoentomology was documented by Theobold (1937), but given the age of this work, these fossils are clearly in need of scientific revision (Wappler *et al.*, 2005; Martin *et al.*, 2011). Some of the outcrops from which the fossils were extracted no longer exist.

Various Tertiary deposits, Slovenia. Fossil sites with insect remains are rare in Slovenia, only seven sites are known (Križnar, 2013). A fossil beetle has been documented from Eocene beds at Socka near Dobrna, and two fossil Diptera from Oligocene beds of Zasavje. Some fossil ant and wasp remains were found within Oligocene rocks (Rupelian age) at Rovte. The richest fossil insect sites (two sites) come from the Tunjice Hills near Kamnik. More than 200 specimens of fossil insects were found in the beds of Middle Miocene age (Early Sarmatian), including Odonata (Fig. 240), Coleoptera, Orthoptera, Diptera, Hemiptera and Hymenoptera (Žalohar & Hitij, 2014).

Beetles (Coleoptera: Dytiscidae: *Copelatus convexus* [left]; family uncertain: *Escheria crassipunctata* [right]) from Kleinkems, SW Germany, *ca.* Eocene–Oligocene boundary. Reproduced from Martin *et al.* (2011) with permission. NHMB

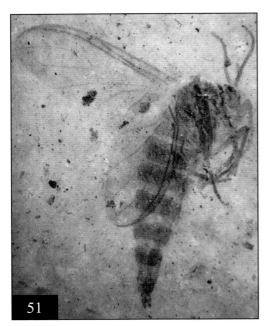

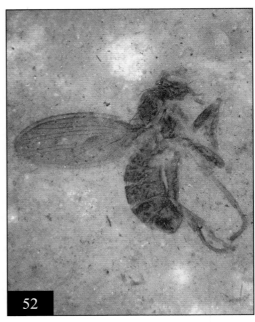

Fly (Diptera: Sciaridae, *cf. Sciara* sp.) from the Miocene of Río Rubiels, Teruel, Spain. PMZU

Fly (Diptera: Dolichopodidae) from the Miocene of Río Rubiels, Teruel, Spain. PMZU

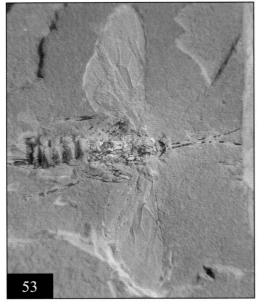

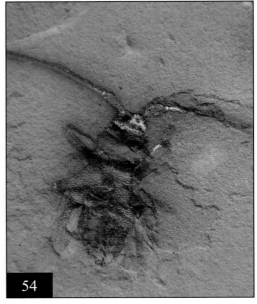

Parasitic wasp *Pimplites praeparatus* (Hymenoptera: Ichneumonidae) from the Late Pliocene of Willerhausen, Germany. GZG

Longhorn beetle *Monochamoides willershausensis* (Coleoptera: Cerambycidae) from the Late Pliocene of Willerhausen, Germany. GZG

Randeck Maar, Germany. This Early/Middle Miocene deposit, 9 km SSE of Kirchheim unter Teck has only just recevied a critical and detailed overview of its fauna and flora (Rasser *et al.*, 2013), although the insects were previously studied by Joachim (2010). The palaeoenvironment appears to have consisted of subhumid sclerophyllous forests and mixed mesophytic forests, and there is an indication for the occurrence of seasonal drought. After plants, insects are the most abundant fossils from the Randeck Maar site. Fifteen orders have been recorded to date, with terrestrial insects rather diverse, but aquatic insects, although common, show a low diversity (Rasser *et al.*, 2013).

Río Rubielos, Teruel, Spain. The Miocene Rubielos de Mora basin is located in the eastern Iberian Chain. Fossil insects are found in the the the oil shale facies, which occur in the upper part of the lacustrine sequence. The insect orders Hemiptera, Diptera (Figs. 51, 52) and Hymenoptera are specially abundant, with Odonata, Dermaptera, Orthoptera, Thysanoptera (Fig. 128), Raphidioptera, Coleoptera, Trichoptera and Lepidoptera also recorded. The most impressive record in Rubielos de Mora concerns Chironomidae (Diptera), which are found as eggs in aggregations, adults fossilized during their emergence from the pupal stage (Peñalver, 2002) and reproductive swarms (Peñalver & Martínez-Delclòs, 1996). The deposit is also important because it includes some wasp families that are otherwise extremely rare in the fossil record (e.g. Peñalver & Engel, 2006). The palaeoentomology of this locality was described by Peñalver (1998). A similar locality rich in fossil insects can be found at Ribesalbes (Castellón) (Peñalver *et al.*, 1996).

Hrútagil, Iceland. The fossil insect orders Plecoptera, Dermaptera, Hemiptera, Coleoptera, Hymenoptera, Trichoptera and Diptera were described from Miocene sedimentary rocks of the Skarðsströnd-Mókollsdalur (9–8 Ma) Formation by Wappler *et al.* (2014). Approximately 180 specimens were examined for their study and the preservation of some of them is excellent. The fauna probably existed in a mixed or borderline temperate-boreal forest. Given that no other Miocene insect faunas are known from this part of the world, the Icelandic fossils provide an important missing link in the palaeobiogeographic history of insects in this region.

Willerhausen, Germany. A locality with abundant arthropods such as insects (Figs. 53, 54) and arachnids from Late Pliocene lake sediments, including some very well preserved material. In total, around 500 fossil species have been described from this deposit; see Meischner (2000) for the most recent overview of this locality. Most of the insects were described by several authors (e.g. Steinbach & Schmidt, 1967; Schmidt, 1967) in two special *Willershausen* issues of the *Berichte der Naturhistorischen Gesellschaft zu Hannover* (Hiltermann & Gersdorf, 1967; Hiltermann & Zobel, 1969), as well as in Beiheft 6 of the same series (Gersdorf & Hiltermann, 1968). For a more recent contribution on ants, see Dlussky *et al.* (2011).

AMBER
Spanish amber with inclusions (Fig. 140) was only discovered relatively recently but has received intensive investigation over the past decade and a half. The identity of the

amber producing tree is still unclear. Thousands of fossil insects have been recovered, many of which are of significant scientific value, as they originate from early in the Cretaceous, when many insect groups were radiating to become pollinators of the first flowering plants. At least 16 insect orders are known from this deposit. For the most recent review see Peñalver & Delclòs (2010).

Charentese amber, from southwest France, has only received attention for its inclusions this century. Many specimens are opaque, which requires synchrotron scanning technology to image and identify the fossils (Fig. 22). In addition to the usual insects associated with trees, this Cretaceous amber has a high proportion of litter and soil dwelling organisms, and is particularly unusual for the relatively large number of brackish and marine groups encountered as inclusions. At least 19 insect orders are known from this amber. For the most recent review of this deposit see Perrichot *et al.* (2010).

Oise amber was discovered in 1996 near Creil, Oise, in France and is still under intensive investigation by researchers in Paris. The quality of preservation is excellent and the fossil insects are diverse. More than 21,000 fossils, mainly insects, have been recovered. It has a relatively 'modern' insect fauna with few extinct families, which appears to be quite distinct from that of the slightly younger Baltic amber. At least 18 insect orders have been recorded. For the most recent reviews of this deposit see Brasero *et al.* (2009) and Nel & Brasero (2010).

Baltic amber, from the Eocene of northern Europe (Fig. 55) is by far the most famous and longest studied amber deposit anywhere in the world, with more than 3500 described fossil species, which are mainly insects representing at least 30 different orders. The fossil assemblage contains a high proportion of aquatic species (Wichard *et al.*, 2009). Unfortunately, many of the early descriptions date from the 1800s and are inadequate by modern scientific standards. To compound this problem, many of the specimens on which the original species descriptions were based (type specimens) have been lost over the years. Despite the intense study of this deposit, there is still considerable controversy regarding the correct family identity of the Baltic amber tree. For the most recent review of this deposit see Weitschat & Wichard (2010).

Rovno amber, from the Ukraine, has only recently been investigated palaeontologically and demonstrated to be different from Baltic amber. Although the two ambers are chemically identical and have many shared fossil species, there are also many unique to this deposit, which is also highly diverse, with at least 23 insect orders recorded to date. A remarkable 227 species of gall midges have been recorded from a single family (Diptera: Cecidomyiidae). For the most recent review of this deposit see Perkovsky *et al.* (2010).

Bitterfeld amber, from Germany (sometimes referred to as Saxonian amber), has always been somewhat in the shadow of amber from the Baltic region. Indeed, its independent origin from the latter has been questioned frequently. The current consensus is that it is a different, younger (Miocene) deposit, despite sharing many fossil species

55

Rare snakefly (Raphidioptera: Inocellidae) in Eocene Baltic amber. PCCG

with the deposits from the Baltic. At least 20 insect orders are known from this deposit. For the most recent review of this deposit see Dunlop (2010).

It has often been speculated that all the northern European Tertiary ambers are contemporaneous and recent research on biting midges suggests this may be the case (Szwedo & Sontag, 2013). However, this short (non-statistical) analysis is by no means conclusive, so here the deposits are treated separately, in their 'conventional' sense.

(Eur)Asia
A considerable number of monograph volumes on fossil insects (in Russian) can be downloaded here: http://www.palaeoentomolog.ru/Publ/publ.html (see also Rasnitsyn & Quicke, 2002). Fossil insects of the Middle and Upper Permian of European Russia (particularly the Vologda Region) were reviewed by Aristov *et al.* (2013) in a substantial work that also described almost 30 new genera and more than 100 new species.

NON-AMBER
Tshekarda, Urals. A very diverse Permian (Kungurian) fossil insect locality with more than 8000 specimens collected and 20 insect orders recorded. These include Ephemeroptera (Fig. 56), Odonata, Orthoptera, Notoptera (grylloblattids), Plecoptera (Fig. 57), Dermaptera, Blattodea, Caloneurodea (Fig. 113), Hypoperlida (Fig. 107), Miomoptera (Fig. 125), Thysanoptera, Psocoptera, Hemiptera, Coleoptera, Megaloptera, Neuroptera, Mecoptera and Trichoptera (Aristov, 2004). The fossils are preserved in fine grained clastic sediments.

Karatau, Kazakhstan. A famous late Jurassic (Kimmeridgian–Oxfordian) fossil insect locality. It has yielded almost 20,000 fossil insects from a lacustrine palaeoenvironment (Rasnitsyn & Quicke, 2002). Orders include Odonata (Fig. 209), Dermaptera, Orthoptera, Blattodea, Psocodea, Hemiptera (Fig. 58), Coleoptera, Neuroptera (Figs. 142, 226), Megaloptera, Hymenoptera (Fig. 148), Diptera (Fig. 59) and Trichoptera (Doludenko *et al.*, 1990; and chapters in Rasnitsyn & Quicke, 2002).

Daohugou, China. A middle Jurassic (Bathonian–Oxfordian) fossil locality, which, like the younger Yixian Formation, has yielded many beautifully preserved insects. Orders recorded include Ephemeroptera, Odonata, Plecoptera, Blattodea, Orthoptera, Hemiptera, Coleoptera, Neuroptera, Hymenoptera (Fig. 61), Diptera and Trichoptera (Fig. 62). Other non-insect fossils include plants and dinosaurs, amongst others. The palaeoenvironment is thought to have been mountain streams and lakes with volcanic input (Fig. 13), with fossils being preserved in grey tuffaceous sandstone and mudstone.

Zaza Formation, Baissa, Siberia. A very productive Lower Cretaceous (Valanginian) insect locality, which has yielded thousands of fossil insects, varying in preservation from wing fragments to complete specimens. Almost 200 families have been recorded, with more than 20 insect orders discovered to date. They include Ephemeroptera, Odonata, Notoptera (grylloblattids), Plecoptera, Blattodea (including Isoptera), Mantodea, Dermaptera (Fig. 60), Orthoptera, Phasmatodea, Psocodea (?Phthiraptera) (Fig. 194),

Thysanoptera, Hemiptera, Megaloptera, Raphidioptera, Neuroptera, Coleoptera (Fig. 173), Mecoptera, Siphonaptera, Trichoptera, Diptera, Lepidoptera and Hymenoptera. The fossil insects are found in the finer grained sediments, representative of lacustrine deposits (Zherikhin *et al.*, 1999).

Yixian Formation, China. A Lower Cretaceous deposit (Hauterivian–Barremian) from northeastern China, where a diverse fauna of fossil insects has been discovered. The insects are beautifully preserved and many species have been described, including Neuroptera (Figs. 63, 144), Odonata, Mecoptera, Diptera (Fig. 64), Hemiptera (see Ren *et al.*, 2010) and Siphonaptera (Fig. 195). The rocks represent a lacustrine palaeoenvironment with the influence of volcanic activity (ash).

Shanwang, China. A Miocene assemblage, located 22 km east of Linqu in central Shandong Province, China. The fossils occur in an accumulation of thousands of diatomaceous layers. Fossil insects are diverse, represented by at least 400 species within 221 genera of 84 families in 12 orders (Hong, 1985; Zhang, 1989; Zhang *et al.*, 1994).

AMBER
Lebanese and Jordanian ambers, at around 130 million-years-old, are the oldest Cretaceous fossil resin deposits yielding a diverse array of fossil insects. They are contemporaneous with the appearance of angiosperms and newly evolving ecosystems, and document the diversification of modern insects and the disappearance of some archaic groups. Some of the oldest 'frozen behaviours' of numerous insect groups in the fossil record (e.g. mating in scatopsid flies, mite parasitism on chironomid midges) are documented from Lebanese amber, which contains at least 20 different insect orders (approximately 17 insect orders are known from the Jordanian deposits). These ambers contain many extinct insect families and also the oldest records of many families still around today. For the most recent reviews of these deposits see Poinar & Milki (2001), Azar *et al.* (2010) and Kaddumi (2007).

Burmese (Myanmar) amber was originally considered Tertiary in age, until subsequent examination of the insect inclusions demonstrated the presence of several archaic families and subfamilies, suggesting an older, Cretaceous origin. This was confirmed by additional palaeontological studies on the host rocks. Burmese amber is found in both Cretaceous primary deposits and also as reworked material in Tertiary rocks. In particular, it preserves a diverse neuropterid (lacewings and allies) fauna. At least 26 insect orders are known from this 99 million-year-old (Shi *et al.*, 2012) deposit, including some of the oldest known ants (Barden & Grimaldi, 2012). For the most recent review of this deposit see Ross *et al.* (2010).

Russian amber originates from both Tertiary (e.g. Sakhalin Island) and Cretaceous (e.g. Taimyr Peninsula, northern Siberia) deposits from various regions. Although many specimens contain fossil insects, relatively few have been formally studied and described. For the most recent review of these deposits see Zherikhin & Eskov (1999).

Misthodotes sharovi (Ephemeroptera: Misthodotidae) from the Permian of Tshekarda, Russia. PIN 1700-338

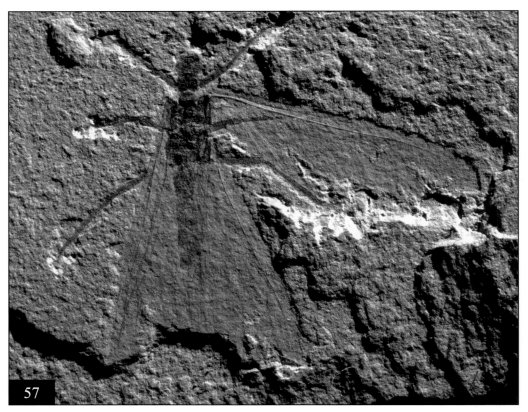

Perlopsis filicornis (Plecoptera: Perlopseidae) from the Permian of Tshekarda, Russia. PIN 1700-1212

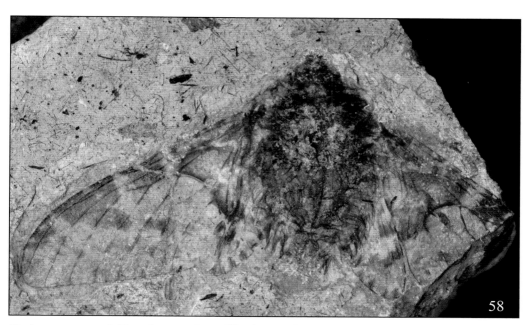

Martynovocossus (=*Pseudocossus*) sp. (Hemiptera: Auchenorrhyncha: Paleontinidae) from the Jurassic of Karatau, Kazakhstan. PIN 2904-445

Praemacrochile ansorgei (Diptera: Tanyderidae) from the Jurassic of Karatau, Kazakhstan. Holotype, PIN

60

Earwig (Dermaptera: Pygidicranidae) from the Cretaceous of Baissa, Russia. PIN 1989-2941

Wasp (Hymenoptera) from the Jurassic of Daohugou, China. RCJN

Caddisfly (Trichoptera) from the Jurassic of Daohugou, China. RCJN

Mantis-fly *Archaeodrepanicus nuddsi* (Neuroptera: Mantispidae) from the Lower Cretaceous Yixian Formation, China. Holotype, CNU-NEU-LB2011001P

Fly (Diptera) from the Lower Cretaceous Yixian Formation, China. RCJN

Indian amber, from Vastan, Gujarat is the only known amber deposit from the Indian subcontinent, and was only discovered this century. The investigation of its inclusions is still at a very early stage, but they have the potential to be informative in terms of past biogeography, because this lowermost Eocene amber was formed before the Indian–Asian tectonic plates collided, approximately 50 million years ago. To date, approximately 12 insect orders have been identified, but only a handful of inclusions have been described. For the most recent review of this deposit see Rust *et al.* (2010).

Chinese amber originates from the coal seams of the Guchengzi Formation of the Fushun Coal Mine in Fushu City, Liaoning Province and is Early Eocene in age. Fossil insects are abundant in this deposit, with most of the descriptions to date published in Chinese. For the most recent review of this deposit see Hong (2002).

Australia
For a taxonomic catalogue of the known fossil insects of Australia see Jell (2004), who provides a more extensive list of deposits than that given below.

NON-AMBER
Newcastle Coal Measures, Belmont, New South Wales. A Permian (Tatarian) locality, which has so far yielded representatives of the orders Mecoptera, Plecoptera, Odonata, Trichoptera, Neuroptera, Psocodea, Coleoptera, Hemiptera, Hypoperlida and Notoptera (grylloblattids) (the last two described by Rasnitsyn & Aristov, 2013). The fossils are preserved in fine-grained volcaniclastic tuff beds (Tillyard, 1918, 1929, 1935, 1937; Willmann, 1989; Jell, 2004; Beattie, 2007). The fauna is considered to be unbalanced in comparison with other localities, due to its lack of Blattodea and Orthoptera (Schlüter, 2003).

Ipswich Coal Measures, Mount Crosby, Queensland. This Triassic (Carnian) locality has yielded more than 1000 fossil insects, dominated by Blattodea and with representatives of Mecoptera, Neuroptera, Trichoptera, Diptera, Hemiptera, Coleoptera, Hymenoptera, Plecoptera, Orthoptera and Odonata (Riek, 1970; Schlüter, 2003; Jell, 2004). Coleoptera and Orthoptera are few in number, with many other orders being represented by just one or two specimens (Schlüter, 2003). Aquatic insect orders are also poorly represented in this deposit (Tindale, 1946). The fossiliferous shales are indicative of restricted, quiet lacustrine conditions (Jell, 2004) (Fig. 11). An additional Triassic Ipswich Coal Measures insect fauna can be found at Denmark Hill, southeastern Queensland (e.g. Lamkin, 2014).

Perth Basin, Western Australia. This Lower Jurassic (Sinemurian–Toarcian) Mintaja locality preserves highly disarticulated insect remains in a single layer of fine, brown siltstone. The fossils are biased towards highly sclerotized elements and taxa, such as elytra and heads. The assemblage includes mainly beetles (Fig. 66), but also documented are Blattodea (Fig. 65), Hemiptera, Mecoptera, Neuroptera, Notoptera (grylloblattids) and Diptera. This fossil fauna was re-discovered very recently (Martin, 2008).

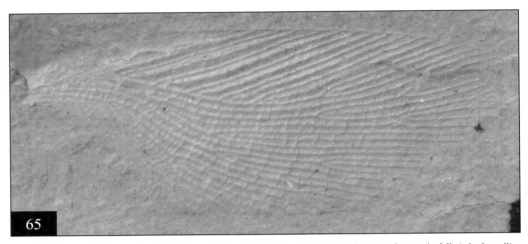

65

Kurablattina mintajaensis ('Blattodea': Liberiblattinidae) from the Lower Jurassic Mintaja locality, Australia. WAM 09.84(c)

66

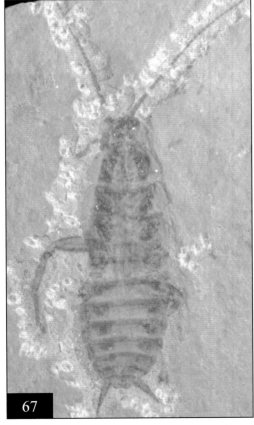

67

Zygadenia sp. (Coleoptera: Ommatidae) from the Lower Jurassic Mintaja locality, Australia. WAM 08.173(p)

'Methana' sp. (Blattodea nymph, ?Mesoblatti-dae) from the Lower Cretaceous of Koonwarra, Australia. MVM P102532

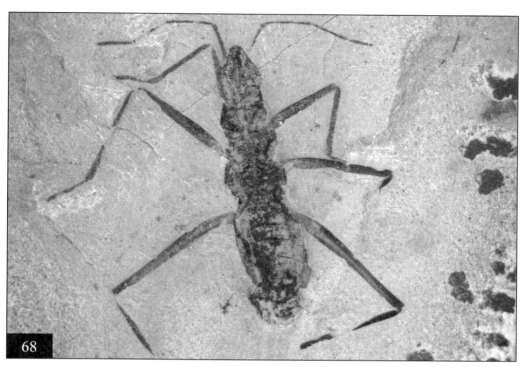

Duncanovelia extensa (Hemiptera: Heteroptera: family uncertain – see Damgaard *et al.*, 2012) from the Lower Cretaceous of Koonwarra, Australia. Holotype, MVM P27004

Peraphlebia tetrastichia (Odonata: family uncertain) from the Lower Cretaceous of Koonwarra, Australia. Holotype, MVM P103204

Talbragar Fish Beds, New South Wales. Fossil insects from this Upper Jurassic locality have only recently been collected in reasonable numbers. Around 100 specimens are known, most of which await formal description. The entomofauna is dominated by Hemiptera, followed by Coleoptera (Cai *et al.*, 2013), then <5% each of Orthoptera, Diptera, Plecoptera, Mecoptera, Odonata (Beattie & Nel, 2012), Neuroptera, Raphidioptera and Hymenoptera (Beattie & Avery, 2012; Selden & Beattie, 2013).

Koonwarra, Victoria. A Lower Cretaceous (Aptian) fossil insect locality that has yielded thousands of fossils preserved in a varved lacustrine sequence, with more than 70 insect species described and 13 orders recorded. The fauna is dominated by Ephemeroptera, Hemiptera (Fig. 68), Coleoptera and Diptera, with smaller numbers of Odonata (Fig. 69), Blattodea (Fig. 67), Plecoptera, Orthoptera, Psocodea, Mecoptera, Trichoptera, Hymenoptera and ?Siphonaptera (Schlüter, 2003). The fauna also has a very high number of immature insects present (Jell & Duncan, 1986; Jell, 2004; Fikáček *et al.*, 2014).

Redbank Plains Series and Dinmore, Queensland. The palaeoenvironment of these Lower Tertiary deposits has been interpreted as lacustrine, originating from two lakes (Riek, 1970; Schlüter, 2003). Redbank Plains is a hardened band of mudstone, dominated by Hemiptera and Coleoptera, with a few Neuroptera, Mecoptera, Orthoptera and Diptera. Dinmore consists of compact clays and clay shales containing representatives of Isoptera, Hemiptera, Megaloptera, Orthoptera and possibly Odonata (Jell, 2004).

AMBER
Cape York amber, from Australia, was discovered in 2003 and is currently being investigated. At least 300 inclusions, representing 25 families of terrestrial arthropods (mainly insects: Coleoptera, Diptera, Hymenoptera, Isoptera, Lepidoptera, Thysanoptera and Neuroptera) have been found in this richly fossiliferous amber deposit, although only a single species of insect has been described so far (Diptera: Dolichopodidae). For the most recent review of this deposit see Hand *et al.* (2010). Previous reports of fossil insects preserved in what was thought to be Tertiary amber from Allendale, Victoria are now considered to be preserved in copal (see later).

New Zealand
Entomological reviews of both newly discovered deposits below are currently in preparation by Uwe Kaulfuss (University of Otago), in conjunction with Alex Schmidt (Göttingen) for the amber.

NON-AMBER
Foulden Maar, Otago. An Early Miocene (23 Ma) maar–diatreme volcano with a crater infilled by highly fossiliferous laminated lacustrine diatomite. The terrestrial element of the fossil assemblage originates from a Lauraceae-dominated subtropical rainforest surrounding the maar lake (Bannister *et al.*, 2012). The fossil insect fauna is currently being formally described by Uwe Kaulfuss (University of Otago). Several orders have been identified to date, including Odonata, Plecoptera, Isoptera, Hemiptera, Coleoptera,

70

Straight-snouted weevil (Coleoptera: Brentidae: Apioninae) from the Miocene of Hindon Maar, Otago, New Zealand. OU

Hymenoptera, Trichoptera and Diptera (Kaulfuss *et al.*, 2011, 2013). Preliminary excavations at Hindon Maar, Otago (also a Miocene diatomite) have yielded well preserved insects from the orders Coleoptera (Fig. 70), Trichoptera and Hymenoptera.

AMBER

South Island amber, from various localities is still in its very early stages of study by Alex Schmidt and colleagues. The amber is mostly of Cenozoic age (Late Oligocene–Early Miocene) and several insect orders (and arachnids) have been discovered, including Collembola (Fig. 91), Coleoptera, Diptera, Hymenoptera, Hemiptera and Lepidoptera (wing scales only) (Kaulfuss *et al.*, 2013). Notable results to date include a diverse soil-dwelling mite fauna (Kiecksee *et al.*, 2013).

Africa

NON-AMBER

African Carboniferous insects are little known (Schlüter, 2003), with only scarce records of Protorthoptera from the Matabola Flats, Zimbabwe (Riek, 1974a) and Mavanova River, Madagascar (Paulian, 1965). Coleoptera and a tentative Isoptera were recently described in Late Cretaceous (Cenomanian–Turonian) marine sediments from Morocco (Engel *et al.*, 2012). Schlüter (1981) provided a systematic account of 14 Jurassic/Cretaceous insect fossils (Odonata, ?Isoptera, Hemiptera and Coleoptera) from three localities in Egypt. Engel *et al.* (2013b) described a new Ethiopian Paleogene termite species from well preserved wings.

Estcourt Formation, Karoo Basin, South Africa. A globally significant Upper Permian (Lopingian) insect and plant deposit. The formation is known from 25 sites over 200 km in South Africa (Schlüter, 2003). More than 70 species have been recorded, with representatives of Protorthoptera, Megasecoptera, Blattodea, Orthoptera, Miomoptera, Hemiptera, Trichoptera and Neuroptera known. The insect fauna is dominated by Hemiptera (Van Dijk, 1997; Van Dijk & Geertseema, 1999).

Molteno Formation, Karoo Basin, South Africa. A very diverse insect locality from the Triassic (Carnian). Around 18 orders have been documented and thousands of specimens collected (Anderson *et al.*, 1998). Much of the early work was completed by Riek (1974b, 1976) who documented 11 orders, 22 families and described 32 species. The insects are preserved as isolated wings, with few articulated remains.

Orapa, Botswana. More than 5500 fossil insects have been collected from this Cretaceous (Turonian) site (Brothers, 1992; Brothers & Rasnitsyn, 2003), including representatives of the orders Orthoptera, Blattodea, Dermaptera, Hemiptera, Diptera, Hymenoptera and Coleoptera, which dominate the fauna (Rayner *et al.*, 1997). The palaeoenvironment is thought to have been a toxic crater lake, where insects died soon after contact with the water, explaining the absence of aquatic insects (Schlüter, 2003).

Mfwanganu and Ruzinga Islands, Lake Victoria, Kenya. These localities have yielded some exceptionally preserved insects, the age of the deposits is Miocene. Little work has been done on these localities, with only a caterpillar of a lepidopteran (Leakey, 1952), an ant colony (Wilson & Taylor, 1964) and a nest of sweat bees (Thackray, 1994) described. More than 120 specimens have been collected, with representatives of Hemiptera, Coleoptera, Lepidoptera and Hymenoptera recorded to date. The insects are preserved in volcaniclastic sediments, which preserve great detail. Indeed, these sites can probably be classed as Lagerstätten (Schlüter, 2003).

AMBER

Ethiopian amber, from Cretaceous sandstone, and which contains bountiful fossil inclusions, was first reported in 2010. It provides the earliest African evidence of important ecological groups and is of major significance for understanding the biogeography and evolutionary history of the African biota. Hexapod orders identified to date include: Collembola, Psocodea, Hemiptera, Thysanoptera, Zoraptera, Lepidoptera, Coleoptera, Diptera and Hymenoptera. For the most recent review of this deposit see Schmidt *et al.* (2010).

The Americas
NON-AMBER
Mazon Creek, Illinois, USA. A very famous and important Upper Carboniferous (mid-Pennsylvanian) fossil locality. Various early insects have been found, including Protodonata, Palaeodictyoptera, Paoliida (Fig. 119), Megasecoptera, Protorthoptera and 'Blattodea' *s.l.* (Carpenter, 1997). Other than insects, there is an exceptional fauna of other invertebrates, including the strange marine invertebrate *Tullimonstrum gregarium*

(the state fossil of Illinois), as well as beautifully preserved vertebrates and plants. The fossils are preserved in ironstone nodules, found scattered in old strip coal mines. They provide evidence of both terrestrial and marine palaeoenvironments (Shabica & Hay, 1997; Wittry, 2012).

Elmo, Kansas, USA. An important Permian locality (Artinskian). More than 15,000 specimens have been collected and 17 orders and 150 species have been described, including the orders Protodonata (Fig. 72), Palaeodictyoptera (Fig. 104) and Megasecoptera (Beckemeyer, 2000). This includes the largest ever discovered insect *Meganeuropsis permiana* (Protodonata: Meganeuridae), which had a wing span of 710 mm. The rock types represent a freshwater lake palaeoenvironment with a vegetated border (Beckemeyer, 2000). An equally productive (but less well-known) site is located approximately 270 km further south, in Oklahoma (Beckemeyer & Hall, 2007).

Cascade, Virginia, USA. A Late Triassic (Carnian) assemblage of fossil insects preserved as aluminosilicate films on very fine-grained shales from the Solite Quarry, Cow Branch Formation, part of the Newark Supergroup of Early Mesozoic rift basins from eastern North America. Fraser *et al.* (1996) reported the orders Blattodea, Coleoptera, Diptera, Hemiptera, Orthoptera, Thysanoptera and Trichoptera. The flies were studied in detail by Blagoderov *et al.* (2007); Thysanoptera and Coleoptera have also been described.

Mendoza and Los Rastros Provinces, South America. These localities are upper Triassic in age (Rhaetian). The deposits are found predominantly in Argentina, but they do extend into Brazil. The insect fauna is diverse, including Odonata, Plecoptera (Fig. 74), Orthoptera, 'Blattodea' *s.l.* (Fig. 76), Miomoptera, Hemiptera, Coleoptera (Fig. 134) (Lara *et al.*, 2012), Diptera (Lara & Lukashevich, 2013), Mecoptera (Fig. 73), Hymenoptera (Lara *et al.*, 2014), Notoptera (Fig. 76) and Glosselytrodea. The palaeoenvironment of deposition was lacustrine. A review of South American deposits was given by Martins-Neto *et al.* (2003; see also Martins-Neto *et al.*, 2007, 2008). Slightly younger Triassic insect remains from Argentina were described by Brauckmann *et al.* (2010).

Crato Formation, Brazil. A very important and diverse fossil insect fauna from the Lower Cretaceous (Aptian). The fauna and flora has recently been reviewed by Martill *et al.* (2007). The insect fauna is represented by more than 20 insect orders, with more than a hundred species described to date. The fauna includes the new insect order Coxoplectoptera (Figs. 95, 96) and a very diverse fauna of neuropteroid insects (lacewings, snakeflies and dobsonflies), including the only known Southern Hemisphere snakeflies and the proposed extinct order Schwickertoptera (see papers in Martill *et al.*, 2007). The insects are beautifully preserved (Figs. 77–81) in a very fine-grained limestone, representing an arid and saline lacustrine palaeoenvironment (Fig. 15).

Okanagan Highlands, British Columbia, Canada (and Washington State, USA). The series of deposits collectively referred to as the Okanagan Highlands spans a 1000 km transect from northern Washington State to central British Columbia. Fossil insects

Syntonoptera schucherti (Syntonopterida: Syntonopteridae) from the Upper Carboniferous of Mazon Creek, USA. Holotype, YPM 19

Megatypus schucherti (Protodonata: Meganeuridae) from the Permian of Elmo, Kansas, USA. Holotype, YPM 1021

associated with forest, lakes and swamps from upland communities in a warm and seasonable equable climate are found in lacustrine shales and are preserved in stunning detail (Figs. 82, 156). Important fossil insect sites include Driftwood Canyon, Horesefly and McAbee. The fossil assemblage reflects a world in transition, with many modern elements and unusual extinct taxa (Archibald *et al.*, 2011, 2013b).

Green River Formation, USA. A very famous fossil insect locality from the Eocene. The deposit represents an extremely large fossil lake system, 65,000 km^2 in area and 600 m thick (Grimaldi & Engel, 2005). From the Parachute Creek Member, Lake Uinta, a diverse fauna of insects has been documented, including 14 orders, 100 families and more than 300 species of both aquatic and terrestrial insects (Figs. 83, 84, 122). Many species were described by one of the founders of palaeoentomology (Samuel H. Scud-

Mendozachorista volkheimeri (*incertae sedis* ?Mecoptera: Mendozachoristidae) from the Late Triassic of Mendoza Province, Argentina. Holotype, MCNAM-PI 24527

Platyperla marquati (Plecoptera: Platyperlidae) from the Late Triassic of Mendoza Province, Argentina. Holotype, MCNAM-PI 24312

Mancusoblatta pulchella ('Blattodea' *s.l.*: Mancusoblattidae) from the Late Triassic of La Rioja Province, Argentina. Holotype, PULR-I 288

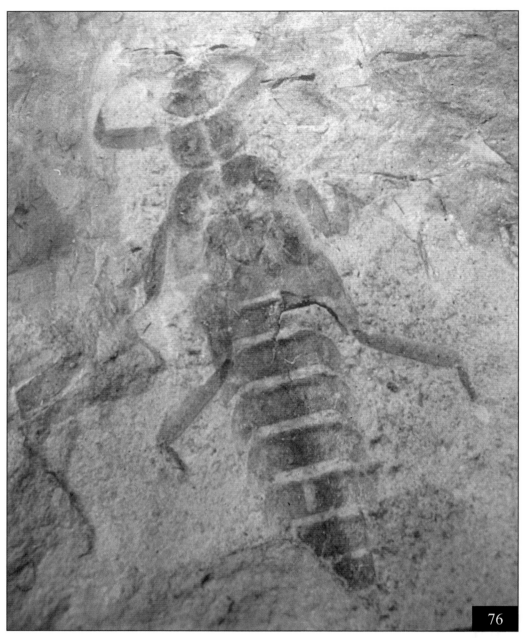

76

Triasseuryptilon acostai (Notoptera: Grylloblattodea) from the Late Triassic of Mendoza Province, Argentina. Holotype, MMNH 1518 der, 1890). Despite the long history of research on these insects, some orders have been formally described for the first time only very recently, e.g. Raphidioptera by Engel (2011). Notable fossil insects include beautifully preserved rare butterflies. Numerous beautiful and undescribed specimens from the Fossil Butte Member were figured and discussed in the excellent book by Grande (2013).

Florissant Formation, USA. Late Eocene to Early Oligocene in age, this site has become world famous for its fossil insects (see Meyer, 2003 and Meyer & Smith, 2008 for more comprehensive accounts; Emmel *et al.*, 1992 for butterflies in particular), with fine detail such as eyes, lepidopteran wing scales and setae preserved. There have been 200 families and more than 1000 fossil insect species described so far, although many require taxonomic revision (e.g. Makarkin & Archibald, 2014). The preservation is exceptional (Figs. 85–87, 172), with the fossils being preserved in fine-grained shale formed by fine ash deposits from volcanic eruptions. The three fossiliferous shale units, which include most of the fossil insects, are lithologically heterogeneous and consist of thinly laminated shale interbedded with tuffaceous mudstone and siltstone beds, tuffs, and pumiceous sandstone and conglomerate beds (Evanoff *et al.*, 2001). Theone Henning *et al.* (2012) sampled across these lithologies in a comparative study of bias and taphonomy. Specimens were smaller and less variable in size in the siltstone, but otherwise no significant differences were found, including in the diversity and relative abundance of individuals in the different layers. Much of the deposits now form part of the *Florrisant Fossil Beds National Monument*. Most of the early work on the fauna was completed by Scudder (1890) and Cockerell (e.g. 1907, 1908, 1909, 1914).

Barstow Formation, USA. A Miocene death assemblage of fossil insects preserved in a saline-alkaline lake system from southern California. The concretion horizons yield all ontogenetic stages of the diving beetle *Schistomerus californensis* (Dytiscidae), fly larvae and pupae (Ceratopogonidae and Culicidae) and Hymenoptera. Also known from this deposit are Collembola, Odonata, Plecoptera, Orthoptera, Isoptera, Hemiptera and Thysanoptera (Park & Downing, 2001).

Rancho La Brea, USA. This deposit comprises of a number of tar pits in Los Angeles, with fossils dating back to the Pleistocene. As well as the famous large Pleistocene mammals, a number of insect fossils have been discovered in the asphalt impregnated sediments, including Orthoptera, Hemiptera, Coleoptera (Fig. 88) and Diptera (Miller, 1997). The presence of carcass-exploiting insects in the Rancho La Brea biota provides insight into the taphonomy of the asphaltic vertebrate bone masses and the palaeoenvironmental conditions under which they accumulated (Holden *et al.*, 2013). In addition to this famous locality, equally fossiliferous coeval deposits are also known at Carpinteria (Santa Barbara County), Maricopa (Kern County) and McKittrick (Kern County), all preserving rich fossil assemblages of Late Pleistocene age (approximately 38,000 years-old) (e.g. Heads & Wang, 2013). Recently, computed tomography was used to identify fossil bee pupae (Hymenoptera: Megachilidae) inside rolled-up leaves, from specimens that had originally been collected in the 1970s (Holden *et al.*, 2014).

77

Cearagryllus perforatorius (Orthoptera: Baissogryllidae) from the Cretaceous Crato Formation, Brazil. RCDP

78

New family of cicada (Hemiptera: Cicadomorpha) from the Cretaceous Crato Formation, Brazil. RCDP

79

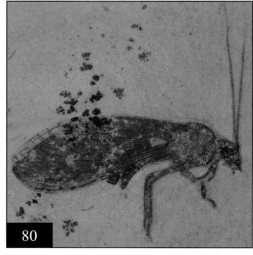

80

Wasp (Hymenoptera) from the Cretaceous Crato Formation, Brazil. RCDP

Lacewing (Neuroptera: Mesochrysopidae) from the Cretaceous Crato Formation, Brazil. RCDP

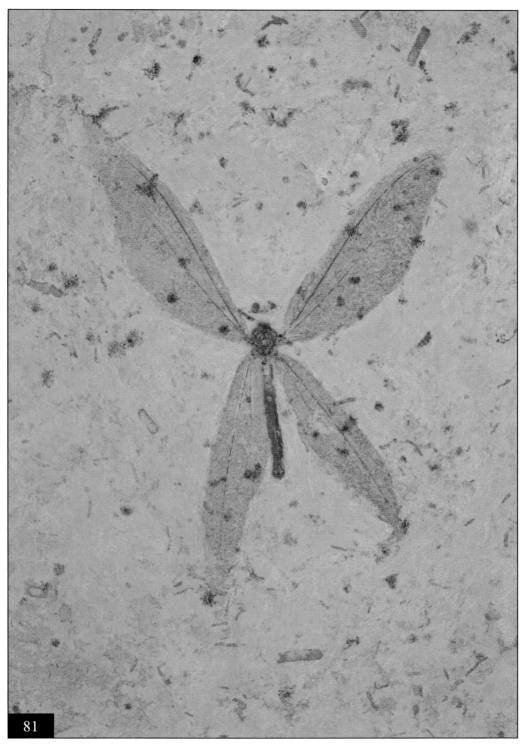

81

Lacewing (Neuroptera: Araripaneuridae) from the Cretaceous Crato Formation, Brazil. RCDP

Fugus gnat (Diptera: Mycetophilidae) from the Early Eocene Driftwood Canyon in the Okanagan Highlands, British Columbia. BCP

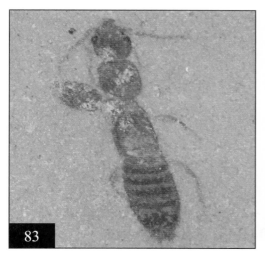

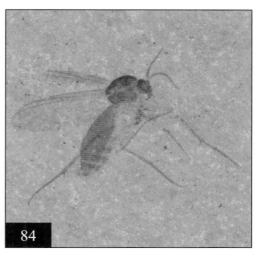

Rove beetle (Coleoptera: Staphylinidae) from the Tertiary of Green River, USA. RCDP

Gnat (Diptera: Sciaridae) from the Tertiary of Green River, USA. RCDP

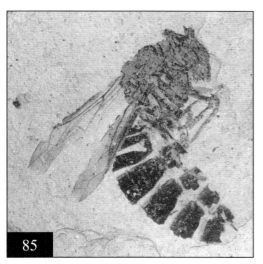

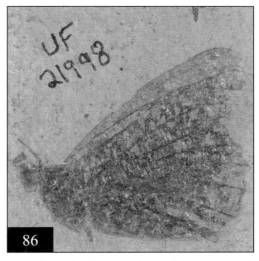

Palaeovespa florissantia (Hymenoptera: Vespidae) from the Tertiary of Florissant, USA. FLFO-50

Oligodonta florissantensis (Lepidoptera: Pieridae) from the Tertiary of Florissant, USA. Holotype, FLFO UF21998

Green Lacewing (Neuroptera: Chrysopidae) from the Tertiary of Florissant, USA. FLFO

Siri Scientific Press

Water beetle *Cybister* sp. (Coleoptera: Dytiscidae) from the Pleistocene tar pits of Rancho La Brea, California, USA. RCDP

AMBER

New Jersey (Raritan) amber is the most significant amber deposit in the United States. This Cretaceous (Turonian) deposit was discovered in the 1990s and has yielded thousands of fossil insects, many of which are still being studied (e.g. Dikow & Grimaldi, 2014). Particularly notable is the high diversity of ant subfamilies. It also contains an unusually high abundance of scale insects (Coccoidea) and Lepidoptera, relative to other ambers of a similar age. At least 15 insect orders are known from this 90–94 million-years-old deposit. For the most recent review of this deposit see Grimaldi & Nascimbene (2010) and for more specific coverage of certain insect inclusions see Grimaldi (2000). Some non-amber fossil insects have also been recovered from the amber locality (Lubkin, 2003).

Canadian amber is of particular interest because it represents the last known diverse fossil insect assemblage before the end-Cretaceous extinction event. It comes from two main areas: Grassy Lake in Alberta and Cedar Lake in Manitoba, the latter being a secondary deposit of the former. Unfortunately, little research has focussed on this fauna, despite the large collections preserved in Canadian museums, which include 11 insect orders identified to date. For the most recent review of this deposit see McKellar & Wolfe (2010). A smaller amber deposit with fossil insects is known from the Early Eocene of British Columbia, but few insects have been described.

Dominican amber, from the Caribbean island of Hispaniola (Dominican Republic not Dominica), probably exhibits the highest degree of preservation of fossil insects of all known ambers (Fig. 89). Despite the relatively late onset of study of this 16 million-years-old Miocene deposit in the 1960s, more than 1000 fossil species (mainly insects) have been described. Most of their closest relatives live in the Neotropics today, but

89

Tiny (body length = 3.9 mm) lace bug *Phatnoma mattijoae* (Hemiptera: Tingidae) in Miocene amber from the Dominican Republic, showing the remarkable preservative qualities of this particular fossil resin. Holotype, NHM II 3047

Termite swarm *Coptotermes sucineus* (Isoptera: Rhinotermitidae), in Miocene amber from Chiapas, Mexico. CU

some do not. For example, the fossil termite, *Mastotermes electrodominicus*, has its closest affinities with extant Australian species. For the most recent review of this deposit see Penney (2010b).

Mexican amber, from the state of Chiapas in southern Mexico, is considered to be the same age as Dominican amber and was produced by the same type of tree. However, the quality of preservation of its inclusions is not always as good, possibly due to exposure to increased temperature and pressure, resulting from past volcanic activity in the region. Nonetheless, sometimes the fossils are extremely well preserved (Fig. 90). These fossil insects have received less attention than those in Dominican amber, yet comparison of both faunas (one being continental, the other insular) has great potential to help us understand the origins of Caribbean insect biodiversity. For the most recent review of this deposit see Solórzano Kraemer (2010) and for a more extensive account see Solórzano Kraemer (2007).

Diversity of fossil insects

Given that more than 99% of all insect species that have ever existed are extinct, full coverage of the entire insect fossil record would be an immense undertaking well beyond the scope of this work. The most recent synthesis was the *Treatise on Invertebrate Paleontology* volume by Carpenter (1992); revised volumes in this series are now being published, but the Hexapoda volume is not yet complete. Here we provide a general overview of the fossil record for each insect order, without getting bogged down with long lists of specific localities or species. The orders (as defined here) are considered in their loose sense, because in many cases it can be difficult to differentiate unequivocally the modern forms from their more primitive relatives. Readers who wish to delve further can do so via the more extensive texts cited throughout this book (e.g. Beutel *et al.*, 2014) and newer works that had not been published at the time of writing. For example, the descriptions of at least two new fossil insect orders are in preparation for fossils preserved in Cretaceous Burmese amber. In some instances we refer to the fossil insect database (EDNA). This database is not fully up-to-date in terms of numbers of species and whether or not species names have been synonymized. Nonetheless, our reference to it is intended to give a broad overview of the relevant fossil record. Numbers of described extant species are mostly rounded off approximate values. Russian palaeoentomologists tend to use a different order level nomenclature to that commonly used in the West, so these names are also provided where appropriate.

Hexapoda: 'Entognatha'

Springtails (Collembola)
Geological range.—Devonian–Recent

Identification.—Living springtails are easily identified by their small size, absence of wings, four-segmented antennae and six-segmented abdomen with a jumping organ (furcula) on the fourth segment.

Extant Biodiversity.—8130 species described (Janssens & Christiansen, 2011).

Palaeontology.—Both rounded (symphypleonean) and elongated (arthropleonean) springtails are common and diverse as fossils in amber (Fig. 91) from most known deposits. Collembolan fossils such as *Rhyniella praecursor* from the Devonian (400 million years ago) Rhynie Chert of Scotland are among the oldest recorded land animals. A fossil springtail has been found attached to the wing of a mayfly in Dominican amber, shedding light on a potential dispersal technique for the order (Penney *et al.*, 2012a).

Coneheads (Protura)
Geological range: Recent

Identification.—Coneheads are identified by their minute size (<1.5 mm), slender body with simple morphology (12 abdominal segments, no antennae or eyes). Their forelegs are projected forward and function as sensory appendages (covered in many sensory structures), rather than being used for locomotion; the tarsi consist of a single segment. These sensory structures are important in the taxonomy of the order.

Extant Biodiversity.—800 species described (Zhang, 2011).

Palaeontology.—No fossils found to date.

Two-pronged bristletails (Diplura)
Geological range: ?Devonian–Recent

Identification.—Diplurans are identified by their leg morphology – the articulation between the trochanter and femur, and femur and tibia is monocondylic (joint with a single point of articulation), most other hexapods are dicondylic (two points of articulation). Eyes are absent, body size is small (<7 mm), abdomen with ten segments.

Extant Biodiversity.—800 species described (Zhang, 2011).

Palaeontology.—The fossil record of diplurans is extremely poor. Campodeidae have been described from Baltic amber (Fig. 92), and Procampodeidae and Japygidae are known from Dominican and Mexican ambers respectively. Non-amber fossils occur in the Pliocene onyx marble of Arizona and from the Cretaceous Crato Formation of Brazil (Wilson & Martill, 2001), with an additional, highly controversial specimen from the Upper Carboniferous of Mazon Creek, USA, tentatively considered as Dermaptera rather than Diplura by Staniczek *et al.* (2014). Given the primitive nature of these hexapods, it has been proposed that they already existed by the Early Devonian.

Hexapoda: Ectognatha (Insecta & Dicondylia) († = extinct order)

Bristletails (Archaeognatha = Microcoryphia)
Geological range: Devonian–Recent

Identification.—Bristletails can be identified by their wingless, cylindrical body (covered with minute scales), large compound eyes (which meet at the top of the head), well developed ocelli, long and segmented maxillary palps, multi-segmented antennae and cerci with a long median filament. The mandible articulation has a single condyle, whereas all higher insects have two.

Extant Biodiversity.—500 species described (Grimaldi & Engel, 2005).

Palaeontology.—Bristletails are the most primitive living insects, with their geological history dating back to the Mid-Devonian. However, their fossil record is relatively sparse and often consists of poorly preserved or fragmentary material. The best preserved specimens are found in various Tertiary and Cretaceous ambers (Fig. 93). The majority of fossil species have been described from Eocene Baltic amber (in need of revision), with

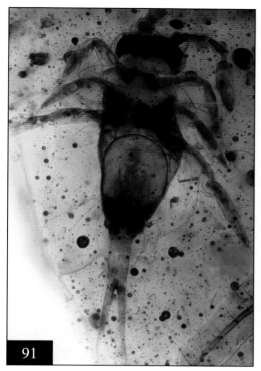

91

Springtail (Collembola: Entomobryidae) in Miocene amber from New Zealand. OU(GC)

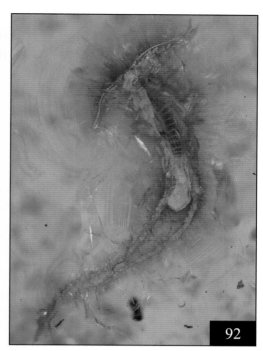

92

Campodea darwinii (Diplura: Campodeidae) in Eocene Baltic amber. RCDP

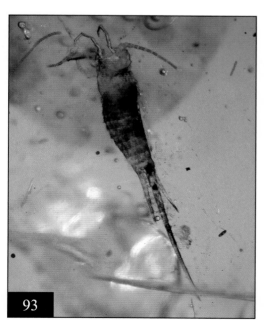

93

Neomachiellus dominicanus (Archaeognatha: Meinertellidae) in Miocene Dominican amber. RCDP

94

Lampropholis dubia (Zygentoma: Lepismatidae) in Eocene Baltic amber. PCYCT

a few rock records from the Carboniferous of France and North America, the Permian of Russia and North America, and a single record from the Triassic of Russia. A Devonian fossil from Gaspé, Québec was originally described in this order by Labandeira *et al.* (1988), but was most likely misidentified.

Silverfish (Zygentoma) (= Lepismatida)
Geological range: Cretaceous–Recent

Identification.—Silverfish are wingless, medium-sized insects. Eyes small or absent, most families lack ocelli (an exception is Lepidotrichidae). Coxae enlarged. The body is flattened, bearing bristles or scales, cerci are present with a long median filament. See Blanke *et al.* (2014) for the most recent opinion on the classification of this order.

Extant Biodiversity.—500 species described (Beutel *et al.*, 2014).

Palaeontology.—The fossil record of silverfish is almost entirely restricted to Tertiary and Cretaceous ambers, with records from most of the fossiliferous deposits (Fig. 94). Two compression fossils have been recovered from the Cretaceous Crato Formation of Brazil, and there are dubious specimens described from the onyx marble thermal deposits of Arizona, but their true identity remains to be confirmed. Some fossils identified from the Devonian of Gilboa, New York and the Late Carboniferous of the Czech Republic may also be silverfish, but these placements are considered uncertain by palaeoentomologists (Grimaldi & Engel, 2005). Given that the order can be expected to have existed as far back as Devonian times, there is a large gap in the fossil record for this order.

Chimera wings (†Coxoplectoptera)
Geological range: Jurassic–Cretaceous

Identification.—Adults resemble mayflies and are identified by having two pairs of wings with dense venation. The hind wing is large with an enlarged anal area. Numerous crossveins separating the costal brace from the costal margin. They have large eyes, a skewed prothorax, raptorial forelegs and free coxae. Nymphs are aquatic, shrimp-like with strongly armoured head and gills.

Palaeontology.—The fossil record is so far limited to two deposits. One larva is known from the Jurassic of Transbaikalia (Tshernova, 1977) and adults and larvae have been described from the Crato Formation of Brazil (Figs. 95, 96) (Staniczek *et al.*, 2011).

Syntonopterids (†Syntonopterida)
Geological range: Carboniferous–Permian

Identification.—Large to very large primitive mayfly-like insects. They have a slender body with four wings similar in length, but with the hind wings slightly broader basally.

Coxoplectoptera (Mickoleitiidae) from the Cretaceous Crato Formation, Brazil. Left: *Mickoleitia longimanus.* Holotype, SMNS 66550; Above: *Mickoleitia* sp. larva. SMNS 66547

Palaeontology.—Several fossils (Figs. 31, 71) have been described from Europe (including the UK and France), the Urals (western Russia) and North America (see Rasnitsyn & Quicke, 2002). Prokop *et al.* (2010) described a new fossil from the UK and considered syntonopterids sister to Ephemeroptera, though Prokop & Nel (2011) included Syntonopteridae within Ephemeroptera.

Mayflies (Ephemeroptera) (= Ephemerida)
Geological range: Permian–Recent

Identification.—Mayflies are identified by their large forewings and reduced hind wings with dense wing venation. The adults have 2–3 long, filamentous 'tails' (cerci +/- caudal median filament) from their abdomen. Antennae are short and fine. The mouthparts are vestigial in adults and males have enlarged eyes. Nymphs are aquatic with lateral gills.

Extant Biodiversity.—3250 species described (Zhang, 2011).

Palaeontology.—Well represented in the fossil record, with both adults and nymphs known, representing more than 200 described species. They are first recorded in the

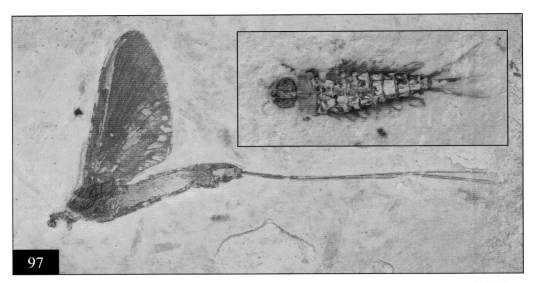

Ephemeroptera adult and larva (inset) from the Cretaceous Crato Formation, Brazil. RCDP

Siphloplecton sp. (Ephemeroptera: Metretopodidae) in Eocene Baltic amber. RCDP

Permian, however enigmatic forms, most likely stem-group mayflies are recorded in the Carboniferous. They are common as fossils in rock (especially as larvae) (Fig. 97) and amber (Fig. 98) deposits around the world. *Triplosoba pulchella* from the Upper Carboniferous of Commentry, France was assigned to its own order (†Triplobosida = Protephemerida) and was previously considered the oldest mayfly until the single known specimen was revised and transferred to Palaeodictyopterida *sensu* Bechly by Prokop & Nel (2009). A Carboniferous trace fossil described from the Wamsutta Formation of Massachusetts by Knecht *et al.* (2011) was originally considered to have originated from a primitive mayfly, but this proposal was questioned by Marden (2013).

Geropterans (†Geroptera)
Geological range: Late Carboniferous

Identification.—Geropterans can be identified by having two pairs of wings with dense wing venation, pronotal lobes present, lacking an archedictyon. Nymphs unknown.

Palaeontology.—Geroptera is known from one family from the Late Carboniferous of Argentina (Riek & Kukalova-Peck, 1984). The monophyly of this order has been debated (see Grimaldi & Engel, 2005 for discussion).

†Griffinflies (Protodonata) (= Meganisoptera)
Geological range: Carboniferous–Late Permian

Identification.—Griffinflies resemble giant dragonflies and are identified by two pairs of membranous wings with a dense venation. As a rather general rule, they differ from the latter by lacking a pterostigma and in having a more simple wing venation. Some species were very large (largest wingspan 710 mm). They had very large eyes.

Palaeontology.—Known mainly from wings, with occasional body parts. Griffinflies have been regarded as stem-group Odonata. Fossils have been found in the Carboniferous–Permian of Europe, Asia and North America (Fig. 72). The largest insect *Meganeuropsis permiana* is known from the early Permian of Kansas and Oklahoma. Eurasian fossils of this order were revised by Nel *et al.* (2009) and Li, Y. *et al.* (2013). According to Nel *et al.* (2001), the Jurassic fossil species *Liadotypus relictus* was misplaced in this order because it possesses a pterostigma.

Damselflies and dragonflies (Odonata)
Geological range: Triassic–Recent

Identification.—Odonatans are often large insects that can be identified by having four long and narrow wings all of a similar size and with dense venation. In contrast to the griffinflies mentioned above, as a general rule, the wings have a distinct pterostigma. At rest the wings are either held out to the sides (dragonflies, suborder Anisoptera) or are folded over the abdomen (damselflies, suborder Zygoptera). The thorax is skewed, the abdomen is long and slender and the male terminalia have a grasping appendage.

Italophlebia gervasuttii (Odonata: Triassolestidae) from the Upper Triassic of Ponte Giurino, Valle Imagna, Italy. MCSNB

Mesuropetala muensteri (Odonata: Mesuropetalidae) from the Jurassic of Solnhofen, Germany. BMMS

Araripegomphus sp. (Odonata: Araripegomphidae) from the Cretaceous Crato Formation, Brazil. CU

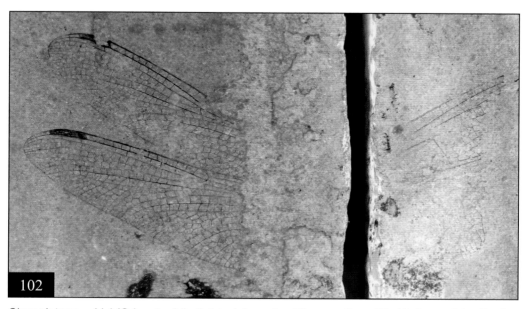

Sloveniatrum robici (Odonata: Libellulidae) from the Miocene Coprolitic Horizon of the Tunjice Hills, Slovenia. Holotype, NHMS T-280

103

Damselfly *Eoprotoneura hyperstigma* (Odonata: Protoneuridae) from the Cretaceous Crato Formation, Brazil. RCDP

Extant Biodiversity.—5900 species described (Zhang, 2011).

Palaeontology.—Fossils of most modern odonate families are known from the Jurassic or the Cretaceous. Additional extinct suborders include: Protozygoptera, Archizygoptera, Protanisoptera and Triadophlebiomorpha. Odonates are very rare in amber, with records usually consisting only of parts of wings; they are more common in rock (Figs. 99–103).

Dunbaria fascipennis (Palaeodictyoptera: Spilapteridae) from the Permian of Elmo, Kansas, USA. YPM 1002

Schlüter *et al.* (2003) described the unusual preservation of three-dimensional dragonfly larvae within transparent gypsum crystals from the Miocene of northern Italy. Many papers on fossil Odonata have been published or are in preparation by Günter Bechly at the SMNS in Stuttgart, Germany. A search of the fossil insect database (EDNA) returned 1002 species names for Odonata, although many of them are considered to be synonyms. A large dragonfly forewing (10.7 cm long) was recently described from the Jurassic of Inner Mongolia by Zhang, H.C. *et al.* (2013). See also griffinflies (Protodonata), regarded as stem-group Odonata, which include very large to enormous Upper Carboniferous and Permian dragonfly-like species.

6-wings (†Palaeodictyoptera) (= Dictyoneurida, Triplobosida [= Protephemerida])
Geological range: Carboniferous–Permian

Identification.—Palaeodictyopterans are identified by two pairs of wings, with the hind wing broad and triangular. Wings often patterned. Large paranotal lobes on the prothorax, with a well developed archedictyon (wing-like projections on the prothorax). They were medium-sized to large, with a wingspan up to 550 mm. These insects had sucking beak-like mouthparts. Also distinctive are the unusually long cerci, about twice the length of the abdomen (Fig. 7).

Palaeontology.—Palaeodictyopterans are among the earliest records of pterygote insects (Grimaldi & Engel, 2005) and several hundred species have been described from Europe, Asia and North America (Fig. 104).

Diclipterans (†Dicliptera)
Geological range: Early Permian

Identification.—Diclipteran forewings are broad with a distinct pterostigma and reduced number of crossveins (to a single rs-m crossvein). Hind wings are vestigial or absent. Pronotal lobes and archedictyon are absent.

Palaeontology.—Fossils are known from the Permian of Eurasia, however it is likely that the group may extend into the Late Carboniferous (Grimaldi & Engel, 2005).

Megasecopterans (†Megasecoptera) (= Mischopterida)
Geological range: Carboniferous–Permian

Identification.—Megasecopterans are identified by two pairs of wings; occasionally patterned. Wings with Sc and R close together, distinct crossveins and petiolate wing base. A small archedictyon is rarely present. Some species had falcate wings and a pronotum bearing spiky projections. Nymphs were terrestrial (no gills).

Palaeontology.—Fossils are found in the Carboniferous and Permian of Europe, Urals (Fig. 9), China, North and South America and South Africa (Sinitshenkova, 2002). More than 100 fossil species have been described.

Diaphanopterans (†Diaphanopterodea) (= Paramegasecoptera)
Geological range: Carboniferous–Permian

Identification.—Diphanopterans were moderate to large-sized insects, with two pairs of wings with a simple MA and wing flexion. They were able to fold their wings over the abdomen when at rest. There is a complete loss of the archedictyon. They had sucking beak-like mouthparts. Reduction of tarsus in legs to three tarsomeres. The nymphs were covered in hair-like filaments.

Palaeontology.—Diaphanopterodea are amongst the earliest winged insects and have been found in the Carboniferous of North America, Europe and Siberia, and the Permian of Europe, Urals and North America (Sinitshenkova, 2002). More than 50 species have been described. The family Alexrasnitsyniidae (Fig. 105) was described by Prokop &

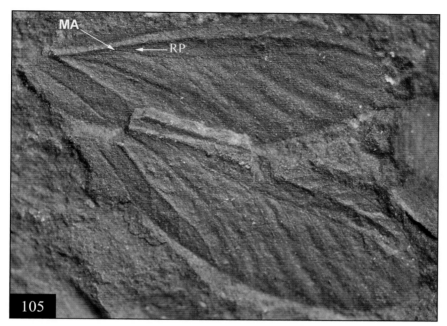

Alexrasnitsynia permiana (Diaphanopterodea: Alexrasnitsyniidae) from the Middle Permian of Lodève, France. Reproduced from Prokop & Nel (2011) with permission. Holotype, MLF LdLAP 318A

Nel (2011) in recognition of Professor Alex Rasnitsyn's contributions to the study of palaeoentomology.

Hypoperlids (†Hypoperlida)
Geological range: Carboniferous–Permian

Identification.—Small extinct group of moderately small to large insects with a diverse external appearance in terms of both body morphology and wing venation (Rasnitsyn & Quicke, 2002). Hence, unambiguous diagnostic features for this order are unclear.

Palaeontology.—Hypoperlids (Figs. 106, 107) have been described from Asia, the Czech Republic, North America and Europe. Several new species were described recently by Novokshonov & Aristov (2004) and Aristov *et al.* (2013).

Stoneflies (Plecoptera) (= Perlida)
Geological range: Carboniferous–Recent

Identification.—Stoneflies are identified by their elongated, flattened body and four membranous wings (hind wing slightly wider) which curve around the body when at rest. Two cerci are present on the abdomen. Larvae aquatic.

Extant Biodiversity.—3750 species described (Zhang, 2011).

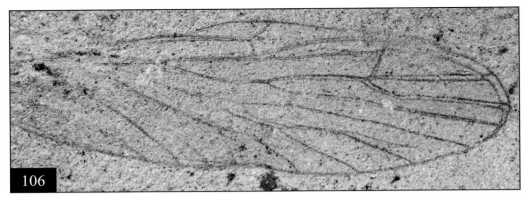

Idelopsocus arcuatus (Hypoperlida: Hypoperlidae) from the Permian of Soyana, Russia. Holotype, PIN 3353-456

Synomaloptila longipennis (Hypoperlida: Synomaloptilidae) from the Permian of Tshekarda, Russia. Holotype, PIN 118-24

Platyperla platypoda (Plecoptera: Platyperlidae) from the Jurassic of Siberia, Russia. PIN 2375-215

Palaeontology.—Stoneflies have a long but fragmented fossil record dating back to the Carboniferous (including stem-group plecopterans occasionally grouped together as Protoperlaria). *Gulou carpenteri* was described by Béthoux *et al.* (2011) as the only genuine stem group Plecoptera reported from the Pennsylvanian (Carboniferous). Fossil stoneflies are most frequent as fossils in rock (Figs. 74, 108, 174), but have been recorded from various Tertiary and Cretaceous amber deposits. More than 250 fossil species have been described.

Webspinners (Embiodea) (= Embiida)
Geological range: Cretaceous–Recent

Identification.—Webspinners have two pairs of simplified membranous wings in the males only (females wingless). They have a cylindrical and elongated body and short legs, with enlarged tarsi (containing silk glands) on first pair of legs. There are two cerci on the abdomen (unequal in size in males).

Extant Biodiversity.—460 species described (Zhang, 2011).

Palaeontology.—The fossil record of webspinners is poor, with records from various ambers (Fig. 109), and compression fossils from the Tertiary of Florissant, Colorado and the Jurassic of China. Engel *et al.* (2011) provided a checklist of known fossil species.

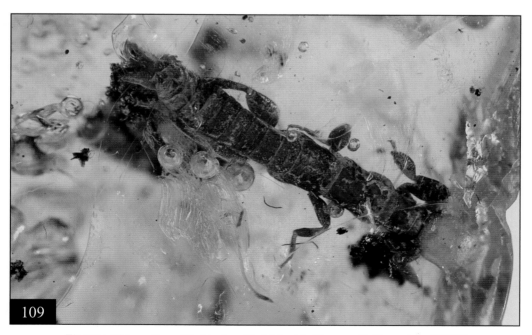

Electroembia antiqua (Embiodea: Embiidae) in Eocene Baltic amber. RCDP

110

Zorotypus (Zorotypus) goeleti (Zoraptera: Zorotypidae) in Miocene Dominican amber. CU

Angel insects (Zoraptera) (= Zorotypida)
Geological range: Cretaceous–Recent

Identification.—Zorapterans are minute insects (<3 mm) with two adult morphs – winged and eyed (alates) and eyeless and apterous. In winged forms the hind wing is smaller than the forewing. The antennae are moniliform. Tarsi two-segmented, stout metafemoral spines and unsegmented cerci. Gregarious insects, often found in groups. See Mashimo *et al.* (2014) for a review of the uncertain relationhsips of this order.

Extant Biodivesity.—37 species described (Zhang, 2011).

Palaeontology.—The fossil record of zorapterans is poor. Four different zorapteran species have been described from Dominican amber (Fig. 110) (both winged and apterous species) (Engel, 2008). They are also known in ambers from Myanmar, Ethiopia and Jordan, but are unknown as compression fossils from sediments.

Earwigs (Dermaptera) (= Forficulida)
Geological range: ?Carboniferous–Recent

Identification.—Earwigs are identified by their slender body, two strong pincer-like sclerotized cerci (curved in males) and moderately long antennae. They have four wings, but the forewings are hardened and shortened tegmina, the hind wings are fan-shaped, membranous and are folded beneath the leathery forewings.

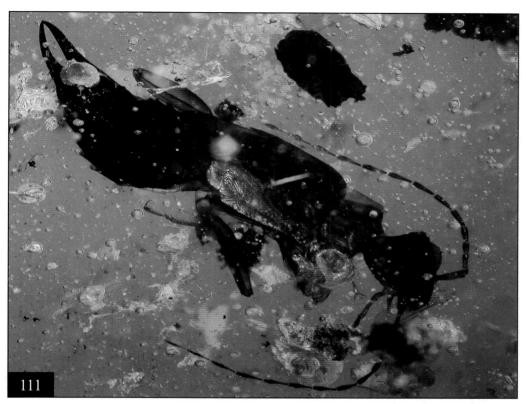

111

Unidentified earwig (Dermaptera: Forficulidae) in Miocene Dominican amber. RCDP

Extant Biodiversity.—2000 species described (Zhang, 2011).

Palaeontology.—Fossil earwigs are known in most fossiliferous Tertiary and Cretaceous ambers and from various rock deposits (Figs. 42, 60, 111). The Archidermaptera are a group of primitive earwigs dating from the Triassic (Grimaldi & Engel, 2005), with described fossils from the Upper Jurassic of Kazakhstan and the Lower Jurassic of England. They have elongate cerci with as many as 40 segments. More than 80 fossil earwig species have now been described, including so-called missing links between the primitive and modern groups (Zhao *et al.*, 2010). Nel *et al.* (1994) provided a checklist of known fossil earwigs. For a possible Carboniferous form see Staniczek *et al.* (2014).

Rock and ice crawlers (Notoptera = Mantophasmatodea + Grylloblattodea)
Geological range: Jurassic–Recent

Identification.—Notopterans are soft-bodied hemimetabolous insects, lacking wings and ocelli. They have long, thin antennae and resemble some stick insects and orthopterans (but lack the jumping hind legs). Rock crawlers have a strongly enlarged arolium.

Extant Biodiversity.—51 species described (Zhang, 2011; Wipfler *et al.*, 2012).

112

Rock crawler *Raptophasma kerneggeri* (Notoptera: Mantophasmatidae) in Eocene Baltic amber. Holotype, GPIH

Paleuthygramma tenuicorne (Caloneurodea: Caloneuridae) from the Permian of Tshekarda, Russia. Holotype, PIN

Palaeontology.—Rock crawlers (suborder Mantophasmatodea), first identified from specimens preserved in Baltic amber (Fig. 112), and subsequently in the extant fauna from tropical Africa, caused a considerable degree of excitement (and controversy) when they were described as a newly discovered insect order in 2002. They are now classified as a suborder, together with their closest relatives the ice crawlers (Grylloblattodea) within the order Notoptera (e.g. Schoville, 2014). This scheme was questioned by some entomologists, but the close relationship has recently been confirmed (Wipfler *et al.*, 2014). Fossil rock crawlers are known from Eocene Baltic amber and from the Middle Jurassic of Daohugou, Inner Mongolia, China; winged stem-group fossil ice crawlers (Fig. 76) are known from the Permian, Jurassic and Cretaceous (Grimaldi & Engel, 2005; Coram & Jepson, 2012).

Caloneurodeans (†Caloneurodea) (= Caloneurida)
Geological range: Carboniferous–Permian

Identification.—Membranous wings, anal area lost in hind wings. Fore and hind wings have a similar shape, texture and venation. Unbranched and nearly parallel veins CuA and CuP in both wings. Strongly concave and convex wing veins. They have very long multi-segmented antennae, five-segmented tarsi and unsegmented cerci.

Palaeontology.—Fossils are known from the Carboniferous of Europe, Siberia, USA, Canada and the Permian of Russia (Figs. 9, 113) and USA (Rasnitsyn, 2002a; Aristov

114

Gigatitan vulgaris (Titanoptera: Mesotitanidae) from the Triassic of Kyrghyzstan. Holotype, PIN 2240-4593

et al., 2013). Béthoux *et al.* (2004b) revised and rediagnosed the order and considered it closely related to Orthoptera. Jurassic and Cretaceous fossils from China previously assigned to Caloneurodea were misplaced in this order (Rasnitsyn & Quicke, 2002). More than 20 species have been described.

Titanopterans (†Titanoptera) (= Mesotitanida)
Geological range: Permian–Triassic

Identification.—Two pairs of wings held flat over the abdomen when at rest. Forewings of many species with a stridulatory organ. Large insects up to 400 mm in wingspan. Forelegs raptorial.

Palaeontology.—Fossils are found in the Triassic of Kyrgyzstan (Fig. 114) and New South Wales, Australia (Fig. 11) (Gorochov & Rasnitsyn, 2002). It was only recently that Gorochov (2007) described the first Permian fossil of this order, based on a specimen from Russia. See Béthoux (2007) for a discussion of the orthopteran affinities of these insects.

Protorthopterans (†Protorthoptera)
Geological range: Paleozoic

Identification and Palaeontology.—A large and polyphyletic stem-group of polyneopterous winged insects with a diverse range of characteristics. This is an artificial

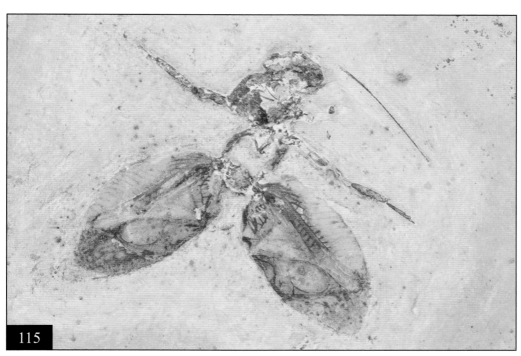

115

Araripegryllus sp. (Orthoptera: Gryllidae) from the Cretaceous Crato Formation, Brazil. RCDP

116

Archepseudophylla laurenti (Orthoptera: Tettigoniidae), katydid with pigment pattern on the wings, from the Lower Oligocene of Céreste, southern France. SMNK

'waste-basket' taxon of unrelated species, but recognized as being mostly composed of extremely primitive hemipteroids (Kukalová-Peck & Brauckmann, 1992). Included here is the order Blattinopseida (Hörnschemeyer & Stapf, 2001), still used as a discrete, valid taxon by some workers (e.g. Rasnitsyn & Quicke, 2002; Rasnitsyn *et al.*, 2005). Recent attempts to 'tidy up' the 'Protorthoptera' problem include Béthoux & Nel (2005); see also Béthoux *et al.* (2012) and references therein.

Grasshoppers and crickets (Orthoptera)
Geological range: Permian–Recent

Identification.—Sadle-shaped pronotum, two pairs of wings, the forewings are leathery and narrower than the membranous fan-like hind wings. Mouthparts are mandibulate and the eyes are large. Grasshoppers have short antennae, whereas crickets and katydids have mainly long antennae. The hind legs are enlarged, modified for jumping. Many orthopterans produce sounds by rubbing either legs, wings or abdomen together (stridulation). Nymphs look like small wingless versions of the adult.

Extant Biodiversity.—23,750 species described (Ingrisch, 2011).

Palaeontology.—Fossil Orthoptera have been recorded from most well studied amber deposits, where they can be reasonably diverse. Their non-amber fossil record is extensive (Figs. 36, 77, 115, 116, 219, 229), with stem group fossils dating back to the Paleozoic (Upper Carboniferous). The first fossil evidence of the two extant suborders Ensifera (crickets, katydids and bush crickets) and Caelifera (locusts and short-horned grasshoppers) occurs in sediments from the Late Permian of France and Early Jurassic of the UK respectively. More than 1000 fossil species have been described. The systematics of the diverse stem-group orthopterans has received renewed attention in recent years, especially at the species level. A number of revisions of Upper Carboniferous fossils led to the identification of a series of successive stem-representatives of the orthopteran lineage (grasshoppers, katydids and crickets). A new taxonomic and nomenclatural framework has been developed in which the taxon Archaeorthoptera includes these stem-orthopterans together with crown-orthopterans (Béthoux *et al.*, 2012).

Fossil water striders (†Chresmododea)
Geological range: Jurassic–Cretaceous

Identification.—Large insects with short, thick antennae and large eyes. Their legs are very elongated, with very long femora, shorter tibiae, and long, multi-segmented flagellate tarsi with more than 40 tarsomeres. Females have two pairs of membranous wings – slender forewings and broad hind wings. Females also have a prominent ovipositor. Nymphs are similar to adults but smaller, therefore having a hemimetabolous development, like orthopterans. They most likely lived on the water surface (Fig. 15).

Palaeontology.—They are exclusively Mesozoic, possibly being one of the few higher taxonomic (insect) victims of the end-Cretaceous extinction. The few fossil species are

117

Chresmoda obscura (Chresmododea: Chresmodidae) from the Jurassic of Solnhofen, Germany. JM

known from the Upper Jurassic of Germany (Fig. 117), Lower Cretaceous of Mongolia, China, Brazil and Spain, and the Upper Cretaceous of Lebanon (for a review of the group see Delclos *et al.*, 2008). Their phylogenetic position and status as a distinct order have been debated (e.g. Grimaldi & Engel, 2005; Zhang *et al.*, 2009). They are currently thought to be closely related to the orthopteroid lineage (Delclos *et al.*, 2008).

Stick insects (Phasmatodea) (= Phasmatida)
Geological range: Cretaceous–Recent

Identification.—Most species have two pairs of wings, but some are wingless. Forewings are short and hardened forming protection for the larger membranous hind wings. Antennae filiform, ranging from short to long. Body shape variable and modified to resemble sticks or leaves.

Extant Biodiversity.—3000+ species described (Brock & Marshall, 2011).

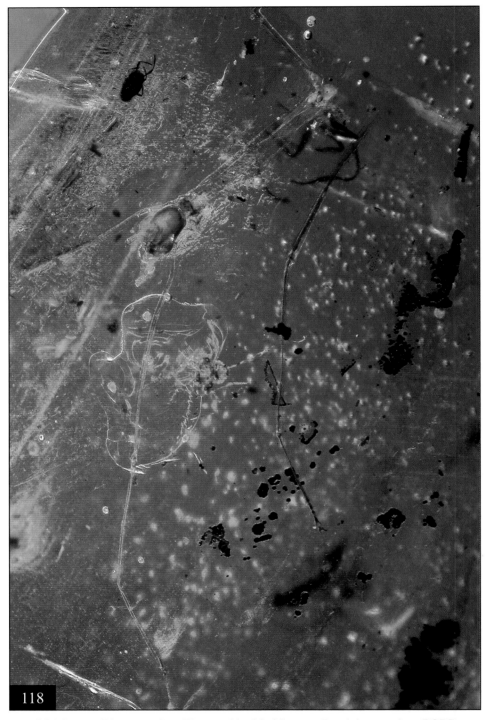

Stick insect (Phasmatodea: Phasmatidae) in Miocene Dominican amber. RCDP

Zdenekia silesiensis (Paoliida: Paoliidae) from the Upper Carboniferous), Sosnowiec–Klimontów, Upper Silesian Coal Basin, Poland. Holotype (forewing), MP ISEA I–F/MP/1488/2ab/08

Palaeontology.—The fossil record of Phasmatodea was reviewed by Tilgner (2000). Fossil stick insects in amber are extremely rare, with the only confirmed specimens recorded from the Tertiary of the Dominican Republic (Fig. 118), Mexico and the Baltic region, in addition to sub-fossils in copal. Non-amber fossils are known from the Tertiary of Germany and USA (Florissant). The only known fossil leaf insect (Euphasmatodea: Phylliidae) (Fig. 230) originates from the 47 million-years-old deposits of Grube Messel in Germany (Wedmann *et al.*, 2007). *Gallophasma longipalpis* was described from earliest Eocene French amber as a key fossil that linked 'Mesozoic Phasmatodea' with extant stick and leaf insects. However, the identity of this fossil as Phasmatodea was subsequently rejected by Bradler & Buckley (2010). Despite previous claims for Mesozoic fossils, no certain affinity of pre-Tertiary phasmid-like insects and the true stick insects has been demonstrated. Nonetheless, stem-group phasmatodean fossils are known from the Mesozoic (e.g. Wang *et al.*, 2014). The fossil record of wingless stick insects (suborder Timematodea) consists of a single specimen in Eocene Baltic amber.

Paoliids (†Paoliida) (= Protoptera)
Geological range: Carboniferous–Permian

Identification.—This extinct order was redelimited by Prokop *et al.* (2013) who considered them the sister group to Dictyoptera. The fore and hind wings are similar, but the latter are broader basally. The diagnosis of the order is based on wing venation (see Prokop *et al.*, 2012, 2013).

Palaeontology.—Fossils have been described from North America, Europe (Fig. 119) (including the UK), the Czech Republic, Russia and Mongolia (Prokop *et al.*, 2013).

Cockroach *Araripeblatta brevis* (Blattodea: Araripeblattidae) from the Cretaceous Crato Formation, Brazil. RCDP

Cockroaches and termites (Blattodea)
Geological range: Cretaceous–Recent

Identification.—Cockroaches: Wings when present – two membranous with forewing being more sclerotized than the hind wing. Long antennae, two simple ocelli-like spots and mandibulate mouthparts. Body is oval in shape and flattened, the thorax is covered by the pronotum, which extends partially over the head. Prominent cerci on the abdomen. Termites: Body elongate, with two pairs of equal length membranous wings (present only in reproductive castes, shedded after mating). Short antennae, mandibulate mouthparts. Termites are social insects with a queen, worker, soldier and reproductive castes. Recent DNA studies have shown that termites are actually a lineage of cockroaches, not a separate order of insects as previously thought. Termites are most closely related to the *Cryptocercus* wood-feeding cockroaches, with which they share many structural characters and behavioural traits.

Extant Biodiversity.—Cockroaches: 4600 species described; termites: 2930 species described (Beccaloni & Eggleton, 2011; Krishna *et al.*, 2013).

Palaeontology.—The systematic placement of many fossil 'roachoids' is uncertain, especially as regards the Paleozoic forms (Beccaloni & Eggleton, 2011). The earliest fossil cockroach-like insects date back to the Carboniferous (Paleozoic) and had an ovipositor for laying eggs (Fig. 7). This was gradually reduced and lost towards the end

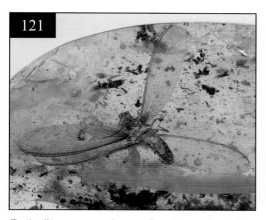

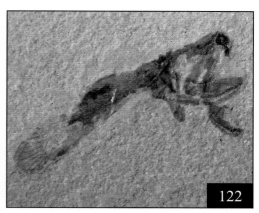

Reticulitermes antiquus (Isoptera: Rhinoter-mitidae) in Eocene Baltic amber. RCDP

Praying mantis (Mantodea) from the Tertiary of Green River, USA. PCYW

of the Mesozoic. It is now considered that modern cockroaches date back to the Mesozoic and that the Paleozoic forms with ovipositors should be considered as extinct relatives of 'Dictyoptera' or Orthoptera, rather than as close relatives of modern cockroaches (Roth, 2003). The oldest 'roach' was described from the earliest Late Carboniferous (Namurian) of China by Zhang, W. *et al.* (2013), who suggested that winged forms might have appeared as early as the Devonian.

The earliest fossil termites pre-dated those of other social insects (bees and ants) by approximately 35 million years. There appears to have been a high diversity of primitive termites during the Cretaceous, including the diversification of some modern families. However, the majority of higher termites radiated in the Tertiary. Both cockroaches and termites have been recorded from most fossiliferous amber deposits (Figs. 90, 121), although cockroaches are more common in rock deposits, such as the Crato Formation, Brazil (Fig. 120), where they are particularly abundant (Martins-Neto *et al.*, 2010). The fossil insect database (EDNA) lists 2500 blattid species and around 300 isopterans, although only approximately 170 of the latter are considered valid.

Praying mantises (Mantodea) (= Manteida)
Geological range: Cretaceous–Recent

Identification.—Mantids can be identified by the following combination of features: Two pairs of wings, both of which are used for flight. Occasionally the wings are reduced or absent. The forewings are hardened and cover the membranous hind wings. Antennae filiform and vary from short to medium in length. Head triangular, highly mobile and with large eyes. Body elongated and forelegs raptorial with one or two rows of spines. Forelegs attached to the anterior part of the prothorax (often elongated). Coloration on body and wings (and sometimes body structures) adapted for camouflage.

Next page: Rare praying mantis in Eocene Baltic amber (Mantodea: Manteidae). PCH

123

Epimastax tschepanikha (Miomoptera: Permosialidae) from the Permian of Russia (the Chepanikha locality in Udmurtia). Holotype, PIN 3286-125

Extant Biodiversity.—2400 species described (Zhang, 2011).

Palaeontology.—Mantids are relatively large insects, so it is unusual to find adults preserved in amber because this mode of preservation tends to be biased towards smaller organisms. Thus, most amber mantid inclusions are juvenile forms. They occur in various Cretaceous and Tertiary (Fig. 123) amber deposits and also in sediments from shales of the USA (Fig. 122), France and Eurasia, and from the Crato limestone of Brazil. It has been proposed that mantids originated as early as the Carboniferous (Béthoux & Wieland, 2009), though Jurassic origins have also been proposed (Svenson & Whiting, 2009). A Paleozoic origin was rejected by Gorochov (2013). For reviews of fossil mantids see Ehrmann (1999, Baltic amber) and Grimaldi (2003, Cretaceous fossils).

Miomopterans (†Miomoptera) (= Palaeomanteida, Protoperlaria)
Geological range: Carboniferous–Permian

Identification.—Miomopterans are minute insects. Fore and hind wings are of similar shape and venation, with no crossveins, hind wing also lacks an anal lobe. They are mandibulate, have thick antennae (15–20 flagellomeres). Tarsi are four-segmented, cerci short.

Palaeontology.—Only known from isolated wings and rare body parts (Figs. 124, 125). The phylogenetic placement of the order has been debated: some authors have placed Miomoptera as a stem group Holometabola (Rasnitsn & Quicke, 2002), whereas now they are considered stem group Paraneoptera (Grimaldi & Engel, 2005). More than 100 fossil species have been described from Europe, Asia, North and South America, Australia and South Africa. The relationships of the order were discussed by Novokshonov & Zhuzhgova (2004).

125

Permonika aestiva (Miomoptera: Palaeomanteidae) from the Permian of Tshekarda, Urals, Russia. PIN 1700-1381

126

Bark louse *Hemipsocus* sp.
(Psocodea: Hemipsocidae) in
Miocene Dominican amber. RCDP

Bark, book and parasitic lice (Psocodea) (= Psocoptera, Psocida, Phthiraptera, Pediculida)
Geological range: Carboniferous–Recent

Identification.—Psocodeans are minute insects with two pairs of wings, the forewing being larger and more complex than the hind wing, both have reduced venation. Some species are wingless. They have large heads with protruding eyes and post clypeus. Psocodea includes both bark lice and parasitic (and book) lice, formerly classified in the separate orders Psocoptera (*ca.* 5700 species) and Phthiraptera (*ca.* 5100 species) respectively. However, recent morphological and molecular analyses have demonstrated that parasitic lice represent a group within the bark lice, and thus the single order Psocodea is now recognized for both groups.

Extant Biodiversity.—10,800 species described (Zhang, 2011).

Palaeontology.— Parasitic lice (as adults) have not been formally described from amber, although one of the authors (DP) is aware of a potential specimen in Dominican amber. Bark lice (Fig. 126) are very common and reasonably diverse in amber, they have been found in all major fossiliferous deposits. They are also found in the rock fossil record, with several species described from the Permian of Russia, America and Australia, and a single Carboniferous species described from New Mexico, USA (Rasnitsyn, 2004). Prior to 1999 no postembryonic fossil parasitic lice had been described. The phthirapteran (and even insect) nature of those that have been described since has been rejected in most cases (Dalgleish *et al.*, 2006) (see also pages 162–163).

 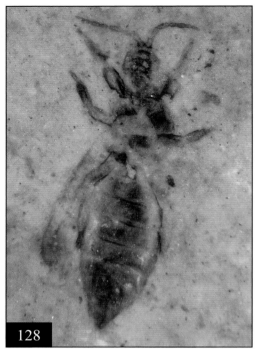

Thrips (Thysanoptera: Phlaeothripidae) in Eocene Baltic amber. RCDP

Thrips (Thysanoptera) from the Miocene of Río Rubiels, Teruel, Spain. PMZU rm-rr-152

Thrips (Thysanoptera) (= Thripida)
Geological range: Permian–Recent

Identification.—Thrips are minute insects (<1 mm) with two pairs of wings fringed with fine 'hairs' and with reduced venation. Their mouthparts are asymmetric (right mandible reduced). The body has a separate prothorax, an ovipositor is present in females.

Extant Biodiversity.—5800 species described (Mound, 2011).

Palaeontology.—Thrips are encountered reasonably frequently in amber (Fig. 127), including from all the major Tertiary and Cretaceous deposits (although many of the species have not been formally described). Non-amber fossils (Fig. 128) are much less common and date back to the Permian (e.g. Aristov *et al.*, 2013) with the stem-group Lophioneuridae, the earliest true thrips are from the Triassic of Virginia and Kazakhstan (Grimaldi *et al.*, 2004).

True bugs (Hemiptera [Auchenorrhyncha, Sternorrhyncha, Coleorrhyncha, Heteroptera])
Geological range: Permian–Recent

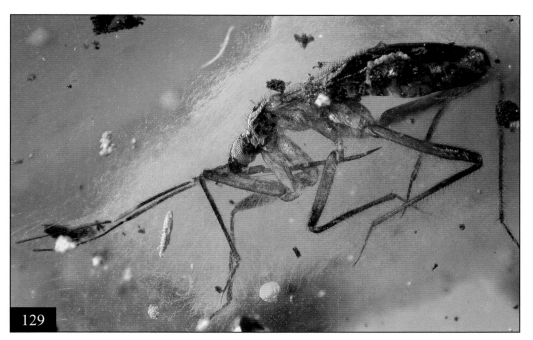

Predatory bug (Hemiptera: ?Nabidae) in Miocene Dominican amber. RCDP

Scale insect *Puto* sp. (Hemiptera: Putoidae) in Eocene Baltic amber. RCDP

Scale insect *Matsucoccus cf. saxonicus* (Hemiptera: Matsucoccidae) in Eocene Baltic amber. RCDP

Mimamontsecia cretacea (Hemiptera: Fulgoromorpha: Mimarachnidae) from the Cretaceous La Cabrua outcrop of Montsech, Spain. Holotype, GZG.RF.9311

Plant hopper (Hemiptera *s.l.*) preserved next to a fish, from the Cretaceous Crato Formation, Brazil. RCDP

Identification.—Minute to large-sized insects. The majority of species have two pairs of wings (some species are wingless or have forewings only). Wings are mainly membranous; forewings in many species (Heteroptera) are hardened at the wing base. Mouthparts formed into a pointed tube (proboscis or rostrum) extending from the underside of the head, used for piercing or sucking.

Extant Biodiversity.—103,600 species described (Zhang, 2011).

Palaeontology.—Found throughout the fossil record, in both rock (Figs. 132, 133) and amber (Figs. 129–131), the earliest being from the Permian. There have been debates about the classification of the suborders of true bugs, which were traditionally divided into Heteroptera and Homoptera; the latter is paraphyletic. The most recent classifications have Heteroptera plus Sternorrhyncha, Auchenorrhyncha and the relictual Coleorrhyncha (see Grimaldi & Engel, 2005 for discussion). See Szwedo *et al.* (2004) for an annotated catalogue of fossil planthoppers (Fulgoromorpha). The fossil insect database (EDNA) includes more than 3000 species names for fossil Hemiptera.

Beetles (Coleoptera)
Geological range: Permian–Recent

Identification.—Beetles range from minute to very large in size. They have two pairs of wings, with the forewings hardened into elytra, the hind wings are membranous (folding under the protective elytra). The head is usually prognathous and the prothorax freely articulates from rest of the thorax, and is shield-like. They have heavily sclerotized abdominal sternites and less sclerotized tergites. Ocelli and cerci are absent.

Extant Biodiversity.—386,500 species described (Slipinski *et al.*, 2011).

Palaeontology.—Beetles are very common in the fossil record, both in rock and amber (Figs. 134–137). They are first recorded in the Permian, their diversity increasing before the late Jurassic (Grimaldi & Engel, 2005). Isolated elytra are often found in great numbers in the rock record, often reaching thousands in numbers, but in some cases they can be difficult to identify beyond family or even order. Fossil beetles in Quaternary sediments are often used in climate reconstructions or as indicators of human activity. Slipinski *et al.* (2011) suggested there were approximately 600 fossil beetle species, but the fossil insect database (EDNA) contains almost 4800 species names. Béthoux (2009) treated the Late Carboniferous *Adiphlebia lacoana* from Mazon Creek, North America as a beetle that is the sister group of all other Coleoptera. However, this fossil is rather enigmatic and is better considered as a member of a polyneopterous lineage with possible relationships to Dictyoptera and Paoliida (Kirejtshuk *et al.*, 2013) or Hypoperlida (Aristov *et al.*, 2013). Kirejtshuk *et al.* (2013) recently described *Coleopsis archaica* (Tshekardocoleidae) from the earliest Permian (Asselian or early Sakmarian) of Germany as the oldest fossil beetle.

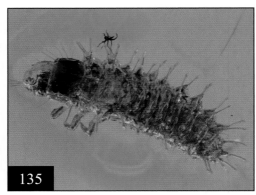

Beetle *Argentinosyne frengüelli* (Coleoptera: Schizocoleidae) from the Triassic Los Rastros Formation, Argentina. Holotype, PULR-I 227

Chequered beetle larva (Coleoptera: Cleridae) in Eocene Baltic amber. RCDP

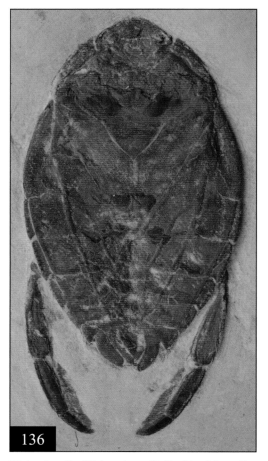

Diving beetle (Coleoptera: Dytiscidae) from the Cretaceous Crato Formation, Brazil. RCDP

Cretopoena gratshevi (Coleoptera: Eucnemidae) from the Cretaceous Shar-Tolgoy Formation, Mongolia. Holotype, PIN 4271-241

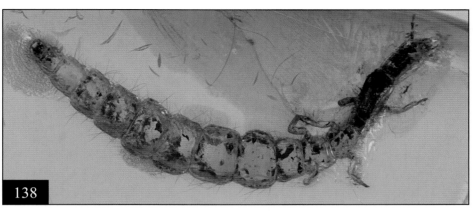

Snakefly larva (Raphidioptera) in Eocene Baltic amber. RCDP

Glosselytrodeans (†Glosselytrodea) (= Jurinida)
Geological range: Permian–Jurassic

Identification.—Two pairs of membranous wings subequal in size and shape. Forewing with an expanded precostal area, forming a bulge at the base of the wing. Hind wings lack precostal area. Wings with numerous crossveins. Multi-segmented cerci present.

Palaeontology.—Glosselytrodean classification is still unsettled. A more precise assignment than 'within the clade Paraneoptera + Holometabola' is not possible based on current knowledge (Béthoux *et al.*, 2007). They are considered an unnatural assemblage consisting of two distinct groups: the Permian Permithonidae and several Late Permian/Triassic–Jurassic families. Permithonidae are considered stem group Neuropterida and Grimaldi & Engel (2005) suggested this should be referred to as Protoneuroptera, with the other families comprising Glosselytrodea. Some of the families are probably paraphyletic (Huang *et al.*, 2007). Approximately 30 species have been described (Zhang, 2011), distributed in Central Asia, China, Russia, Western Europe, North and South America and Australia. They probably had a global distribution during the Late Paleozoic and Early Mesozoic (Huang *et al.*, 2007).

Snakeflies (Raphidioptera) (= Raphidiida)
Geological range: Jurassic–Recent

Identification.—Snakeflies are easily recognized by their elongated prognathous head and prothorax, long ovipositor in females and the subcosta (Sc) running into the costa (C) in the wing. They have two pairs of subequal membranous wings with a pterostigma.

Extant Biodiversity.—250 species described (Zhang, 2011).

Palaeontology.—Snakeflies are extremely rare as fossils in amber, but have been recorded in most fossiliferous Tertiary (Fig. 55) and Cretaceous (Fig. 140) deposits, including

Snakefly *Siboptera cf. fornicata* (Raphidioptera: Mesoraphidiidae) from the Jurassic of China. The image has been treated with photoshop to enhance contrast. RCDP

Snakefly *Cantabroraphidia marcanoi* (Raphidioptera: Mesoraphidiidae) in Cretaceous El Soplao Spanish amber. Reproduced from Pérez-de la Fuente *et al.* (2012b) with permission. Holotype, MGM

sometimes as larvae (Fig. 138). Diverse Cretaceous and Jurassic snakeflies, preserved in sediments are found in Canada, Brazil, China (Fig. 139), South Korea, Spain, England, Mongolia, Russia (Cretaceous) and China, Kazakhstan, England and Germany (Jurassic). Tertiary snakeflies are known from Spain, France and North America, with a large fauna known from Florissant, Colorado (Engel, 2003, 2011; Jepson & Jarzembowski, 2008; Makarkin & Archibald, 2014). Bechly & Wolf-Schwenninger (2011) discussed the phylogeny and fossil history of the order and described the smallest known species, a fossil in Cretaceous Lebanese amber. Shcherbakov (2013) proposed the new order Panmegaloptera for Megaloptera+Raphidioptera, but it remains to be seen how well this hypothesis will be received by entomologists. Numerous important contributions have also been published by the Aspöcks from Austria. More than 100 fossil species are currently recognized. See Engel (2002) for a catalog of fossil Raphidioptera species.

Fishflies, alderflies and dobsonflies (Megaloptera) (= Corydalida)
Geological range: Permian–Recent

Identification.—Megalopterans are moderate to large-sized insects with two pairs of similar-sized wings, held roof-like over the abdomen when at rest. The hind wings have a broad anal area. They have long filiform antennae. Male corydalids have long sickle-shaped, tusk-like mandibles. The larvae are aquatic and have lateral abdominal gills.

Extant Biodiversity.—350 species described (Zhang, 2011).

Palaeontology.—Megaloptera is considered to be one of the most primitive of the holometabolous insect orders. Shcherbakov (2013) proposed the new order Panmegaloptera for Megaloptera+Raphidioptera, but it remains to be seen how well this hypothesis will be received by entomologists (see also discussion in Aspöck *et al.*, 2012). They are rare as fossils in amber, having been described only from Tertiary deposits of the Dominican Republic, the Baltic region and from Oise (France). Non-amber fossils

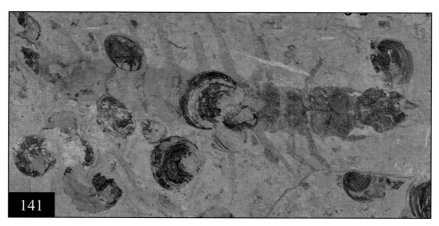

Fishfly larva *Eochauliodes striolatus* (Megaloptera: Corydalidae) from the Jurassic Jiulongshan Formation, Mongolia. Reproduced from Liu *et al.* (2012) with permission. CNU-MEG-NN2011008

include various extant and extinct families, which originate from the Permian of Russia and Asia, the Triassic of South Africa, the Jurassic of Asia and Europe, the Cretaceous of Russia, and the Tertiary of Europe and Turkey. Fossil larval forms (Fig. 141) are known from various deposits. The fossil insect database (EDNA) lists 27 species names. Liu *et al.* (2012, 2014) generated the first phylogenetic hypotheses including all fossil and extant fishfly and alderfly (respectively) genera worldwide.

Lacewings (Neuroptera)
Geological range: Permian–Recent

Identification.—Lacewings are recognized by their two pairs of intricate densely veined wings, which are similar in size and held roof-wise over the body when at rest. They range in size from the sparsely veined bark-louse-sized wax wings (Coniopterygidae)

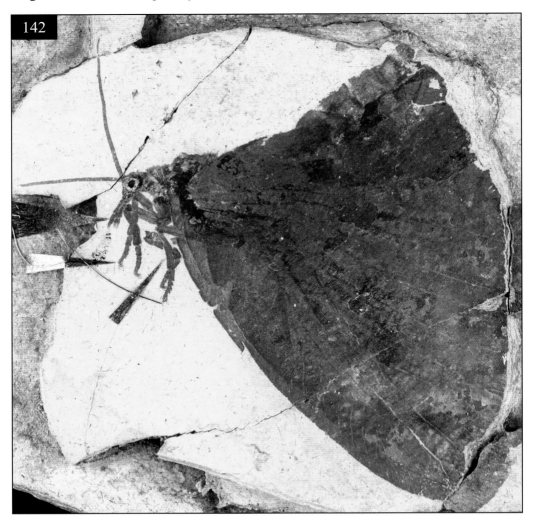

142

Meioneurites (Parameioneurites) spectabilis (Neuroptera: Kalligrammatidae) from the Upper Jurassic of Karatau, Kazakhstan. Holotype, PIN 2784/1069

to the densely veined dragonfly-like antlions (Myrmeleontidae). The predacious larvae tend to be highly specialized and cryptic, with the majority being terrestrial. This order also includes the mantispids (mantis-flies), which bear a resemblance to praying mantises as a result of their raptorial forelegs.

Extant Biodiversity.—5900 species described (Zhang, 2011).

Palaeontology.—The fossil record of Neuroptera extends back to the Permian. Neuropterans are known from both rock and amber deposits (Figs. 142–147). They

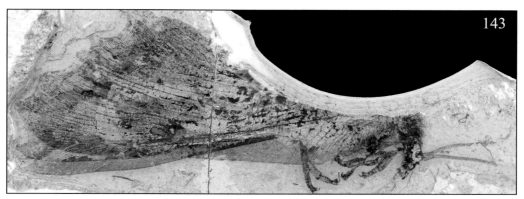

Parakseneura sp. (Neuroptera: Parakseneuridae) from the Middle Jurassic of Mongolia. Reproduced from Yang *et al.* (2012) with permission. CNU-NEU-NN2011020

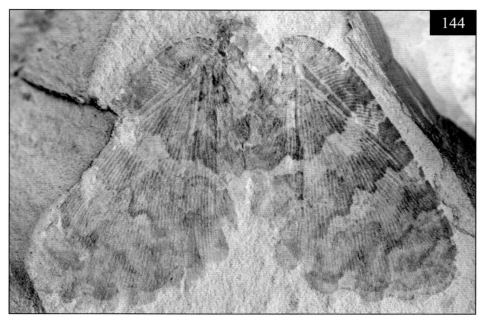

Silky lacewing *Undulopsychopsis alexi* (Neuroptera: Psychopsidae) from the Early Cretaceous Yixian Formation of western Liaoning Province, China. Reproduced from Peng *et al.* (2011) with permission. Holotype, CYNB044

are usually quite rare, but in some deposits, such as the Cretaceous Crato Formation of Brazil (Fig. 145) they can be rather common. Several unusually large forms evolved during the Mesozoic, especially in the extinct family Kalligrammatidae (Figs. 13, 142, 226), often referred to as 'the butterflies of the Jurassic', as a result of their large and patterned wings (e.g. Engel, 2005). The new fossil family Parakseneuridae (Fig. 143) was described from the Middle Jurassic of Mongolia by Yang *et al.* (2012), representing the most primitive family in the order. The fossil insect database (EDNA) lists 649 fossil Neuroptera species names, although some of these are synonyms.

145

Owlfly *Cratoscalapha* sp. (Neuroptera: Ascalaphidae) from the Cretaceous Crato Formation, Brazil. RCDP

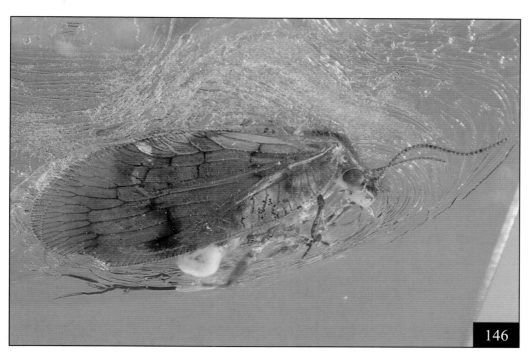

Brown lacewing *Prolachlanius cf. resinatus* (Neuroptera: Hemerobiidae) in Eocene Baltic amber. RCDP

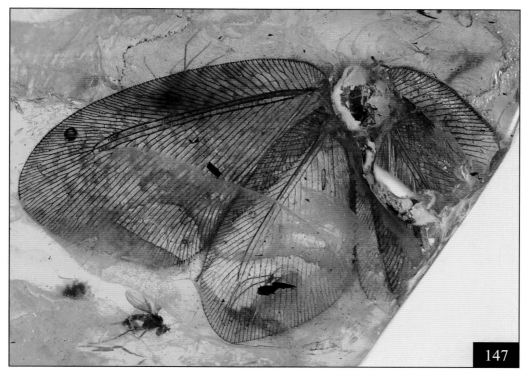

Silky lacewing *Propsychopsis* sp. (Neuroptera: Psychopsidae) in Eocene Baltic amber. RCDP

Rafaelids (†Schwickertoptera)
Geological range: Cretaceous

Identification.—Large neuropteroid-like insects with large compound eyes, a distinct ovipositor and RP and MA veins with independent stems (fused in all Neuropterida).

Palaeontology.—Known only from two species in a single family (Rafaelidae) from the Crato Formation, Brazil (see Martill *et al.*, 2007).

Ants, bees, wasps and sawflies (Hymenoptera)
Geological range: Triassic–Recent

Identification.—Probably the most diverse group of insects on the planet today (when undescribed species are taken into consideration, e.g. Klopfstein *et al.*, 2013). They have two pairs of membranous wings (some species of female wasps and worker castes of ants are wingless). The forewings are larger than the hind wings (held together by small hooks: hamuli). The mouthparts are mainly mandibulate, however some hymenopterans,

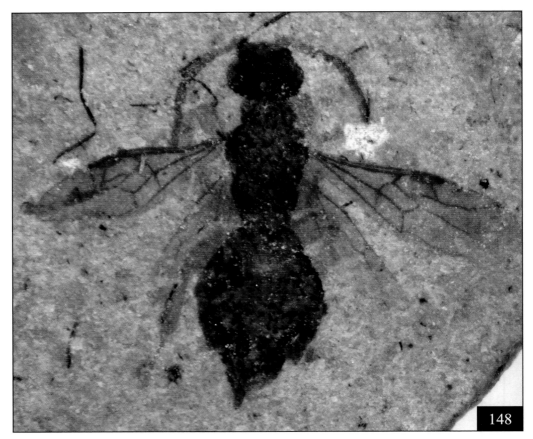

148

Bethylonymellus cervicalis (Hymenoptera: Bethylonymidae) from the Upper Jurassic of Karatau, Kazakhstan. Holotype, PIN 2784/1189

Praeaulacus sharteg (Hymenoptera: Praeaulacidae) from the Upper Jurassic of Shar Teg, Mongolia. Holotype, PIN 4270/1544

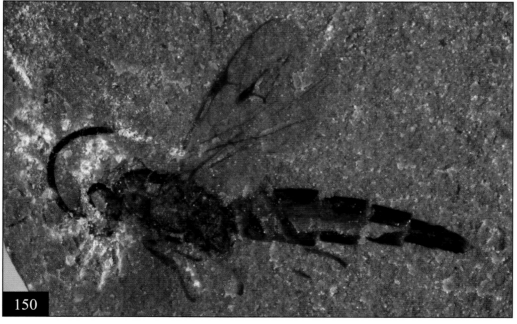

Praescopinus excellens (Hymenoptera: Pelecinidae) from the Upper Jurassic of Shar Teg, Mongolia. Holotype, PIN 2784/1550

e.g. bees have modified mouthparts which form a 'tongue'. The eyes are large. Females possess a hardened ovipositor modified for different uses (stinging, sawing or piercing). Many hymenopterans have a constriction between the first two abdominal segments of their abdomen, forming a structure known as the 'wasp-waist' or petiole. The order is split into two main groups: Apocrita (ants, bees and wasps) and Symphyta (sawflies). The latter lack a petiole.

Extant Biodiversity.—146,000+ species described (Klopfstein *et al.*, 2013).

Palaeontology.—Hymenopterans are well represented in the fossil record, both in rock (Figs. 148–152) and amber (Figs. 153–155). They are first recorded in the Mid-Upper Triassic (Rasnitsyn, 2002b). However, Ronquist *et al.* (2012) proposed that the early radiation of Hymenoptera dates back to the Carboniferous, with diversification into major extant lineages much earlier than previously thought, well before the Triassic. In reply, Engel *et al.* (2013a) noted that Hymenoptera have a robust fossil record which reveals Xyelidae (the most basal hymenopteran family) in the latest Triassic (see also Lara *et al.*, 2014, for the first Triassic fossil of this family from the New World), the

'*Cretosphex*' sp. (Hymenoptera: Angarosphecidae) from the Cretaceous Crato Formation, Brazil. RCDP

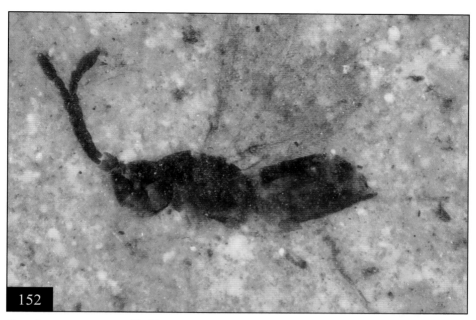

Gonatocerus greenwalti (Hymenoptera: Mymaridae) from the Tertiary Kishenehn Formation of Montana, USA. Reproduced from Huber & Greenwalt (2011) with permission. Holotype, MNNH 543763

Ensign wasp *Evaniella eocenica* (Hymenoptera: Evaniidae) in Eocene Baltic amber. RCDP

Parasitic wasp (Hymenoptera: Ichneumonidae) in Eocene Baltic amber. RCDP

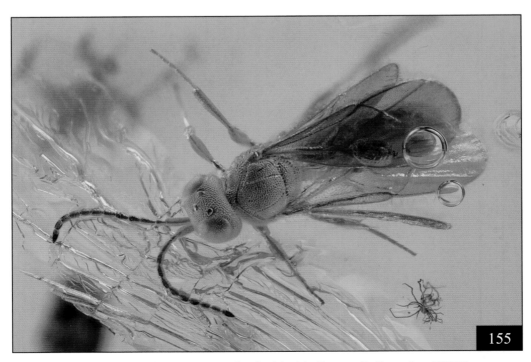

Scelionid wasp (Hymenoptera: Scelionidae) in Eocene Baltic amber. RCDP

parasitoid diversification in the Jurassic, an initial aculeate origin around the Jurassic–Cretaceous boundary, and subsequent Cretaceous radiations of various families. Crown-group Hymenoptera appear to have originated in the Middle to Early Triassic (certainly no earlier than the latest Permian) (Engel *et al.*, 2013a). The fossil record of ants was reviewed recently by LaPolla *et al.* (2013); they are particularly common and diverse in Tertiary (but not Cretaceous) ambers. Gao *et al.* (2013a) described a huge fossil sawfly from the Mesozoic of China, which had a wingspan of almost 10 cm. The fossil insect database (EDNA) lists almost 3100 fossil Hymenoptera species names, although some of these are synonyms.

Scorpionflies and hangingflies (Mecoptera) (= Panorpida)
Geological range: Permian–Recent

Identification.—Mecopterans represent a relict order of a once very diverse group. They are small to medium-sized and are easily recognized by their long projecting beak (or rostrum) and, in scorpionflies, an enlarged abdominal segment nine in males, which superficially resembles a scorpion's sting. The wings are long and narrow and often have distinct banding patterns. Most species have two pairs of wings, some just one pair and others are wingless.

Extant Biodiversity.—750 species described (Zhang, 2011).

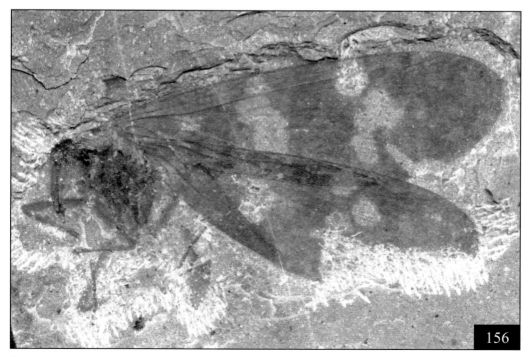

156

Scorpionfly *Eorpa ypsipeda* (Mecoptera: Eorpidae) from the early Eocene McAbee locality in the Okanagan Highlands of British Columbia, Canada. Paratype, 2003.2.5-CDM-029

157

Hylobittacus fossilis? (Mecoptera: Bittacidae), front view of head, in Eocene Baltic amber. RCDP

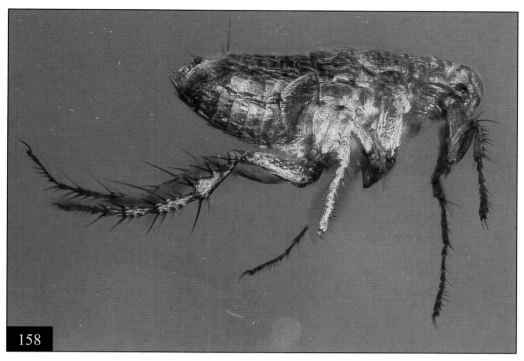

158

Rhopalopsyllus sp. (Siphonaptera: Rhopalopsyllidae) in Miocene Dominican amber. CU

Palaeontology.—Scorpionflies are rare as inclusions in amber, with records from the Mexican, Bitterfeld, Baltic (Fig. 157), Ukrainian (Rovno) and Burmese (Myanmar) deposits. However, the non-amber fossil record (Fig. 156) is incredibly diverse; the fossil insect database (EDNA) lists approximately 750 described species, with some of these in synonymy. They were particularly prevalent in the Late Permian, Triassic and Jurassic periods, but their numbers had waned significantly by the Cretaceous. Although the majority of extant Mecoptera are predators or scavengers, it is thought that some of the extinct forms may have played an important ecological role as plant pollinators. Some of the fossil species had long, siphon-like mouthparts that could fertilize early gymnosperms through feeding on their nectar (Ren *et al.*, 2009).

Fleas (Siphonaptera) (= Pulicida)
Geological range: Cretaceous–Recent

Identification.—Tiny wingless insects with their body laterally compressed and with piercing and sucking mouthparts. The antennae are small and can be retracted into small grooves on the head. Their hind legs are enlarged and adapted for jumping. A strong tarsal claw is adapted to grip on to their hosts. They have backward pointing hairs and bristles. The larvae are grub-like and live in the nest or living place of the host. Recent DNA research suggests that fleas are actually specialized Mecoptera (Whiting, 2002).

Extant Biodiversity.—2500 species described (Whiting *et al.*, 2008).

Palaeontology.—The fossil record of modern-type fleas is sparse, with only a handful of specimens recorded from Tertiary ambers (see Perrichot *et al.*, 2012 for the latest review). Ctenophthalmidae have been described from Eocene Baltic amber, and the families Pulicidae and Rhopalopsyllidae (Fig. 158) are known from Miocene Dominican amber. However, very interesting are the recent descriptions of transitional (giant) fleas (Fig. 195) from the Lower Cretaceous Yixian Formation of northeastern China (Huang *et al.*, 2012; Gao *et al.*, 2013b). Fossils previously thought to be primitive, close relatives of fleas are known from the Mesozoic deposits of Koonwarra, Australia, but their siphonapteran affinities are debatable (Gao *et al.*, 2013b).

Flies (Diptera)
Geological range: Triassic–Recent

Identification.—One pair of membranous wings, with the hind wings reduced to small club-like structures (halteres). Nematocera have elongated bodies and feathery antennae, as seen in midges, mosquitoes and crane flies. Brachycera have a more roundly proportioned body and much shorter antennae. They have large eyes and sucking mouthparts (sometimes modified for piercing). Only about half the expected diversity has been described and fly systematics are far from being fully resolved.

Extant Biodiversity.—155,000 species described (Zhang, 2011).

Palaeontology.—Flies are common in both the rock (Fig. 159) and amber fossil record (e.g. Krzemińska & Krzemiński, 2009). Indeed, they represent the most diverse and abundant inclusions in most amber deposits (Figs. 160–165); there may be as many as 1000 species in Baltic amber alone (Hoffeins & Hoffeins, 2013). The earliest records

159

Phantom crane fly *Probittacomorpha christenseni* (Diptera: Ptychopteridae) from the Eocene Fur Formation of Mors, Denmark. GMCD DK131

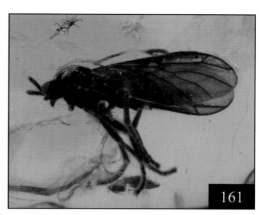

Dagger fly (Diptera: Empididae) in Eocene Baltic amber. RCDP

March fly *Plecia clavifemur* (Diptera: Bibionidae) in Eocene Baltic amber. RCDP

Big-headed fly (Diptera: Pipunculidae) in Eocene Baltic amber. RCDP

Black fly *Greniera affinis* (Diptera: Simuliidae) in Eocene Baltic amber. RCDP

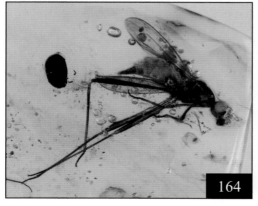

Stilt-legged fly *Electrobata myrmecia* (Diptera: Micropezidae) in Eocene Baltic amber. RCDP

Spider parasite *Villalites cf. electrica* (Diptera: Acroceridae) in Eocene Baltic amber. RCDP

of flies are from the Lower/Middle Triassic of France, with additional Middle/Upper Triassic records from Kyrgyzstan, Australia, North America and the UK (Krzemiński & Krzemiński, 2003), and there is also a single specimen in Triassic amber from Italy (Schmidt *et al.*, 2012). By the Jurassic they had become a very diverse group (Blagoderov *et al.*, 2002, 2007). The order Nakridletia described by Vršanský *et al.* (2010) for the extinct family Strashilidae (Fig. 1), previously considered to be pterosaur ectoparasites, have recently been considered to be flies closely related to the extant family Nymphomyiidae (Huang *et al.*, 2013). Evenhuis (1994) produced a catalogue of more than 3100 fossil Diptera species (now available online and updated periodically).

Skleropterans (†Skleroptera)
Geological range: Carboniferous

Identification.—Known only from Commenty, France, these insects differ from Coleoptera and Strepsiptera in the structure of the thoracic sclerites and venation of the forewings, particularly in the following character combination: the absence of lateral carina on the prothorax, the narrow separation of the bases of its forewings, the very narrow anal region of the forewings that widen apically and the absence of a sub-marginal anal (adsutural) vein going along the entire posterior margin of the tegmina (Kirejtshuk & Nel, 2013).

Palaeontology.—A new monotypic, extinct holometabolous insect order erected for the species *Stephanastus polinae* (family Stephanastidae), represented by an exoskeleton from the Gzhelian lacustrine deltaic shale in the Commentry Shales Formation of France. Discussion following the publication of the paper by Kirejtshuk & Nel (2013) questioned the need for this new order.

166

Stylopid *Stichotrema cf. weitschati* (Strepsiptera: Myrmecolacidae) in Eocene Baltic amber. RCDP

Stylopids or twisted-wing parasites (Strepsiptera) (= Stylopida)
Geological range: Cretaceous–Recent

Identification.—Strepsipterans are an enigmatic group of tiny insects whose phylogenetic placement has often perplexed entomologists, being allied with beetles (their currrently designated sister group) and dipterans (see Pohl & Beutel, 2013 for discussion). They exhibit great sexual dimorphism. Males have one pair of wings, the forewings are reduced to halteres and the hind wing has very reduced venation (no crossveins). They have large eyes (that look like raspberries), reduced mouthparts (they are unable to feed) and antler-shaped antennae. Females are wingless and have a legless, grub-like body and reduced mouthparts. Larvae are grub-like. They spend most of their life as an endoparasite inside another insect.

Extant Biodiversity.—600 species described (Zhang, 2011).

Palaeontology.—Strepsipterans have been recorded from various amber deposits, including Dominican, Baltic (Fig. 166), Rovno, Burmese and Charentese (France), but they are rarely found as inclusions. Non-amber larval forms have been described from the Tertiary of Germany (Kinzelbach & Lutz, 1985; Kinzelbach & Pohl, 1994; Pohl, 2009).

Caddisflies (Trichoptera)
Geological range: Triassic–Recent

Identification.—Two pairs of wings covered in fine hairs, forewings narrowest. The mouthparts are reduced in adults. They have long antennae and an elongate body. Larvae are aquatic with well developed terminal hooks, they often build elaborate cases.

Extant Biodiversity.—14,300+ species described (Holzenthal *et al.*, 2011).

Palaeontology.—Caddisflies have been recorded from all well studied amber deposits and also occur as non-amber fossils. Although their larval cases are abundant in Mesozoic and Cenozoic lacustrine deposits (e.g. Sukatsheva, 1999), the first trichopteran larva was described by Ivanov (2006), from the Mesozoic of Siberia. The oldest fossils of

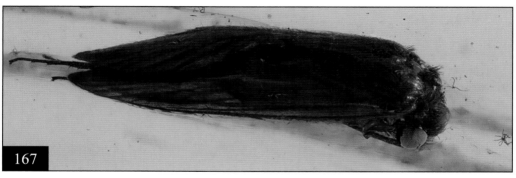

Caddisfly (Trichoptera) with green eyes, in Eocene Baltic amber. RCDP

caddisflies are Triassic, however the Cretaceous was the most important time in the evolution of the order (Sukatsheva, 1982; Sukatsheva & Jarzembowski, 2001; Malm *et al*., 2013). In some amber specimens caddisfly eyes can appear bright metallic green or blue (Wichard *et al*., 2005) (Fig. 167). The fossil insect database (EDNA) lists close to 750 described species, but some of these will be synonyms. Wichard (2013) recently revised many of the Baltic amber species (Spicipalpia and Intergipalpi). The closest relatives of caddisflies are butterflies and moths, despite their very different life histories (together they form the superorder Amphiesmenoptera). It is thought that the two groups had diverged from a common ancestor by the Early Jurassic.

Butterflies and moths (Lepidoptera)
Geological range: Jurassic–Recent

Identification.—Two pairs of membranous wings that are covered in tiny overlapping scales (some moths are wingless). Eyes are large with one ocellus present above each eye (median ocellus absent). The true distinction between butterflies, skippers and moths is somewhat ambiguous, but as a general rule, butterfly antennae are clubbed, while moth antennae tend to be long and slender in females and feathery in males. The mouthparts are formed into a long, coiled tube known as a proboscis. Larvae are known as caterpillars and have a sclerotized head, chewing mouthparts, three pairs of thoracic legs and short, unsegmented prolegs on the abdomen.

Extant Biodiversity.—175,000 species described (Beutel *et al*., 2014).

Palaeontology.—Micro-moths are occasionally found in amber (Fig. 224), but larger moths and butterflies are extremely rare. The Tertiary fossil record of adult butterflies

Ascololepidopterix multinerve (Lepidoptera: Ascololepidopterigidae) from the Middle Jurassic of Mongolia. Reproduced from Zhang *et al*. (2013) with permission. Holotype, CNU-LEP-NN-2012-028

(Figs. 86, 169) for the entire world consists of approximately 50 specimens and only seven of these occur in amber, all from the Miocene deposits of the Dominican Republic and including the families Riodinidae (metalmarks) and Nymphalidae (brush-footed butterflies) (Peñalver & Grimaldi, 2006). Caterpillars of both families also occur in Dominican amber and larval forms of other families, such as Papilionidae have been recorded in Baltic amber. In addition, larvae of at least 22 different moth families have been reported from Baltic amber (Weitschat & Wichard, 2002). The rareness of fossil Lepidoptera in terrestrial deposits (particularly from the Tertiary) is mainly due to taphonomic processes rather than an absence in palaeocommunities, and just as today, they were a dominant insect group at least as far back as the Palaeogene. Coevolutionary dynamics with their angiosperm host plants are thought to have influenced their diversification significantly. There appears to have been a distinct increase in diversification rate in multiple lineages around 90 million years ago, which is concordant with the radiation of angiosperms. Almost all extant families appear to have begun diversifying soon after the end Cretaceous extinction event (Wahlberg *et al.*, 2013). Some of the best preserved rock fossils originate from the Florissant Formation of North America (Emmel *et al.*, 1992) (Fig. 86). The oldest fossils of lepidopterans are from the Jurassic of Europe and Asia, the oldest being from Dorset, UK (Whalley, 1985). Zhang, W. *et al.* (2013) provided a list of known Mesozoic Lepidoptera and described seven new genera and species of moths from three families (one new) from the late Middle Jurassic Jiulongshan Formation in northeastern China (Fig. 168), supporting the conclusion that the Lepidoptera–Trichoptera divergence had occurred by the Early Jurassic. Sohn *et al.* (2012) referred to 229 fossil species in their catalogue of fossil Lepidoptera.

169

Unidentified butterfly (Lepidoptera) from the Eocene Fur Formation, Denmark. GMCD DK136

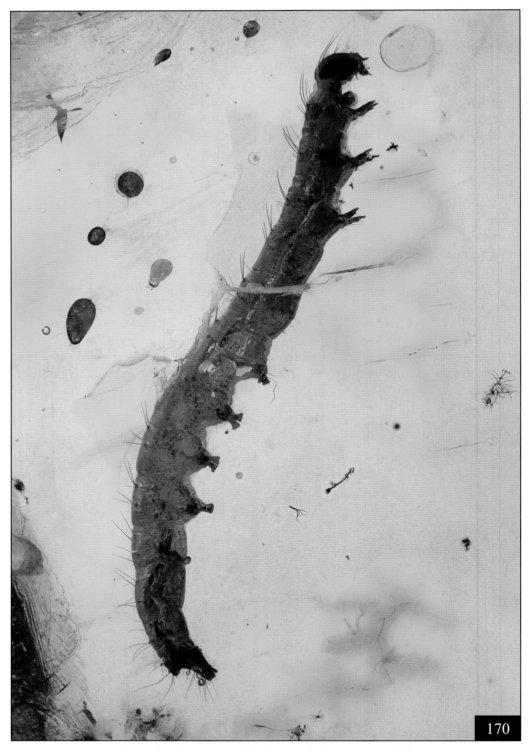

170

Caterpillar (Lepidoptera) in Eocene Baltic amber. RCDP

Insect behaviour and ecology in the fossil record

The concept of behavioural fixity in the fossil record proposes that organisms in the past would have behaved in a similar manner to their close living relatives (Boucot & Poinar, 2010). Fossilized behaviour, sometimes referred to as frozen behaviour or palaeoethology, is reasonably common in the insect fossil record and especially so for organisms preserved in amber (e.g. Penney, 2010a; Penney & Green, 2011). A general overview of fossil behaviour in different ambers was provided by Arillo (2007), with additional and more specific coverage of Baltic amber by Weitschat (2009) and Dominican amber by Poinar (2010).

Fossilized behaviours and ecological interactions occur at many different levels, from communities, populations of a single species (e.g. ant, termite, fly swarms), interspecific interactions (e.g. predation, parasitism and symbiosis, including phoresy) and intraspecific interactions (e.g. mating, mate guarding). However, Arillo (2007) duly noted that virtually all examples of animal behaviour 'frozen' in amber are distorted as a result of the interaction of the organism struggling against the sticky resin. Nonetheless, there are some excellent examples of behavioural interactions in amber, which are presumably the result of rapid entombment and immediate demise of the inclusions.

Some pieces of amber contain hundreds of insects belonging to different species. Such co-occurring fossils are called syninclusions and they can provide many clues to the structure of the palaeoecosystems. Younger, sub-fossilized copal (the intermediate stage between resin and amber) is often retrieved in much larger pieces than amber and so syninclusions can be studied to a much greater extent, thus providing us with a proxy for understanding the bias of fossilization in amber. This is an area of research that has been poorly investigated, but one that has great potential for quantitative palaeoecological studies (e.g. Penney & Preziosi, 2013). Although considerably rarer, mass death assemblages of various insect species also occur in the rock fossil record. Some of the behaviours discussed below can be dated back to the Lower Cretaceous as a result of their occurrence in Jordanian and Lebanese ambers (Kaddumi, 2007; Azar *et al.*, 2010), or even earlier where they appear in sediments. Other behaviours currently known from younger fossil resins may very well be found in older deposits in the future. When examining fossil insects it is important to look for the bigger picture. Most specimens have more information to divulge than merely the presence of a single fossilized individual. 'Frozen' behaviour is far less common in the non-amber insect fossil record, but it does occur, as it does elsewhere in the non-insect fossil record (see Boucot & Poinar, 2010).

Fossil insect assemblages: palaeobiocoenosis or taphocoenosis?
The first question to ask about any fossil insect deposit is *does the assemblage represent a palaeobiocoenois or a taphocoenosis*? A biocoenosis can be defined as *a group of all interacting organisms that live in a particular habitat and form an ecological community*. A palaeobiocoenois is *a fossilized sub-sample of a group of co-occurring and interacting organisms*. A taphocoenosis (or thanatocoenosis) results from the localized accumulation of the remains of dead organisms, where the cause, time and place of death (or habitat in life) of the individuals were not necessarily the same. This usually occurs when the remains of organisms that have perished at various times and in differ-

ent places were transported by water and deposited in a central location. The accumulation of dead matter can include the remains of insects, plants, molluscs and the bones of terrestrial animals. Under such circumstances, the insect remains are usually fragmentary in nature (e.g. isolated wings, beetle elytra, legs, etc.) because dead insects often become disarticulated as a result of transport from the site at which they died. Thus, it is important to understand the different taphonomic processes that led to the preservation of fossil insects in both sediments and amber. An excellent review on this topic was provided by Martínez-Delclòs *et al.* (2004).

Terrestrial fossil insect assemblages in amber are more likely to represent a palaeobiocoenosis than terrestrial insect fossil assemblages in rocks, which would have been preserved in an aquatic setting and so more likely represent a taphocoenosis. Nonetheless, both can provide unique insights into past insect behaviour and ecology and furnish important clues for reconstructing palaeohabitats. It should be noted that mass insect burial slabs can also be misleading when making palaeoecological inferences based on the fossils due to the inherent bias of the fossil record. For example, in a comparative taphonomic study of extant beetles, Smith (2000) found that the relative abundances of families in a live assemblage were significantly different to those found in the associated death assemblage.

A particularly splendid rock specimen (Fig. 171) originates from the Lower Permian of Tshekarda in the Urals and includes various different insect taxa, such as *Tshekardobia osmylina* (Hypoperlida: Hypoperlidae), *Glaphyrophlebia uralensis* ('Protorthoptera': Blattinopseidae), *Perlopsis filicornis* (Plecoptera: Perlopseidae) and an unidentified mecopteran. Perrichot & Girard (2009) reported on an unusual piece of Cretaceous amber (5 × 3 × 2.5 cm) from Archingeay, France that contained a total of

171

Mass burial slab from the Permian of Tshekarda, Russia, containing fossils of various insect orders, including Hypoperlida, Protorthoptera, Plecoptera and an unidentified mecopteran. PIN 1700-3287

274 syninclusions as follows: 86 arthropods (19 families in 13 orders), 181 microbes and seven feathers. Penney *et al.* (2012b) described an unusual spider-dominated palaeobiocoenosis in sub-Recent copal from Colombia.

Intrapopulation interactions

There are various reasons why individuals of a species may have been preserved together in the fossil record. Mass preservation of fly larvae from the poorly understood species *Cuterebra* (=*Lithohypoderma*) *ascarides* (Diptera: Oestridae) occurs in deposits of the Eocene Parachute Creek Member of the Green River Formation, Utah, USA. Similarly, midge larvae (Diptera: Chironomidae) can also be found together in large numbers (Fig. 172). Mass mortality slabs containing numerous beetle larvae of *Coptoclava longipoda* (Coleoptera: Coptoclavidae) (Fig. 173) are known from the Lower Cretaceous of Baissa, Transbaikalia. In the above cases, the aquatic nature of these larvae explains how they became preserved together in large numbers. The mass burial slabs of adult stoneflies *Plutopteryx beata* (Plecoptera: Baleyopterygidae) (Fig. 174) from the Jurassic of Bayan-Teg, Mongolia are thought to represent synchronized mass emergence (Rasnitsyn & Quicke, 2002). Another mass burial, this time consisting of grylloblattid forewings of *Atactophlebia termitoides* (Notoptera: Atactophlebiidae) (Fig. 175) from the older Upper Permian of Tikhiye Gory, Tatarian Republic, Russia, has been interpreted as three sequential subimaginal stages as a result of their different sizes (Rasnitsyn & Quicke, 2002).

   Numerous taphonomically relevant observations were made by Coram & Jepson (2012) on a slab of rock from the Lower Cretaceous Lulworth Formation of Dorset, containing more than 1000 beetle elytra (Fig. 176). They noted that the remains were disarticulated (indicating transport of the dead insects), densely concentrated (suggesting accumulation prior to burial), the specimen contained virtually only beetle elytra (suggesting differential transport of the insect remains, either by wind and/or water currents), that most were preserved with their convex surface facing downwards (relating to the hydraulic properties of the remains in water) and that the elytra showed no preferred alignment (suggesting very weak water currents). Thus, not all mass preservation slabs are directly indicative of naturally occurring and interacting communities.

   Fly swarms (Figs. 180–182) of various families, such as Dolichopodidae, Chironomidae, Keroplatidae, Mycetophilidae, Sciaridae, Psychodidae and Phoridae occur in various ambers, and occasionally mating pairs (Figs. 183–188) are also preserved. Swarms of winged ants and termites (Fig. 90) are also relatively common in fossil resins. In the latter group it is more usual to find mass accumulations of shed wings that were rubbed off by the alates following their mating (nuptial) flights. Multiple syninclusions of flying insects such as primitive lacewings (Neuroptera: Nevrorthidae) (Fig. 178) are much rarer, but multiple caddisflies (Trichoptera) in amber are not uncommon (Fig. 179), especially in Baltic amber. Non-flying members of social insect orders may also be found preserved together in large numbers, such as worker termites and ants going about their daily business, including activities such as carrying eggs and pupae (Brandao *et al.*, 1999). Burnham (1978) provided a comprehensive review of the social insect fossil record, although many new taxa have been described since this publication, extending the known range of some groups back from the Cenozoic to the Mesozoic.

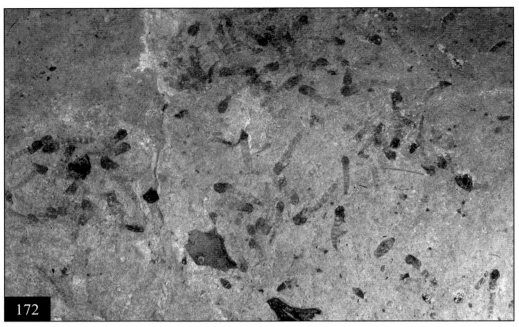

Mass burial slab of midge larvae (Diptera: Chironomidae) from the Eocene Florissant Fossil Beds National Monument, Colorado, USA. FLFO

Mass burial slab from the Lower Cretaceous of Baissa, Transbaikalia, containing fossils of *Coptoclava longipoda* (Coleoptera: Coptoclavidae). PIN 3064-6828 (inset PIN 1989-2692)

Mass burial slab from the Jurassic of Bayan-Teg, Mongolia, containing fossils of *Plutopteryx beata* (Plecoptera: Baleyopterygidae), possibly indicative of synchronized emergence. PIN 4023-2330 (inset PIN 4023-77)

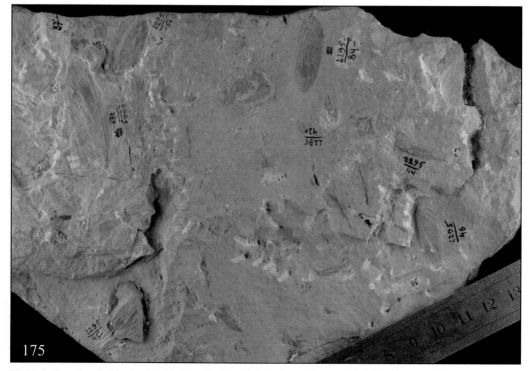

Multiple fossils of *Atactophlebia termitoides* (Notoptera: Atactophlebiidae), possibly representing sequential subimaginal stages due to size variation, from the Permian of Tikhie Gory, Russia. PIN

Slab containing massed beetle elytra, from the Lower Cretaceous Soft Cockle Beds of the Lulworth Formation (Lower Purbeck Limestone Group), Dorset, UK. MNEMG 1999.3

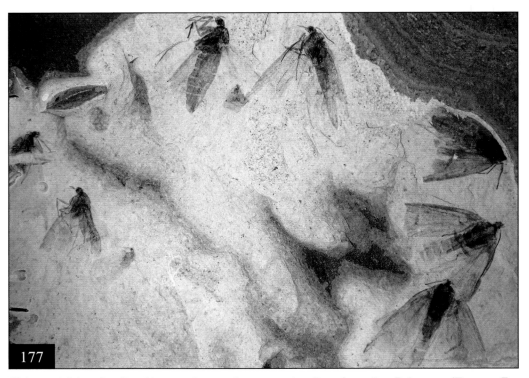

Slab containing fossil evidence of a moth mass migration, from the Paleocene/Eocene Fur Formation of the Isle of Mors, Denmark. PCAB

Lacewing syninclusions *Rophalis relicta* (Neuroptera: Nevrorthidae) in Eocene Baltic amber. RCDP

Caddisfly syninclusions (Trichoptera: ?Polycentropodidae) in Eocene Baltic amber. RCDP

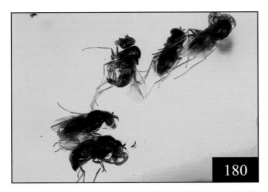

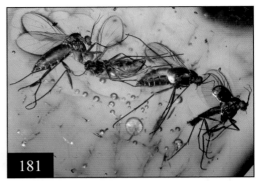

Unidentified long-legged flies (Diptera: Doli-chopodidae) in Eocene Baltic amber. RCDP

Unidentified predatory fungus gnats (Diptera: Keroplatidae: Orfeliini) in Eocene Baltic amber. RCDP

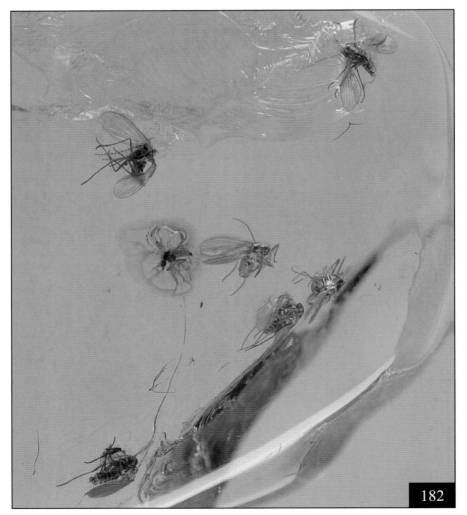

Partial swarm of moth flies *Trichomyia* sp. (Diptera: Psychodidae) in Eocene Baltic amber. RCDP

Swarming is also evident (but much rarer) in non-amber deposits. For example, a Paleogene (55 million years ago) mass moth migration of an estimated 1700 individuals was documented from the Tertiary Fur Formation of Denmark by Rust (2000). The fossils (Fig. 177) consist of complete individuals, isolated wings and wingless bodies from at least seven different species.

Sometimes large numbers of platypodid (flat-footed) beetles (Curculionidae: Platypodinae) are found in a single piece of Dominican amber but these probably do not represent swarms in the strict sense. Batelka *et al.* (2011) proposed that the frequent co-occurrence of the ripiphorid beetle *Quasipirhidius luzziae* as syninclusions in Dominican amber may reflect a unique synchronization of emergence (unknown in living relatives), but was more likely intraspecific aggregative behaviour by males prior to mating with receptive females. Gregarious behaviour in locusts (Orthoptera: Acrididae [?Oedipodinae]) was identified by Arillo & Ortuño (1997) for an assemblage from the Oligocene [now considered to be of Miocene age, Arillo, personal communication] of Izarra, Spain, where the fossil species (which was not named) represents around 20% of all fossil insects. The presence of several earwig nymphs in a piece of Cretaceous amber from Archingeay, south-western France, led Engel (2009a) to propose gregarious behaviour for this species and that the tight association of the nymphs indicated they were probably newly hatched and part of a brood from a single mother who was caring for them, suggesting that maternal behaviour in earwigs had evolved by the latest Jurassic.

Intraspecific interactions: mating
The most obvious evidence of direct intraspecific interaction are males and females preserved whilst mating, with such specimens recorded from most major fossiliferous amber deposits (see Boucot & Poinar, 2010: Table 27 for known occurrences in amber). This behaviour is most commonly observed in fossil flies of various families (Figs. 183–188), but has also been recorded in beetles, true bugs, wasps and even ants (e.g. Arillo, 2007). The fossil scuttle flies (Diptera: Phoridae) in copula (Fig. 188) represent the first example of this fossilized behaviour for this family; in the specimen cited by (Arillo, 2007) and illustrated by Weitschat & Wichard (2002) the pair are actually preserved either pre- or most likely post-copulation, as is a similar specimen figured and described by Brown (1999). Post-copulation mate guarding was proposed by Andersen

183

Mating pair of fungus gnats (Diptera: Mycetophilidae) in Eocene Baltic amber. RCDP

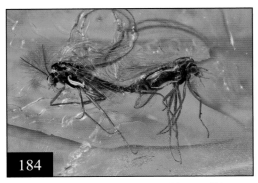

Mating pair of non-biting midges (Diptera: Chironomidae) in Eocene Baltic amber. RCDP

Mating pair of long-legged flies (Diptera: Dolichopodidae) in Eocene Baltic amber. RCDP

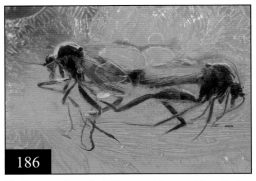

Mating pair of biting midges *Monohelea clunipes* (Diptera: Ceratoponidae) in Eocene Baltic amber. RCDP

Mating pair of dark-winged fungus gnats *Trichosia (Trichosia) meuneri* (Diptera: Sciaridae) in Eocene Baltic amber. RCDP

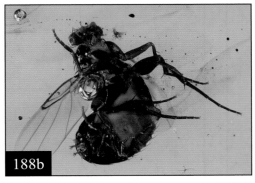

Mating pair of scuttle flies *Limulomyia tyche* (Diptera: Phoridae) in Eocene Baltic amber. RCDP

Mating froghoppers *Anthoscytina perpetua* (Homoptera: Procercopi-dae) from the Middle Jurassic of northeastern China. Reproduced from Li *et al.* (2013) with permission. CNU-HEM-NN2012002p

& Poinar (1992) for a pair of adult pond-skaters (Hemiptera: Gerridae) preserved to-gether in Miocene Dominican amber.

Preservation of insects in copula from non-amber deposits is extremely rare. A unique fossil consisting of a pair of dragonflies *Mesuropetala muensteri* (Odonata: Mesuropetalidae) preserved in the characteristic tandem (mate guarding) posture has been discovered in the Upper Jurassic lithographic limestone deposits of Solnhofen, Germany (Frickhinger, 1999). More recently, Li, S. *et al.* (2013) described a pair of froghoppers, *Anthoscytina perpetua* (Procercopidae) from the Middle Jurassic of north-eastern China copulating in a belly-to-belly mating position (Fig. 189).

Intraspecific interactions: trophallaxis

Trophallaxis is the transfer of food or other fluids among members of a population via stomodeal (mouth-to-mouth) or proctodeal (anus-to-mouth) feeding. In insects it is most highly developed in the social groups such as Isoptera and Hymenoptera, but also oc-curs as 'nuptial feeding' in Mecoptera. Only a single instance of this behaviour has been reported in the fossil record, although it has not been formally described. Arillo (2007) made reference to a piece of Miocene Dominican amber containing a *Nasutitermes* sp. worker termite feeding a soldier termite with a cone-shaped head modified for squirting chemical defence, but lacking mandibles and so unable to feed itself.

Interspecific interactions: parasitism

Evidence of parasitism is scarce in the fossil record. Endoparasites are usually hidden from view inside their hosts or, if exposed, are usually fragile organisms which do not easily fossilize. However, 'instantaneous' entrapment in resin may result in the preser-vation of both ectoparasites and endoparasites that are partially exposed or in the act of exiting their host (Poinar, 1992a). Rarely, the presence of an internal parasite can be

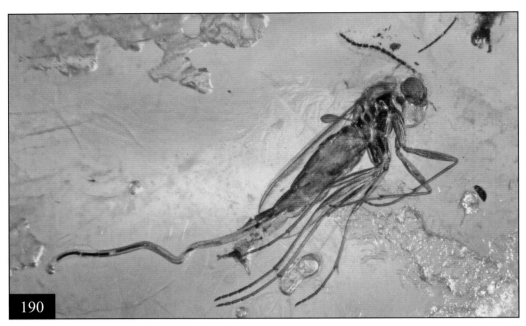

190

Parasitic nematode *Heydenius sciarophilus* (Mermithidae) emerging from a dark-winged fungus-gnat (Diptera: Sciaridae) in Eocene Baltic amber. RCGP

inferred from the presence of an empty egg attached to the cuticle of the host, as in the presumed case of Tachinidae (Diptera) parasitism of a chrysomelid beetle in Dominican amber described by Poinar (2013). The most common examples of parasitism in amber are *Leptus* sp. (Erythraeidae) mite larvae attached to flies of various different families (and occasionally other insect orders) (Figs. 191, 192), and evidence of nematode (e.g. Mermithidae) infections (Fig. 190) also occurs, but these are less common (see Arillo, 2007 for cited examples and Poinar, 2012 for recent descriptions). Seven insect orders (Phasmatodea, Lepidoptera, Trichoptera, Diptera, Coleoptera, Hymenoptera and Hemiptera) are now known as hosts to mermithid worms in various ambers (Poinar, 2012). Additional examples of mite parasitism include water mites attached to aquatic insects, for example in Baltic amber (Wichard *et al.*, 2009). Koteja & Poinar (2005) described parasitic (although they did not exclude a phoretic association) mites on thirteen scale insects (Hemiptera: Coccinea) from a range of Tertiary and Cretaceous ambers, concluding that mites played a major role in controlling scale insect populations during the Cretaceous. The parasitized scale insects belonged to the families Ortheziidae, ?Steingeliidae, Electrococcidae, Kuwaniidae, Pityococcidae and Inkaidae; all but the last being archeococcids. The frequency of this association was highest in Pityococcidae with eight out of 64 specimens associated with mites (Koteja & Poinar, 2005). Extant *Calamiscus* flies (Diptera: Phoridae) are gregarious parasitoids of injured stingless bees in the Neotropical region today. The co-occurrence of a specimen of the genus *Calamiscus* with a fossil bee in a piece of Cretaceous New Jersey amber (Brown, 1997) represents one of the oldest fossil examples of an insect–insect host–parasitoid relationship. The parasitic fly was probably lured to the amber site by the alarm pheromones of the trapped bee, and subsequently became trapped in the sticky resin alongside it.

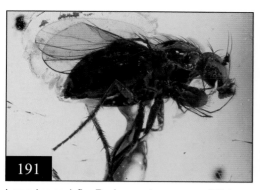

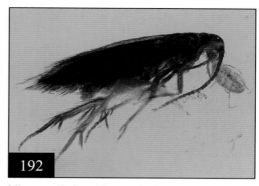

Long-legged fly *Prohercostomus* sp. (Diptera: Dolichopodidae) with parasitic *Leptus* sp. mite in Eocene Baltic amber. RCDP

Micro-moth (Lepidoptera) with parasitic *Leptus* sp. mite in Eocene Baltic amber. RCDP

Parasitic Hymenoptera larvae are occasionally encountered attached to, or even emerging from their hosts, such as the exceptional fossil of a wasp larva (Hymenoptera: Braconidae) preserved whilst emerging from an adult ant (Poinar & Miller, 2002). A parasitic Ichneumonidae larva in close proximity to a clubionoid spider in Dominican amber was presumed to represent a parasitic association by Poinar (1987). Arillo (2007) referred to direct fossil evidence of parasitism, including a Stigmaphronidae (Hymenoptera) laying eggs into a Sciaroidea (Diptera) in Mesozoic Spanish amber, as figured by Alonso *et al.* (2000). The specimen in the figure in question was referred to as Megaspilidae and it is not possible to determine from the photograph, nor is it mentioned in the text, whether or not this behaviour is actually occurring. The review of Spanish amber stigmaphronids by Ortega-Blanco *et al.* (2011) did not mention this particular specimen. Wunderlich (1986: 226) figured a remarkable specimen of Baltic amber containing an ichneumonoid wasp (Hymenoptera) ovipositing into a caterpillar. Dryinid wasps (Hymenoptera: Dryinidae) are parasitoids of Auchenorrhyncha (planthoppers etc.) and occur in both the rock and amber fossil record (Olmi & Guglielmino, 2011 and references therein). They have a distinctive chelate protarsus used to grasp the host during egg laying. The larva develops internally and eventually forms a thylacium (an external gall-like cyst) extending from the host's abdomen; examples of this developmental stage are preserved in Miocene Dominican amber (Grimaldi & Engel, 2005). Parasitic Hymenoptera are common in the fossil record, but it is rare to find direct evidence of their parasitic behaviour. Indeed, most wasps found in amber are tiny parasitoid species and in Cretaceous ambers these taxa offer insights into the antiquity of parasitoid associations, through comparison with modern relatives in which the biology is known. Additionally, the obligate parasitoid–host relationships of many of these species also provide evidence for the presence of other groups within the Cretaceous amber-producing forest, even though these host groups may not have been preserved, or have yet to be recovered as fossils themselves (McKellar & Engel, 2012). Wunderlich (2012) referred to Mantispidae (Neuroptera) larvae as parasitic on spiders in Baltic amber (see discussion under phoresy).

A parasitic hair worm (Nematomorpha) in Miocene Dominican amber was recorded emerging from its cockroach host by Poinar (1999b). Fur and feather lice/eggs

 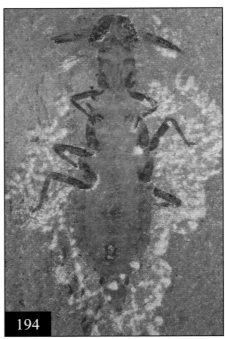

A possible pterosaur parasite *Saurophthirus longipes* (Siphonaptera) from the Cretaceous of Baissa, Siberia, Russia. Holotype, PIN 3064-1898

?Parasitic louse *Saurodectes vrsanskyi* (?Phthiraptera: Saurodectidae) from the Cretaceous of Baissa, Siberia, Russia. Holotype, PIN 4210-7056

Giant flea *Tyrannopsylla beipiaoensis* (Siphonaptera: Pseudopulicidae) (body length 14.7 mm) from the Lower Cretaceous Yixian Formation at Huangbanjigou in Beipiao City, Liaoning Province, China. Holotype, NIGP 154249a

have been noted in association with fur and feather fragments preserved in amber (e.g. Voigt, 1952). Strepsiptera (sometimes referred to as twisted-winged parasites) are tiny insects with complicated life cycles and are rare as fossils in amber. Males are winged but females are wingless and spend their entire life inside an insect host. Males are encountered more frequently as fossils, but even the parasitic females still inside their host have been discovered, e.g. associated with ants (Hymenoptera: Formicidae) in Baltic amber (Pohl & Kinzelbach, 2001) and bees (Hymenoptera: Halictidae) and fulgoroid planthoppers (Achilidae and Delphacidae) in Dominican amber (Poinar, 2004).

The non-amber fossil record of parasitic behaviour (and even the parasites themselves) is sparse and in some cases controversial. A chewing louse from the Eocene of Eckfeld Maar, Germany, described as *Megamenopon rasnitsyni* (Psocodea [Phthiraptera]: Menoponidae) by Wappler *et al.* (2004), has remnants of its host's feathers preserved in its gut and was considered the only indisputable fossil louse by Dalgleish *et al.* (2006). The supposed chewing louse *Saurodectes vrsanskyi* (Psocodea [Phthiraptera]: Saurodectidae) (Fig. 194) from the Early Cretaceous of Baissa, Siberia is thought to have fed on pterosaurs (Rasnitsyn & Zherikhin, 1999). Grimaldi & Engel (2005) questioned the systematic placement of this species but agreed that it was probably an ectoparasite, plausibly with phthirapteran affinities; Dalgleish *et al.* (2006) considered it *incertae sedis*. Vršanský *et al.* (2010) suggested it may even warrant being placed in a new insect order. Supposed pterosaur pre-fleas have been described as follows: *Saurophthirus longipes* (Siphonaptera, see Gao *et al.*, 2013b) (Fig. 193) from the Cretaceous of Transbaikalia, Russia (Ponomarenko, 1976) and *Strashila incredibilis* (Fig. 1) from the Jurassic of Mogzon, Russia (Rasnitsyn, 1992). Vršanský *et al.* (2010) erected the new insect order Nakridletia for the latter species, in addition to two new giant pterosaur parasites *Vosila sinensis* and *Parazila saurica* from the Middle Jurassic of China, both of which were assigned to the new family Vosilidae. However, Nakridletia was synonymized with Diptera by Huang *et al.* (2013).

The oldest definitive fleas are giant forms from the Middle Jurassic and Early Cretaceous of China (Fig. 195) that exhibit many defining features of Siphonaptera, but retain primitive traits such as non-jumping hindlegs. They have stout and elongate, sucking mouthparts for piercing the skin of their hosts, which were most probably hairy or feathered 'reptilians', with radiations to feed on mammals and birds later in the Cenozoic (Huang *et al.*, 2012). *Tarwinia australis* and *Niwratia elongata* described by Jell & Duncan (1986) from the Early Cretaceous Koonwarra sediments of southern Australia were referred to as putative stem-group siphonopterans by Grimaldi & Engel (2005), but Krasnov (2008) considered their affinities to fleas uncertain. Fleas are very rare in amber, but a handful of specimens have been recorded from the Dominican and Baltic deposits (Lewis & Grimaldi, 1997; Perrichot *et al.*, 2012) as evidence of ectoparastic insect behaviour in the fossil record. A review of haematophagous fossil insects (mainly Diptera) was provided by Lukashevich & Mostovski (2003).

An interesting study by Greenwalt *et al.* (2013) identified what they considered to be the remnants of a vertebrate-derived blood meal in an oil shale preserved mosquito (Culicidae: *Culiseta* sp.) from the Middle Eocene Kishenehn Formation in Montana. The abdomen of the fossil insect was shown to contain very high levels of iron, and time-of-flight secondary ion mass spectrometry (ToF-SIMS) analysis was used to iden-

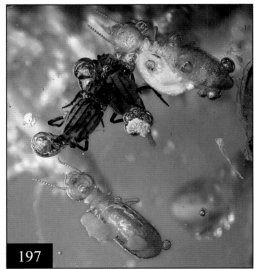

Termite inquiline *Prorhinopsenius alzadae* (Staphylinidae: Trichopseninae) in Miocene Dominican amber. PCYCT

Termite inquiline *Termitodius* sp. (Scarabaeidae: Aphodiinae) with *Coptotermes* (Rhinotermitidae) hosts in Colombian copal. RCDP

tify porphyrin molecules derived from the oxygen-carrying haeme moiety of haemoglobin (Greenwalt *et al.*, 2013).

Interspecific interactions: symbiosis

The definition of symbiosis is controversial, but can be broadly defined as a close and often long-term mutually beneficial interaction between different biological species. There are lots of examples of this today and the fossil record is useful for providing clues as to when such interspecific relationships may have evolved. For example, some extant rove beetles (Staphylinidae: Trichopseniinae) are found only in association with termites. The usual termite hosts for extant species are members of the family Rhinotermitidae, but they are also known to co-exist with Termitidae, Mastotermitidae and Kalotermitidae. The extant genus *Prorhinopsenius* is unusual within the subfamily for including species that live with three host families: Mastotermitidae (*Mastotermes*), Kalotermitidae (*Neotermes*) and Rhinotermitidae (*Prorhinotermes*). Kistner (1998) proposed that multiple host transfer events have occurred throughout their evolutionary history as an explanation for the co-occurrence of Trichopseniini with unrelated termite lineages. The proposed termite host for the fossil species *Prorhinopsenius alzadae* (Fig. 196) was most probably the Dominican amber fossil termite *Mastotermes electrodominicus* (Mastotermitidae). However, to our knowledge they have not been found together as syninclusions. Extant Mastotermitidae are found only in northern Australia, but clearly the family had a rather different distribution in the past.

Termitophilous beetles are also known from other families. For example, extant scarabs of the genus *Termitodius* (Scarabaeidae: Aphodiinae: Rhyparini) are well known as social insect inquilines (i.e. they live in the nest of another species). Sub-fossils possibly belonging to the extant species *T. coronatus* have been found preserved in close association with *Coptotermes* termites (Rhinotermitidae) in Colombian copal

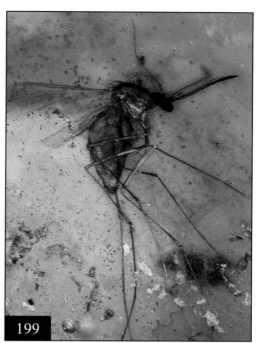

Blood-engorged female sand fly *Lutzomyia/ Pintomyia* sp. (Diptera: Psychodidae) in Miocene Dominican amber. RCDP

Female mosquito *Culex* sp. (Diptera: Culicidae) in Miocene Dominican amber. RCDP

(Fig. 197), with both organisms co-occurring together in reasonably large numbers (the proposed age ranges for Colombian copal are highly variable and some specimens may be only a few decades old). In extant species the larvae live in the sides of the termite nest. Also found in termite nests are termite bugs (Hemiptera: Termitaphididae). Their fossil record is restricted to two species in Miocene Dominican amber and a single species from the contemporaneous Mexican amber. With a body length of 7.1 mm *Termitaradus protera*, the fossil species from the latter deposit, is almost twice the size of all others, fossil or extant (Engel, 2009b).

Alate ants of the genus *Acropyga* (Formicinae) carrying mealybugs (Pseudococcidae: Rhizoecinae) in Miocene Dominican amber were described by Johnson *et al.* (2001), a discovery indicating that the intimate association and relatively uncommon behaviour, which still occurs today, has existed for at least 16 million years. Extant *Acropyga* species are subterranean ants that rely on aphids or mealybugs to provide their sustenance. Females carry the mealybugs in their mandibles while swarming, which they probably then use to inoculate their new nests.

Even insect–microbial associations have been recorded in amber, such as Cretaceous termites preserved in Burmese amber, along with their symbiotic intestinal protozoa that would have facilitated digestion of the plant matter on which the insects fed (Poinar, 2009). Even various species of (presumably) pathogenic viruses and microbes, such as trypanosomes and plasmodia inside their insect vectors, including sand flies (Psychodidae) (Fig. 198), biting midges (Ceratopogonidae), mosquitoes (Culicidae) (Fig. 199) and triatomine bugs have also been described from amber (Poinar, 2011a), in some cases dating back as far as the Cretaceous (Poinar & Telford, 2005). Poinar (2011b) described *Vetufebrus ovatus* (Haemospororida: Plasmodiidae) from two oocysts attached to the midgut wall and sporozoites in the salivary glands and ducts of a fossil bat fly (Diptera: Streblidae) in Dominican amber, suggesting that representatives of the Hippoboscoidea were vectoring bat malaria in the New World by the mid-Tertiary. Triatomine bugs preserved in Dominican amber, which are thought to have fed on bats, may also have been vectors of disease in the amber forest (Poinar, 2010). See Luka-shevich & Mostovski (2003) for a review of haematophagous (blood-feeding) insects in the fossil record. The potential for identifying viruses in fossil insects based on observa-tions of virus-induced cellular structures was discussed by Lovisolo & Rösler (2003).

Fossil flatus (or wind) preserved in amber, as bubbles exiting the anal region of an insect, is presumably indirect evidence of insect–intestinal microbial associations (Boucot & Poinar, 2010). Such fossil evidence, some of which dates back approxi-mately 100 million years to the Mesozoic (e.g. Poinar, 2009), is important for studies that aim to identify when these kinds of associations first evolved.

Interspecific interactions: phoresy
Phoresy refers to a short-term symbiotic relationship, especially among arthropods, in which one organism disperses by being transported by another organism of a different species. In the fossil record, this phenomenon is most often observed in amber pre-served pseudoscorpions (Arachnida: Pseudoscorpiones) attached to flies, beetles, wasps or moths (Figs. 201, 203) (reviewed by Poinar et al., 1998), but careful examination of inclusions can also reveal the presence of microscopic phoretic mites (usually belonging to the family Uropodidae, but also other families) on insects such as cerambycid (Dun-lop et al., 2013), cryptophagid (Lyubarsky & Perkovsky, 2012) and anobiid beetles (Fig. 202), Diptera (Poinar & Grimaldi, 1990), Hymenoptera (see summary in Arillo, 2007) and more rarely also on spiders (Dunlop et al., 2011b). X-ray computed tomography is particularly useful for the study of these fossils, not only because of their small size, but also because it permits 3D reconstructions and non-destructive virtual dissection of the mite from the host, which is necessary in order to see important features on the underside of the mite required for identification (Dunlop et al., 2011b). Another exam-ple of palaeophoresy concerns fig nematodes (Diplogasteridae) in Miocene Dominican amber, which used fig wasps (Hymenoptera: Agaonidae) to transport them from flower to flower (Poinar & Poinar, 1999: fig. 23), just as their extant relatives do today.

An interesting, and the first example of springtail (Collembola) phoresy, was documented by Boucot & Poinar (2010), consisting of five individuals of *Sminthurus longicornis* adjacent to the leg of a *Dicranopalpus* harvestman (Arachnida: Opiliones) in Eocene Baltic amber. The collembolans appear to have secured themselves for transit using their antennae, which are completely or partially curved over the leg in four of the springtails. A similar example is that of a sminthurid springtail being trasported by a mayfly in Dominican amber (Figs. 20, 200), representing the first record of Ephemerop-tera as a transporter of other species (Penney et al., 2012a). Again, in this specimen the springtail is holding on using its antennae. Phoresy using winged insects is unknown in extant Collembola, but this is presumably because they are a poorly studied group and the tiny living individuals would quickly release their hold on the host if disturbed, so

Male mayfly *Borinquena parva* (Ephemeroptera: Leptophlebiidae) with a phoretic springtail (Collembola) holding on with its antennae, in Miocene Dominican amber (see Fig. 20). RCDP

Wasp (Hymenoptera: Braconidae) with phoretic pseudoscorpion, in Baltic amber. BSPGM

Anobium sp. (Coleoptera: Anobiidae) with phoretic mites, in Eocene Baltic amber. RCDP

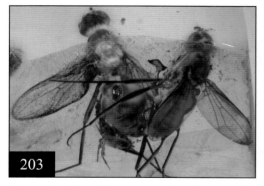

Hyperphoretic mites on a phoretic pseudo-scorpion attached to *Cypselosomatites succini* (Cypselosomatidae), in Baltic amber. PCH

Mantis-fly larva (Neuroptera: Mantispidae) phoretic on a spider, in Baltic amber. MfN

this behaviour may have been overlooked in the extant fauna. Hence, phoresy probably occurs in some extant sminthurids as suggested by the above-mentioned examples of 'frozen' behaviour preserved in amber. Phoresy in extant Collembola, particularly in association with winged insects, would help explain their widespread distribution and their occurrence on remote and newly formed islands (Boucot & Poinar, 2010).

Hyperphoresy, when one organism is being transported by another that is also in the process of being transported, is extremely rare in the fossil record but does occur (Fig. 203). The specimen illustrated shows hyperphoretic mites hitching a ride on the legs of a phoretic pseudoscorpion which is attached to the rare fly *Cypselosomatites succini* (Cypselosomatidae) in Eocene Baltic amber. Trophophoresy refers to queen *Acropyga* ants (Formicidae) emerging from their nests and carrying a mealybug in their mandibles as the seed food source for a new nest. Such specimens in Dominican amber were first described by Johnson *et al.* (2001) and further discussed by LaPolla (2005).

The neuropteran family Mantispidae (mantis-flies) undergo an unusual development known as hypermetamorphosis. This is where the first-stage larva is radically different in appearance from subsequent instars. The purpose of the mobile first-stage (often called planidia or triungulin) larva is to find a suitable host or food resource upon which the subsequent grub-like stages can develop. In mantispids the larvae of some species feed on spider eggs. What better way to find such a resource than to hitch a ride on the back of a spider? Such an example of a phoretic, spider-boarding mantispid larva was recently described from a fossil in Baltic amber by Ohl (2011) (Fig. 204), with additional examples in Wunderlich (2012). Wunderlich referred to the larvae as ectoparasites, however, the few observations that first instar larvae pierce the spider's cuticle to feed have not been further studied and understood in detail, but this would mean that they are also parasitic in addition to being phoretic spider egg predators. Additional hypermetamorphic larvae belonging to the orders Coleoptera (Meloidae and Rhipiphoridae) and Strepsiptera have been identified in Dominican, Baltic and Cretaceous Burmese ambers and from the Eocene brown coal of Halle-an-der-Saale, Germany (see Poinar & Boucot, 2010: Table 5).

Interspecific interactions: predators and prey
Unequivocal fossilized examples of insects as both predators and prey are uncommon. There have been several reports of various insects trapped on the silken threads of spider webs or wrapped in spider silk in ambers from various deposits dating back to the Lower Cretaceous (Peñalver *et al.*, 2006). Sometimes spiders and other arachnids are preserved together with their presumed insect prey. For example, a pseudoscorpion with an ant held firmly in its claws, preserved in Mexican amber, was figured by Ross & Sheridan (2013). There is great potential for all sorts of remarkable fossils preserved within the blink of an eye to exhibit 'frozen' predatory behaviour. An excellent example is that of a dancefly (Diptera: Empididae: *Empis* sp.) engulfed in resin whilst carrying its gall midge (Diptera: Cecidomyiidae) prey (Fig. 205). These predatory flies catch their prey during flight and are major predators of mating swarms of male non-biting midges.

However, not all apparent predator–prey associations in amber are so straight forward to confirm. Once caught in the amber forming resin, many insects would have

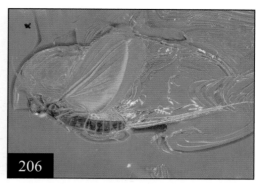

Dagger fly *Empis* sp. (Diptera: Empididae) carrying Cecidomyiidae prey, in Eocene Baltic amber. PCYCT

Mayfly *Paraleptophlebia prisca* (Ephemeroptera: Leptophlebiidae) showing evidence of struggle, in Eocene Baltic amber. RCDP

Theridiidae spider with caddisfly (non-prey) syninclusion in Eocene Baltic amber. RCDP

Zodariidae spider with ant (potential prey) syninclusion in Eocene Baltic amber. PCYCT

struggled in an attempt to escape from it. This is evident from bent wings, disarticulation of body parts, and also through lines of distortion in the resin preserved around the inclusion (Fig. 206). Certainly some insects (e.g. ants) would have bitten anything that came into close proximity during their struggle to escape and such stress related behaviour may be erroneously interpreted as a predator–prey interaction.

Similarly, the presence of a predator and a potential prey species preserved close to each other often requires careful interpretation before a predator–prey association can be confirmed. For example, spiders are often preserved close to insects (Figs. 207, 208), but were they in process of preying on them? In the examples illustrated the theridiid spider would not have been preying on the caddisfly. These spiders have poor eyesight and use webs to catch their prey; the fossil (Fig. 207) is of a mature male that would have been trapped whilst wandering in search of a female rather than hunting for food. In the example of the Zodariidae preserved with the ant (Fig. 208) there is more compelling evidence to suggest a predator–prey association, despite the fact that the spider is not directly consuming it. Zodariids are commonly known as armoured ant-eating spiders on account of the specialized ant diet of many extant species. Jumping spiders (Salticidae) preserved with other insects are common in Tertiary amber. Salticids are

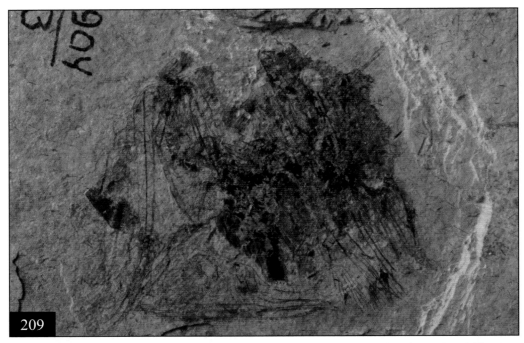

A possible pterosaur regurgitate containing Odonata wings, from the Jurassic of Karatau, Kazakhstan. PIN 2904-3

active diurnal hunters with excellent eyesight and would certainly have been attracted to struggling insects trapped in resin. Thus, there is usually better justification for inferring a predator–prey association, especially if the jumping spider is oriented towards the insect syninclusion, and especially if there are distortion lines preserved in the amber around the potential prey item, which would be indicative of a struggling insect.

A remarkable example of insects as prey is their occurrence in the gut contents of a leptodactylid frog preserved in Miocene Dominican amber, described by Anderson (2004). The contents included a cricket (Orthoptera: Gryllidae), indeterminate Hymenoptera and partially digested remains of other unidentifiable insects consisting only of the more sclerotized body parts. An unusual slab from the Karabastau Formation, Late Jurassic of Karatau, Kazakhstan (Fig. 209) consists of what has been interpreted as a pterosaur regurgitate including odonatan wings. There are several examples, but none have been described formally in the scientific literature (Zherikhin, 2002a).

Sometimes, insect remains are preserved in the fossilized excrement (coprolites) of other animals. The hard exoskeleton of insects makes them relatively indigestible and they are occasionally recovered from such samples, some dating back as far as the Carboniferous (this subject is discussed in more detail under Sub-fossil insects). The earliest fossil record of a putative insect chemical defense response against predators was that of a soldier beetle (Cantharidae) in Burmese amber described by Poinar *et al.* (2007), suggesting that chemical defense mechanisms in beetles have existed for at least 100 million years.

Individual behaviours: general

Insects may be preserved still exhibiting their behaviour immediately prior to their demise. For example, flies (and more rarely other insects) laying eggs are sometimes found as fossils in amber (Figs. 210–212). However, it is unclear whether the oviposition in resin was a natural behaviour. In most cases this is unlikely and several ideas have been proposed to explain this phenomenon. These include the trauma of resin entrapment causing an involuntary relaxation of the ovipositor sphincter muscles; eggs in the oviduct may have been forced out by the pressure exerted by the resin; or possibly the drive to reproduce was so strong that entrapped females released their eggs in a last ditch attempt to produce offspring (Boucot & Poinar, 2010). Such specimens can also provide clues to the behaviour and ecology of poorly studied extant taxa, for example with regard to egg clutch size and whether or not eggs are laid individually or together. A similar phenomenon is sometimes encountered with regard to insect coprolites or frass (Fig. 214) (Vršanský *et al.*, 2013). Maybe these are post-mortem processes, although in this case one may expect to encounter them more frequently. Another example of stress following entrapment in resin includes the loss of appendages as the unfortunate insect struggled to escape. Examples of this are rather common (Fig. 213), especially so in arachnids such as harvestmen and spiders. In some cases fossilized haemolymph

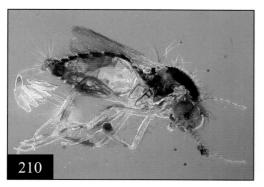

Biting midge (Ceratopogonidae) with eggs, in Miocene Dominican amber. RCDP

Unidentified fungus gnat (Mycetophilidae) with eggs, in Eocene Baltic amber. RCDP

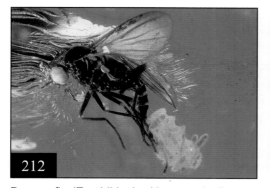

Dagger fly (Empididae) with eggs, in Eocene Baltic amber. RCDP

Phantom midge *Chaoborus ciliatus* (Chaoboridae) with autospasized legs, in Eocene Baltic amber. RCDP

214

Bristletail *Machilis* sp. (Archaeognatha: Machilidae) with frass, in Eocene Baltic amber. RCDP

(blood) droplets can be seen exuding from the exposed limb joint, signifying that the loss of the appendage happened following entrapment in the resin (Penney, 2005). Autotomy (self removal) or autospazy (loss caused by an external force) of legs is a common defensive/escape mechanism in arthropods and the limb grows back gradually following successive moults. Vickery & Poinar (1994) illustrated an example of leg re-growth in an amber cricket (Orthoptera). Flight is another common escape response in insects and sometimes amber beetle (Fig. 215) and earwig inclusions are preserved with their wings unfolded and outstretched, as if about to take off. Alternatively, in some instances these may represent insects that have just landed on freshly secreted resin.

Some insects utilized the freshly secreted tree resin in their routine activities and so it is not surprising that evidence of these behaviours is occasionally preserved in amber. Poinar (1992b) reported two examples preserved in Miocene Dominican amber. The first was of a stingless bee *Proplebeia dominicana* (Hymenoptera: Apidae: Meliponini) with a ball of resin attached to each of its hind legs; an excellent photograph of this appears on the front cover of Poinar & Poinar (1999). The bee would have been collecting the resin as building material for nest construction (propolis), a behaviour that may help explain the high frequency with which these bees are found as inclusions. The second example was of an assassin bug (Hemiptera: Reduviidae: Apiomerinae) with lumps of resin on the tibiae of its forelegs. Extant members of this subfamily are sometimes referred to as bee assassins or resin bugs on account of their specialized predation on bees and the habit of coating their forelegs with resin in order to increase adhesion to the prey item during the capture process. In order to keep the resin in the correct place these bugs have long, erect setae on their foreleg tibiae.

Another example of the use of materials by insects is the construction of protective cases in the larvae of some Lepidoptera, but especially in Trichoptera (caddisflies), and these can be rather common in the insect fossil record. This is particularly true of caddisfly cases in the rock record (Grimaldi & Engel, 2005), because the majority of

Beetle *Malthodes* sp. (Coleoptera: Cantharidae) with wing extended, in Eocene Baltic amber. RCDP

Beetle larva in its protective case (Coleoptera: Chrysomelidae: Cryptocephalinae), in Eocene Baltic amber. RCDP

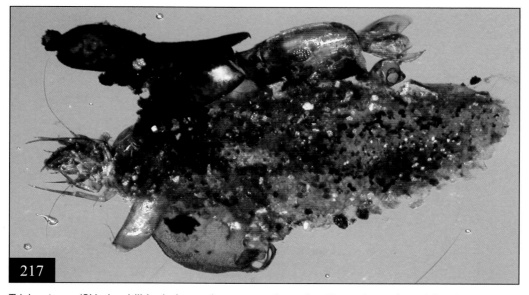

Trichoptera (?Hydrophilidae) larva in case adorned with arthropod cuticle, including a pseudoscorpion claw, an ant head and a spider carapace, in Miocene Dominican amber. RCDP

trichopteran larvae would have been permanently aquatic. However, they are also found in amber from time to time (Fig. 217). The specimen illustrated is a caddisfly larva (Trichoptera: ?Hydrophilidae) inside its case of sand grains, which it has decorated with debris consisting of arthropod remains. These are unlikely to have been the prey of the larva because they are all remains of terrestrial taxa and include a pseudoscorpion claw (Arachnida: Pseudoscorpiones), an ant head (Hymenoptera: Formicidae) and the abdomen and carapace of a goblin spider (Arachnida: Araneae: Oonopidae), all voracious predators in their own right.

Some beetle larvae (e.g. Chrysomelidae: Camptosomata) also inhabit protective cases but their origins are somewhat different. In living species, the hard cases are constructed by the mother, then inherited and retained by her offspring, which then elaborate the protective domicile using their own faeces, before sealing themselves inside to pupate. Instances of Cryptocephalinae larvae within their faecal cases (Fig. 216) have been documented from both Miocene Dominican and Eocene Baltic ambers (Chaboo *et al.*, 2009). These relatively recent finds represent the first fossil evidence for maternal inheritance of architectural structures in beetles. Related to growth and development is the process of moulting, and while arthropod exuvia are found reasonably frequently in amber, ecdysis itself (the process of emerging from an old skin) is seldom encountered. Nontheless, it has been documented for various insects (e.g. Ephemeroptera, Coleoptera, Odonata and Plecoptera) from both amber and non-amber fossils (Poinar & Poinar, 1999: fig. 99; Zherikhin, 2002a: fig. 24; Wichard *et al.*, 2009: figs. 02.06 and 04.13, respectively). Flies and wasps emerging from pupae were figured by Weitschat (2009).

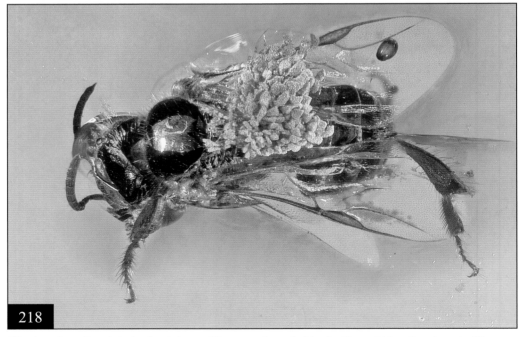

218

Stingless bee *Proplebeia dominicana* (Hymenoptera: Apidae) with orchid pollinarium, in Miocene Dominican amber. MCZ 31141

It is widely accepted that insect pollination of plants underwent major evolutionary changes during the Mesozoic (e.g. Labandeira, 2000; Labandeira & Currano, 2013). However, most of the evidence for this is based on the presence of anthophilous features in fossil insects (or inference thereof based on the ecology of their extant relatives) and the co-occurrence of entomophilous (insect attracting) syndromes in fossilized flowers. This topic was reviewed by Crepet *et al.* (1991) and Grimaldi (1999), but neither paper provided 'direct' evidence of insect pollination in the fossil record. Indeed, the presence of pollen grains on insect body fossils or in insect coprolites is very rare, and even when it does occur it does not exclude flower visitation without pollination (Michez *et al.*, 2012). Krassilov & Rasnitsyn (1999) documented structurally preserved plant remains (including pollen) from the gut remains of Permian, Jurassic and Cretaceous insects (see also Krassilov *et al.*, 2007). However, the first direct fossil evidence of a plant–pollinator interaction was that of an orchid pollinarium (also representing the first fossil record of orchids) attached to the mesoscutellum of an extinct stingless bee *Proplebeia dominicana* (Hymenoptera: Apidae: Meliponini) (Fig. 218) in Miocene Dominican amber (Ramírez *et al.*, 2007). More recently, Compton *et al.* (2010) used SEM to reveal the presence of *Ficus* pollen inside pollen pockets of a tiny fig wasp '*Ponera*' *minuta* (Hymenoptera: Agaonidae) from the Eocene, Insect Limestone of the Isle of Wight, England.

Individual behaviours: communication (including crypsis)
Many insects communicate via sound using stridulation organs or through colourful visual displays. Although it is impossible for audible sound to be preserved in the fossil record, the sound producing organs have been identified as far back as the Middle Triassic, on the wings of *Clathrotitan* (Orthoptera: Clathrotitanidae), a very large insect from New South Wales, Australia (Fig. 11). In an interesting study, researchers predicted the probable frequency of the sound generated by the fossil bushcricket *Pseudotettigonia amoena* from the Paleogene of Denmark (Fig. 219), based on comparisons with extant close relatives (Rust *et al.*, 1999). A similar study on the palaeoacoustic ecology of a 165 million-years-old (Jurassic) katydid (Orthoptera: Haglidae) was recently reported by Gu *et al.* (2012). If insects were making sound in the past then they were listening to

219

Psuedotettigonia amoena (Orthoptera: Tettigoniidae) from the Paleocene/Eocene Fur Formation of the Isle of Mors, Denmark. GMCD DK347

it also. Plotnick & Smith (2012) described exceptionally well preserved tympanal ears found in crickets and katydids from the *ca.* 50 million-years-old (Eocene) Green River Formation of Colorado, which are practically identical to those seen in modern representatives of these orthopteran groups.

Wing patterns and banding are common in living insects and are also sometimes seen in amber preserved fossils, especially certain flies and fulgoromorph hemipterans, such as Achilidae, e.g. *Protepiptera kaweckii* (Fig. 222), where the patterns can exhibit a reasonable degree of intraspecific variation. However, such details are sometimes clearly visible in rock preserved insects dating back to the Paleozoic. For example, *Dunbaria fasciipennis* (Palaeodictyoptera: Spilapteridae) from the Lower Permian of Kansas is characterized by beautifully patterned wings. Patterns, but not colour, are often preserved in fossil insects from the Crato Formation of Brazil. The only known specimen of the antlion *Neurastenyx? cryptohymen* (Neuroptera: Palaeoleontidae) (Figs. 15, 220), described from this locality by Heads *et al.* (2005 [as *Baisopardus c.*]), is preserved with the right pair of wings superimposed and the left pair of wings splayed out. This unique fossil demonstrates clearly that the wing patterning possibly served two different functions. At rest the effect was cryptic, whilst during flight the signal would have been quite different. Mesozoic insects of the butterfly-like cicadas of the family Palaeontinidae also exhibit wing patterning in some specimens (Figs. 13, 221). Abdominal banding is also sometimes preserved in both amber and rock fossils. This is usually seen in Diptera, such as hoverflies (Syrphidae) (Fig. 223), which were presumably Batesian mimics of hymenopterans, as are many of the extant species today.

Eye spots are another form of wing patterning seen in extant insects (e.g. some Lepidoptera and Mantodea). In most cases these form a defensive mechanism against potential predators because they are usually only briefly exposed when the insect is alarmed, for example in the case of the eyed hawkmoth. However, in the extinct family of neuropteran insects, the Kalligrammatidae, decorative wing spots were permanently on display (Figs. 13, 226) (Fang *et al.*, 2010; Makarkin *et al.*, 2009).

The epitome of wing patterning in modern insects occurs in butterflies and moths (Lepidoptera), which exhibit the widest diversity of visual effects of any extant organisms. The colours are of structural rather than chemical origin and are created as a result of light scattering as it reflects off the surface of the minute wing scales, each of which is basically a biophotonic nanostructure. The different colours result from ultrastructural differences on the surface of the scales. Butterflies are very rare as fossils, but moths occur reasonably frequently in amber. However, they rarely preserve their wing scales because they become detached very easily once trapped in resin (Fig. 224). Rock fossils of butterflies and moths often exhibit light- and dark-toned areas on their wings which can retain ultrastructural details of their scales. McNamara *et al.* (2011) reported the first example of fossilized structurally coloured insect scales, in moths from the 47-million-years-old Messel oil shale of Germany. They examined fossils tentatively assigned to Zygaenidae: Procridinae (forester moths) in which the wing scales had not been replaced by minerals and remained organic in nature. Thus, they retained their original structural fidelity, but some had become fractured or realigned as a result of diagenetic compaction. Although the original colour of the moths was not preserved in the fossils, the researchers used a combination of electron microscopy, reflectance

Antlion *Neurastenyx? cryptohymen* (Neuroptera: Palaeoleontidae) from the Lower Cretaceous Crato Formation, Brazil. Holotype, SMNS 65470

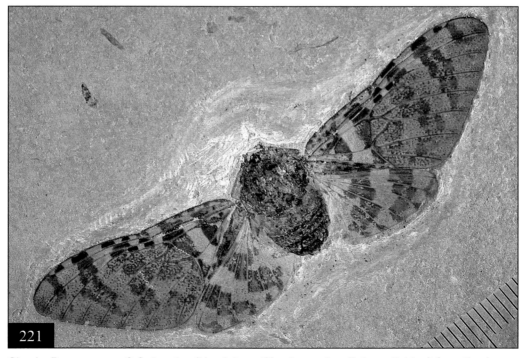

Cicada *Baeocossus cf. fortunatus* (Hemiptera: Cicadomorpha: Palaeontinidae) from the Lower Cretaceous Crato Formation, Brazil. KMNH

Planthopper *Protepiptera kaweckii* (Auchen-orrhyncha: Fulgoroidea) with wing pattern, in Eocene Baltic amber. RCDP

Hoverfly *Palaeoascia* sp. (Diptera: Syrphidae) with abdominal banding, in Eocene Baltic amber. RCDP

Micro-moth (Lepidoptera) shedding wing scales, in Eocene Baltic amber. RCDP

Undescribed treehopper (Auchenorrhyncha: Membracidae) in Miocene Dominican amber. CU

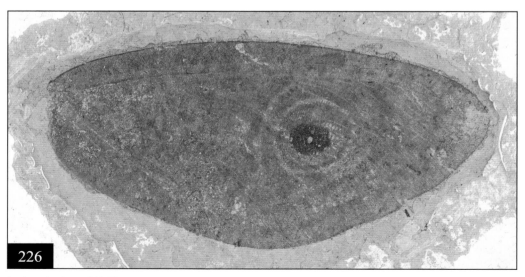

Isolated wing of *Kalligramma turutanovae* (Neuroptera: Kalligrammatidae) from the Late Jurassic of Karatau, Kazakhstan. PIN 2997-5147

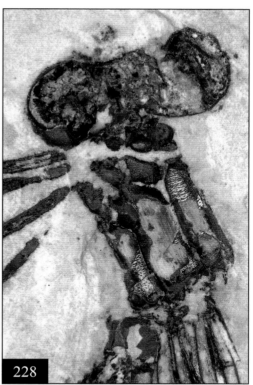

Jewel beetle *Lampetis weigelti* (Coleoptera: Buprestidae) from the Eocene of Grube Messel, Germany. SFNGM Mel3999a

Damselfly *Cretarchistigma*? *essweini* (Hemiphlebiidae) with remants of the original metallic-green body colour, from the Cretaceous Crato Formation, Brazil. SMNS 66393

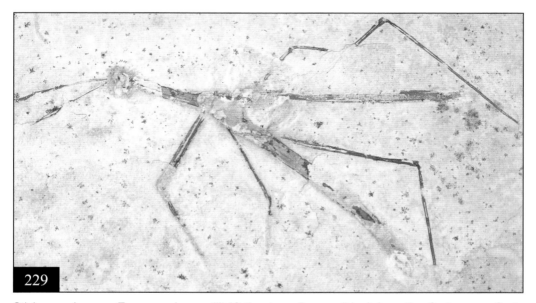

Stick grasshopper *Eoproscopia martilli* (Orthoptera: Proscopiidae) from the Cretaceous Crato Formation, Brazil. Holotype, SMNS 66000-135

micro-spectrophotometry and 2-D discrete Fourier analysis to reconstruct their colour in life. Thus, plastic scale developmental processes and complex optical mechanisms for interspecific signalling had clearly evolved in lepidopterans and other insect orders by the mid-Eocene. The presence of colour in fossils from this deposit is well known (e.g. McNamara *et al.*, 2012a) (Fig. 227) and similar biophotonic structures have been observed in beetles (Parker & McKenzie, 2003). Remnants of structural coloration have also been reported in damselflies from the Mesozoic of Brazil (Fig. 228) (Martill *et al.*, 2007).

In an interesting study, McNamara *et al.* (2012b) examined approximately 700 specimens of different beetle taxa known to exhibit metallic structural colours from seven Lagerstätten: Randecker Maar (early Miocene), Clarkia (early Miocene), Enspel (late Oligocene), Florissant (late Eocene), Eckfeld (middle Eocene), Messel (middle Eocene), and Green River (middle Eocene). Colours were well preserved in most specimens from Clarkia, Enspel, Eckfeld and Messel, but were typically poorly preserved in specimens from Randecker Maar and absent in specimens from Florissant and Green River. The differences were independent of taxonomy and the age and depositional context of the biotas. Instead, the observed variation was attributed to differences in their late diagenetic histories, such as the maximum depth to which the sediments had been buried, as well as to recent weathering (McNamara *et al.*, 2012b). Subsequently, McNamara *et al.* (2013) used an experimental taphonomy approach using extant beetles to demonstrate that elevated temperature is the primary agent of alteration of biophotonic nanostructures during burial, whereas elevated pressure alone has no discernible effect.

Many tree hopper species (Hemiptera: Auchenorrhyncha: Membracidae) are easily recognized by the thorn-like projections on the pronotum (Fig. 225). In many species this gives them a highly cryptic appearance when sat flush against a twig or stem because they look just like a thorny outgrowth. However, in some extant species these structures are highly extravagant and very brightly coloured and so must serve a function other than camouflage. Given that colour is not preserved in amber, interpreting the palaeoethology or presumed behaviour of the fossil species based on the idea of behavioural fixity is not always straight forward.

Many insects masquerade as plants through crypsis or behavioural mimicry in order to avoid predators or to approach prey in a stealth-like manner. Some examples in the extant insect fauna include stick and leaf insects (Phasmatodea), grasshoppers and katydids (Orthoptera), moths and butterflies (Lepidoptera) and praying mantids (Mantodea). One of the oldest reliable fossil records of plant masquerade by insects is the stick mimicking Proscopiidae (Orthoptera) (Fig. 229) described by Heads (2008) from the Early Cretaceous Crato Formation of Brazil. According to the review of this topic by Wedmann (2010), the first records of stick mimesis in Phasmatodea are from Eocene Baltic amber and the Eocene Messel pit in Germany. The oldest fossil record of a leaf-insect (Phasmatodea: Phylliinae) is from the Eocene of Messel (Fig. 230), described by Wedmann *et al.* (2007); although plant mimicry in stem-group phasamatodea dates back at least to the Early Cretaceous (Wang *et al.*, 2014). Several species of advanced leaf-mimicking katydids (Orthoptera: Tettigoniidae: Pseudophylleinae) have been recorded from the late Eocene–early Oligocene of France and England (Nel *et al.*, 2008).

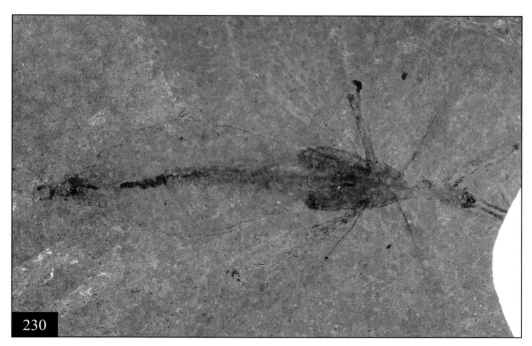

230

Leaf insect *Eophyllium messelensis* (Phasmatodea: Phylliidae) from the Eocene of Grube Messel, Germany. Holotype, SFNGM Mel 12560

More recently, Wang *et al.* (2010) described two lacewings (Neuroptera): *Bellinympha filicifolia* and *B. dancei* from the Middle Jurassic of China, the wings of which bear a remarkable resemblance to the pinnate leaves of gymnosperms, thus providing good evidence for the existence of leaf mimesis in insects 165 million years ago. It appears that this enigmatic neuropteroid lineage became extinct during the Early Cretaceous, alongside the decline of Cycadales and Bennettitales at that time, and perhaps owing to the changing floral environment that resulted from the rise of angiosperms (Wang *et al.*, 2010). Also from this deposit, Wang *et al.* (2012) described a near-perfect mimetic association between a new hangingfly species *Juracimbrophlebia ginkgofolia* (Mecoptera: Cimbrophlebiidae) and a ginkgoalean plant. This is an excellent example of leaf mimesis, whereby the appearance of the multilobed leaf of *Yimaia capituliformis* (the ginkgoalean model) is accurately replicated by the wings and abdomen of the cimbrophlebiid hangingfly mimic.

Pérez-de la Fuente *et al.* (2012a) described the new genus and species of green lacewing *Hallucinochrysa diogenesi* (Neuroptera: Chrysopoidea) in Cretaceous (Albian) amber from the El Soplao amber site in Spain. The specimen consists of a larva with specialized cuticular processes forming a dorsal basket carrying a dense trash packet of gleicheniacean fern trichomes. Such trash-carrying behaviour is well known in some groups of extant insects, where it serves several functions, including camouflage from predators and prey, in addition to acting as a physical defence against attack.

In summary, the fossil record of plant mimicking by insects is sparce, and some previously proposed examples may have been in error, but recently discovered fossils show that there is much still waiting to be discovered (Wedmann, 2010).

Insects also mimic other organisms, including other insects. One example in the fossil record concerns an assassin bug (Hemiptera: Reduviidae) mimicking a wasp, described from the Palaeocene of the Svalbard Archipelago (Norway) by Wappler *et al.* (2013). Indeed, so good was this presumed mimicry that the fossil was originally described as a hymenopteran. A similar example concerns the description of a spider-mimicking planthopper (Fulgoromorpha) from the Early Cretaceous of Baissa, Transbaikalia (Shcherbakov, 2007), which was considered to by a jumping spider mimic. However, this conclusion is rather dubious given that jumping spiders (Salticidae) do not appear in the fossil record until the Tertiary (Penney, 2010c; Penney & Selden, 2011).

Sub-fossil insects

Quaternary sub-fossil insects are not old enough to have mineralized in the same manner as in the more classical palaeontological settings described earlier. Nonetheless, they are of particular interest because they provide a valuable window on change over both ecological and geological time frames, e.g. the last ice age. Insect remains from the Quaternary Period represent the direct precursors of the modern entomofauna, and many of the sub-fossils are either identical to living species or close relatives of them.

In addition to copal, the precursor of amber, sub-fossil insect remains are remarkably abundant in Quaternary freshwater deposits that accumulated under anaerobic conditions, e.g. peat bogs or at the bottom of ancient ponds. They are frequently found at archaeological sites in what were once waterlogged sediments, and are also found in permanently frozen ground or in dry situations (e.g. caves in hot deserts) where desiccation has facilitated long-term preservation.

Originally, the historical authors assigned the remains from the Pleistocene peat bog or asphalt deposits to extinct species, supporting the idea of a high evolutionary rate induced by the climate changes during the Pleistocene. Subsequently, more detailed studies of sub-fossil insects, sometimes based even on examination of their well preserved genitalia, revealed that the majority of Pleistocene sub-fossil beetles belong to recent species (Elias, 2009) and resulted in the Pleistocene evolutionary stasis paradigm (e.g. Coope, 2004).

For the past two decades, sub-fossil midges (Diptera: Chironomidae) preserved in lake sediments have started to be used in palaeolimnology to quantitatively reconstruct various factors, such as nutrients, macrophytes, salinity, lake depth, anoxia and temperature. As their accuracy as a palaeoecological tool has progressed, their distribution has been studied in many parts of the world (Larocque-Tobler, 2014; Massafero et al., 2014 and references therein). Often it is only the chitinized head capsules of the larvae that are preserved, so a parataxonomy is used to separate taxa based on the few morphological features that can be assessed.

Copal

Copal is sub-fossilized tree resin not old or polymerized enough to be classed as amber. Given that the transformation of resin into copal and then into amber is dependent on several factors, such as temperature and pressure, there is no set age at which one turns into the other and the classification (with respect to age) of these different transitional stages is still being debated. Some authors have proposed an arbitrary age of two million-years-old to demarcate the transition from copal to amber, whereas others have suggested classifying anything that can be carbon dated as copal and anything too old for radiocarbon dating as amber (Anderson, 1997). The debate continues (e.g. Vavra, 2009), and reaching a consensus terminology has been hampered by both amber researchers and dealers complicating the issue with terms such as sub-fossil resin, young amber and copal amber, etc. In some cases, researchers even use different terminologies to differentiate between copals from the New and Old World, despite the fact they were produced by the same tree genus (e.g. Stroiński & Szwedo, 2011).

Bark louse *Epipsocus* sp. (Psocodea: Epipso-cidae) in Quaternary Colombian copal. RCDP

Rove beetle (Coleoptera: Staphylinidae) in Quaternary Colombian copal. RCDP

Stingless bee *Trigonisca ameliae* (Hymenop-tera: Apidae) in Quaternary Colombian copal. Holotype, NHM II 3059 [1]

Worker ant (Hymenoptera: Formicidae) in Quaternary Colombian copal. PCYCT

Copal preserves insects in the same way as amber, and given the younger age, the inclusions are often preserved with stunning life-like fidelity (Figs. 231–234). Remarkably, and in contrast to amber, very little research has focused on sub-fossils in copal because of its young age. Such specimens are not deemed old enough to be of any significance by many palaeontologists and for similar reasons few analytical studies have been undertaken. Copals with insect inclusions originate mainly from New Zealand (Karui gum), Victoria in Australia, Mizunami in Japan, Santander in Colombia, Sambava in Madagascar, and deposits from Cotui in the Dominican Republic. Most copals are probably Pliocene/sub-Recent in age, with some samples ranging from as young as a few decades up to approximately 10,600 years-old, although ages as old as Tertiary have been proposed in the scientific literature, albeit without any supporting evidence. Indeed, many different ages are banded around for various different copal deposits, very few of which can be considered reliable. In some samples from Madagascar, evidence of enhanced radioactive Carbon content (due to artificial ^{14}Carbon from thermonuclear weapon tests) indicates that those particular samples are very young indeed (Burleigh & Whalley, 1983). Some samples from Colombia were also recently carbon dated as post WWII, whereas others were dated to 10,600 years-old (Penney *et al.*, 2013ab).

However, inclusions in copal (even very young samples) can be informative at many different levels. Copal is often recovered in much larger pieces than amber samples and it often has a high density and diversity of inclusions, in some cases representing rather unusual taphobiocoenoses or sub-fossil assemblages (e.g. Penney *et al.*, 2012b). Thus, inclusions in copal may be useful as a proxy for investigating the bias of preservation in amber, the palaeodiversity and ecology of (sub)fossil resin producing forest ecosystems and also as a potential source of insect DNA to predate any exisiting museum collections (Austin *et al.*, 1997 considered all early claims of DNA extraction from amber to have been in error). However, the recent application of next generation sequencing techniques to two stingless bees in Colombian copal demonstrated that no DNA was present (Penney *et al.*, 2013b). Fossils in copal may also serve as a record of modern extinctions. Some of the few species so far described from Colombian copal are already extinct, such as an orchid bee (Hinojosa-Díaz & Engel, 2007). Furthermore, some insect families are known as inclusions only from copal, e.g. the bark louse (Psocodea) family Ptiloneuridae in copal from Colombia (Azar *et al.*, 2009). The bark louse figured represents a new undescribed species of *Epipsocus* (family Epipsocidae) (Fig. 231), but it would be highly premature to suggest that this was an extinct species, given the diverse and largely unknown extant Colombian psocodean fauna.

Fossil inclusions in copal are readily available in the marketplace, both online and through retail outlets. In many cases they are sold as copal, but sometimes they are passed off as amber and sometimes the terms copal amber or young amber are used. Occasionally fossils described in the scientific literature as preserved in Baltic or Dominican ambers, have subsequently been demonstrated to be much younger sub-Recent sub-fossils preserved in Madagascan copal, e.g. the only named praying mantis described from Baltic amber was subsequently suspected to have actually been preserved in copal from Africa or Asia. Another example relates to the description by Shelford (1911) of the extant cockroach species *Euthyrrhapha pacifica* (Polyphagidae) from Baltic amber, which was only recently identified as actually being preserved in Madagascan copal

(Grimaldi *et al.*, 1994). There are undoubtedly still early examples of nineteenth century descriptions of fossil insects currently accepted as being in Baltic amber that actually refer to specimens in copal, although in many such cases the specimens have been lost.

Copal is softer than amber, but will still take on a high polish. However, because the volatiles are still evaporating from the sub-fossil resin, the surface may become highly crazed after only a few years (this process takes much longer with amber). Nonetheless, in some specimens of Zanzibar (East Africa) copal the polished surface appears to have remained in relatively good condition even after 180 years of exposure to air. Copal is usually lighter in colour and may even appear colourless, compared to the yellow–orange colour usually seen in amber specimens. More often than not, copal specimens tend to be larger and also to contain a wide range of inclusions, usually belonging to extant species. Sometimes fossils in amber show signs of compression and transformation as a result of exposure to high temperature or pressure. We have not come across this phenomenon in copal specimens. A relatively simple test is to apply a small drop of alcohol or other solvent on the surface of the specimen. If the specimen is amber, this will have no effect, but if it is copal it should dissolve the surface slightly

235

Unidentified beetle (Coleoptera) sub-fossil from the middle Pleistocene Holstein-Interglacial Period, Walsrode, Lüneburger, Heide, Niedersachsen, Germany. GZG

SEM of *Cercyon nigriceps* (Coleoptera: Hydrophilidae) sub-fossil elytron from Roman Tanner Row, York, UK. This beetle is very common in occupation deposits and now typically lives in rather foul, mouldering matter such as dungy straw. Whole beetle 1.3–2.0 mm long. Note, the elytron still bears the fine hairs characteristic of this species. ADY

leaving it tacky to the touch. Given the solubility of copal, it is possible to fully dissolve out the inclusions (e.g. in chloroform) in order to examine and even dissect them under a microscope (Penney *et al.*, 2013a). This is usually not possible with amber inclusions, although some researchers have had some success doing this with ambers from Lebanon and India (Azar, 2007; Mazur *et al.*, 2012). Another simple comparison is the surface scratch test. Copal scratches readily with a pin generating a rough powder, whereas amber is much harder and takes considerably more effort to scatch.

Non-copal and archaeo-paleoentomology
Much of the non-copal sub-fossil insect research has been conducted in an archaeo-palaeoentomological context. However, the often diverse sub-fossil entomofaunas, closely allied to extant assemblages, have proven particularly useful for investigating the effects of intense climate change on species distributions, such as those during recent inter-glacial periods (e.g. Matthews & Telka, 1997).

Sub-fossil insects at archaeological sites are incredibly diverse. The sub-fossil entomofauna has been analyzed from several hundred different sites in the UK, mainland Europe, North America, North Africa, the Middle East (Elias, 2009) and Japan (Okuno *et al.*, 2010). Indeed, they are so abundant (a single medieval moat can yield several hundred different species) that they can often provide better insights to early human living conditions and lifestyles than can be obtained from human-made artifactual relics. The remains usually consist of the original exoskeletons (often as isolated elytra, head capsules, etc.), rather than mineral replacements or impressions in sediments. Robust insects such as beetles are most frequently encountered (Fig. 236) and so have been the focus of most studies to date. However, other orders, including Hymenoptera, Hemiptera, Diptera (especially as larval head capsules, pupal cases and adult heads), Ephemeroptera, Trichoptera and Megaloptera (as fragmented larval remains) and Lepidoptera (from larval mouthparts) occur to a lesser degree and would certainly be worthy of investigation; Orthoptera and Odonata are uncommon.

Identification of isolated beetle elytra to species level can be problematic for groups in which the taxonomy of extant species is based on various other morphological features. However, even in these circumstances it is possible to create species level diagnostic criteria based solely on elytral sculpture patterns, as demonstrated by Mazur & Kubisz (2008) for sub-fossil diving beetles (Dytiscidae).

Additional archaeological settings from which sub-fossil insects have been recovered include: ancient trackways through bogs, organic detritus from the bottom of wells, and ancient habitations. Insect remains have been sampled from mummies (and their tombs) and on corpses recovered from peat bogs. Ancient ponds, lakes and peat bogs in close proximity to archaeological sites usually contain insect faunas that are contemporaneous with (and informative about) nearby human occupation. Sub-fossil insect remains can yield unique insights into historical environmental, public and livestock health, including disease and parasites, overcrowding, sanitation, etc. and practices such as farming, animal husbandry, and food types (including storage). Insects that feed on carcasses, e.g. carrion beetles and flies, can provide forensic evidence with regard to both human and animal corpses in both current and historical stettings. Dating of this type of sub-fossil has been achieved using accelerator mass spectrometry and carbon dating of the insect remains (Tripp *et al.*, 2004; Okuno *et al.*, 2010).

As components of animal coprolites

The term coprolite was first used to describe mineralized fossil vertebrate excrement, but has also been applied to faeces and intestinal content preserved through dessication. The hard exoskeleton of insects makes them relatively indigestible and they are occasionally recovered from such samples, some dating back many millions of years, even as far back as the Carboniferous. Insect-bearing coprolites presumed to have been produced by fish are known from the Lower Cretaceous Purbeck Limestone of southern England (Coram & Jepson, 2012). Insect larval cuticular fragments (Diptera: Culicidae and Chaoboridae) in coprolites from the Tertiary Messel oil shale were matched to those in the intestinal contents of 21 fossil specimens of the teleostoid fish *Thaumaturus intermedius* by Richter & Baszio (2001), confirming fish predation on aquatic insects in the fossil record. Insect remains have also been found in the guts of bats (Coleoptera and Lepidoptera), hedgehogs (Coleoptera and others) and anteaters (Isoptera and others), also preserved in the Messel deposits (Labandeira, 2002). Presumed bird coprolites with fossil insect remains (mainly Coleoptera) have been reported from the Early Pliocene of Transdanubia, Hungary (Krzemiński *et al.*, 1997).

However, most studies of insects in coprolites have focused on human derived samples in an archaeological context, with sub-fossil insects reported in specimens taken from caves in eastern Kentucky and other regions of the USA, from Tamaulpias, Mexico and from Peru. Some groups, such as Orthoptera and Coleoptera, can be relatively easy to identify but the fragmentary, sometimes masticated and partially digested remains of others can be rather difficult to determine. Sometimes the insects found in faecal remains were the direct result of being eaten by the individual that produced the faeces and so can contribute to our understanding of dietary composition in historical societies (although intentional versus accidental ingestion needs to be established). In other cases, they may have been feeding or laying eggs on the faeces itself. For example, large insect remains, such as those belonging to termites, grasshoppers and cicadas, representing a high percentage of the coprolite provide evidence of intentional consumption. The presence of weevil larvae tends to suggest unintentional consumption of infested foodstuffs, whereas small-mammal fleas, Diptera pupae and larval exuvia are evidence of post depositional invasion. Small beetles with heavily broken up exoskeletons infer mastication damage through chewing, but whether this was intentional or accidental consumption can be unclear. Thus, careful consideration needs to be given to establishing whether such sub-fossil insects represent dietary components or whether they were merely scavengers. An excellent summary of this topic is given in chapter seven of Elias (2009). A study of pig coprolites from the mid-14th century workmen's village, associated with the construction of the tombs of the XVIII Dynasty at Amarna in Egypt, revealed the earliest sub-fossil evidence of the small eyed flour beetle *Polorus ratzeburgi* (Tenebrionidae) (Panagiotakopulu, 1999).

Insect trace fossils

What are trace fossils?
The fossil record not only preserves body parts of animals, it also preserves the record of an animal's interaction with the palaeoenvironment. These interactions are known as trace fossils and may represent locomotion: such as trackways left on the sediment; resting trace: where an animal has left an imprint of its body as it was resting on the sediment; burrowing: tunnels preserved within the sediment; feeding: evidence of feeding damage on vegetation and bone; and coprolites: fossilized faeces.

Trace fossils are often much more numerous than animal body fossils, and they can provide clues as to what animals were present in cases where the deposits were not conducive to the preservation of body parts. In addition, they are extremely important in palaeoenvironmental reconstructions. For example, they allow us to determine whether an environment was marine, freshwater, terrestrial, oxic or anoxic. Trace fossils can also provide an insight into the behaviour of animals, such as feeding habits, mode of life and even the speed at which it moved.

Classification
The study of trace fossils, like body fossils, uses binomial nomenclature to name and classify them, with the taxonomic units referred to as ichnotaxa (e.g. ichnogenera and ichnospecies). The traces themselves are also categorized by the activities of the producer, which follows the classification first devised by Seilacher (1953). However, this is based mainly on marine traces and this scheme has its problems, especially with regards to insects, because the same structure may represent different uses. For example, burrows in wood may be feeding traces, burrows or breeding chambers, and hence, using the scheme developed by Seilacher, one trace could be classified as Fodinichnia (feeding), Domichnia (dwelling) or Calichnia (breeding) (see Zherikhin, 2002b, 2003). Alternative schemes have been proposed, which take into account some of these problems, e.g. Vialov (1966, 1968, 1975) and Müller (1981), but these systems have not been universally accepted. Zherikhin (2003) proposed a new way to classify insect trace fossils using a combinatory approach instead of a hierarchical one. Recently, Lehane & Ekdale (2013) introduced the category Irretichnia for 'trapping traces' as fossil evidence of predation strategies. Although no insect examples are currently known it would not be unreasonable to expect the description of examples such as antlion (Neuroptera) burrows at some point in the future, particularly given the prevalence of adults in the fossil record (Lehane & Ekdale, 2013).

One major problem with the study of trace fossils is that in most cases the producer of the trace cannot be identified, mainly because many different animals can leave identical tracks or traces. It can even be very difficult to say which higher taxonomic group made a particular trace. For example, a track of a worm may be morphologically the same as that of an insect larva (Zherikhin, 2003). Therefore, caution is needed when trying to identify the maker of the track, except in the rare cases when the trace maker is found at the end of, or alongside the trace. This is why trace fossils are described based on their morphology rather than the organism that made the track.

Insect trace fossils

Insects in the geological past, like today, created many traces which represent their interactions with the palaeoenvironment. For example, tracks in the sediments, burrows in wood and sediment, nests (such as ants and other hymenopterans, termites), as well as damage to vegetation (galls, leaf mines, feeding traces on leaves and in wood) (reviewed by Labandeira & Currano, 2013), feeding traces on bones, and coprolites. These traces can help us to interpret the palaeoenvironment and palaeoecology of fossil insects throughout geological time. The earliest records of insect trace fossils date back to the Paleozoic, since then they have been found throughout the fossil record and up to the present day. What follows is a brief summary of the geological record of insect trace fossils, under the headings of the behavioural type of trace.

Locomotion

Locomotion traces are structures that are preserved on the surface of the sediment created by the insect's body moving over it. These tracks are known from the Paleozoic onwards and are widespread, but unfortunately poorly studied. They are one of the most difficult trace fossils to attribute to a higher taxonomic group, because different invertebrates can make similar tracks. Recent experimental work examining the locomotion traces of extant insects was conducted by Davis *et al.* (2007).

Resting

Resting traces are produced when an insect's body was imprinted into the sediment. These traces can preserve bodily detail and allow for a reasonable interpretation of the trace maker. Insect resting traces are rare in the fossil record (Walter, 1983; Mangano *et al.*, 1997). A fossil described from the Carboniferous was interpreted as the earliest trace of a flying insect, most likely a stem group mayfly (Knecht *et al.*, 2011; Benner *et al.*, 2013), but the insect producer of this trace was questioned by Marden (2013). Wingless insect resting traces are also known from the Carboniferous (Mangano *et al.*, 1997, 2001). Resting traces are also known from the Permian, representing wingless insects, nymphs of either Ephemeroptera or Plecoptera, and large dragonfly-like insects (Braddy & Briggs, 2002).

Burrows

Burrows and shelters may be represented by tunnels made by the insect in sediment, wood, bone or other material. Shelters may be represented by nests (both under and over-ground) and transportable cases. In the fossil record there is an increase in the number of burrows and shelters in the Mesozoic, moving away from the Paleozoic crawling traces. As with locomotion traces, it is difficult to determine the use of the burrow, i.e. whether it was used for feeding or for some other purpose, and the insect that made the trace.

The simplest types of burrows are those preserved within sediments. These occur widely within freshwater and subaerial environments. They are known from the Paleozoic to the present day and are useful for yielding information on the palaeoenvironment (Zherikhin, 2002b). However, the burrow maker is difficult to determine. Given that the ichnotaxonomy is based on the morphology of the burrow it is possible that the burrow could have been made by any invertebrate, not just an insect. In addition, burrows may be mistaken for plant root pseudomorphs.

Some common morphologically simple burrows have been attributed to beetles and beetle larvae, as well as dipteran larvae. Also, U-shaped burrows in freshwater sediments, wood and bone have been described as mayfly nymph burrows. However, these are morphologically similar to U-shaped burrows in marine sediments, which are definitely not of insect origin (Zherikhin, 2002b).

Fossil insect nests

Insect nests have been found preserved in the fossil record, ranging in complexity from simple burrows in fossil soil and wood, to more complex structures with distinct galleries. Much work has been done on these trace fossils in recent years, in particular by Genise and colleagues (e.g. Thackray, 1994; Genise & Bown, 1994, 1996; Genise & Hazeldine, 1998; Genise, 1999, 2000; Genise et al., 2013b; Sarzetti et al., 2014). Nonetheless, the study of fossil insect nests is still in its infancy (Zherikhin, 2003). These fossils are important for palaeoenvironmental reconstructions and for providing additional information for phylogenetic studies in some groups. For example, the body fossil record of bees, which is rather sparse, can be augmented by the discovery of fossil bee nests (Wenzel, 1990; Martins–Neto, 1991; Zherikhin, 2002b), although one needs to be cautious in attributing nests to bees, because similar structures may be made by other organisms (Engel, 2001).

Insect nests are found throughout the fossil record in palaeosols and fossil wood. They range from relatively simple burrows that have been attributed to nests of bees and wasps, and more complex structures with differentiated galleries, to simple pupation chambers. Some of the more complex burrows have been attributed to termites and ants. The interpretation of these nest makers is often backed up by the preservation of body parts, for example termite mandibles (e.g. Nel & Paichler, 1993) or the actual pupae (Holden et al., 2014). Ant nests are rare in the fossil record, despite their great diversity today, however they have been recorded, including fungus growing ant nests (Genise et al., 2013b), carpenter ants in wood (Brues, 1936), and also a mineralized ant nest containing the brood (Wilson & Taylor, 1964). Reports of hymenopteran nest fragments in amber do exist, but these fossils have not been formally documented.

Other than subterranean insect nests, the fossil record has the potential of preserving nests that were attached to surfaces above ground, for example, paper wasps nests and mud cells of sphecid wasps (including as fossils in amber). However, these would be much rarer than their subterranean counterparts due to them being exposed and more susceptible to erosion and general destruction.

Pupation chambers

Pupation chambers can often be overlooked in the fossil record (Zherikhin, 2002b), because the majority of them are small sub-oval structures in sediment. However, some (mainly beetle) fossilized pupation chambers have been described (e.g. Genise et al., 2013a), including those of weevils (Leptopius sp.) from the Tertiary Weipa Bauxite of northern Queensland, Australia (Tilley et al., 1997), which can reach 50 mm in length and are often referred to as booties, because they resemble baby shoes (Fig. 238). In some cases burrows may have been used as pupation chambers. For example, a U-shaped boring in petrified wood from the Late Triassic Chinle Formation of southern Utah was described by Tapanila & Roberts (2012) as the oldest record of a pupation chamber in wood. *Xylokrypta durossi* was described as a new ichnogenus and ichnospecies consisting of a large excavation in wood backfilled with partially digested xylem to create a secluded chamber. The tracemaker exited the chamber by way of a small vertical shaft, constituting a sequence of behaviours most consistent with the entrance of a larva, followed by pupal quiescence and adult emergence. Among the known Triassic insect body fossil record, cupedid beetles were deemed the most plausible tracemakers of *Xylokrypta*, based on their body size and modern lifestyle (Tapanila & Roberts, 2012).

Transportable cases
Some insects construct cases that they transport with them and these can be preserved in the fossil record, sometimes with the insect still inside (Figs. 216, 217), but more often than not they are found without the insect. The most comprehensively studied trace fossils of this type are caddisfly cases. The cases are constructed from various different types of material, such as small bits of rock, plant matter and even fish scales. These cases have been found throughout the fossil record, particularly in the Cretaceous, and much work has been focused on them (e.g. Sukatsheva 1985, 1989, 1990, 1991, 1994, 1999). They can occur en masse in sediments which do not contain any other fossil fauna (Sukatsheva, 1999). Other than caddisflies, cases of chironomid fly larvae (e.g. Kalugina, 1993; Thienemann, 1933; Moretti, 1955; Hiltermann, 1968), microlepidopterans and coleopterans have been found (e.g. Larsson, 1978; Kozlov, 1988; Chaboo *et al.*, 2009).

Oviposition traces
When some insects lay their eggs they can cause damage to vegetation, this damage can be diagnostic due to the structure of the ovipositor and can aid in the identification of the egg layer. This type of damage, which can often be overlooked, has been preserved in the fossil record, e.g. Odonata in the Upper Oligocene of Rott, Germany (Petrulevicius *et al.*, 2011) and the Middle–Upper Triassic Madygen Formation of southwestern Kyrgyzstan (Moisan *et al.*, 2012); see Vasilenko & Rasnitsyn (2007) for a review of earlier records. Oviposition traces in the *Glossopteris* flora from the Lower Permian Barakar Formation of India were reported by Srivastava & Agnihotri (2011) and the oldest record, from the Carboniferous of France, was described by Béthoux *et al.* (2004c). The first record from the Jurassic was described by Na *et al.* (2014), consisting of presumed Odonata oviposition scars on the abaxial surface of a *Sphenobaiera* leaf (Ginkgoales) from the middle Jurassic Daohugou Formation of Inner Mongolia. Additional examples from other localities and ages are known.

Feeding
Feeding traces of insects are very diverse, and thus difficult to fit into a classification such as Seilacher's (1953). Vialov (1975) introduced a more complex scheme, which divided the feeding traces into wood, leaves and stems, coprolites and animal remains. Vialov's (1975) scheme solved some problems, but was not exhaustive, as feeding traces in seeds, for example, were not categorized (Zherikhin, 2002b).

Feeding traces in wood
Insect feeding traces in wood resemble those made in other substrates, very few features can be used to determine the trace maker because of their simple morphology. However, there are occasionally some diagnostic characters preserved (Zherikhin, 2002b). As with many other traces, not only insects make borings in wood, other animals (such as worms and oribatid mites), fungal decay and the mineralization of wood during fossilization may also produce similar structures (Zherikhin, 2002b).

The earliest wood borings in the fossil record are Carboniferous, but most of these have been attributed to animals other than insects (Labandeira *et al.*, 1997), although some have been described as being of insect origin, e.g. roaches (Scott & Taylor, 1983). The most numerous records of wood borings are from the Mesozoic and Cenozoic (Boucot, 1990), most borers are thought to have been beetles, or rarely siricoid wasps. Other potential insect traces in wood are pitch flecks thought to be cambial mines, these are known only from the Cenozoic (Rasnitsyn & Quicke, 2002). False rings in wood may also represent insect damage and galleries in roots may represent termite nests (Hasiotes & Demko, 1996), however this has been doubted (Zherikhin, 2002b).

Fruit and seed damage
Fruit and seeds are often exploited by insects and such feeding has been preserved in the fossil record, although these traces have been poorly studied (Zherikhin, 2002b). The fossil record of fruit damage includes Lower Cretaceous boring in benettite strobili, the cones of cycadophytes were exploited by insects (Crowson, 1991). In the Upper Cretaceous, borings in araucarian cones have been discovered and attributed to insects (Stockley, 1978), also pine cone damage is known from the Miocene (Zablocki, 1960), possibly made by microlepidopterans (Zherikhin, 2002b). Damage to seeds has been recorded in the Paleozoic as small holes, possibly made by dictyopterans (Sharov, 1973). Larch seed damage is known from the Pliocene–Pleistocene of Greenland (Bennike & Böcher, 1990).

Feeding traces on leaves and stems
Leaf and stem feeding is very common in the fossil record, these include external feeding from chewing insects and fossil leaf mines, and damage from 'sucking' insects (Vialov, 1975; Zherikhin, 2002b; Peñalver & Delclòs, 2004). Extensive studies on these types of traces have been undertaken by Conrad Labandeira and colleagues. In some localities these insect trace fossils can be very common and may provide evidence of insects that are not represented among the body fossils from the same site (Krassilov, 2007).

Leaf feeding
Fossil traces of leaf feeding were divided into four categories by Labandeira *et al.* (1994): margin feeding, centre feeding, skeletonization and surface abrasion. These traces can be produced by herbivores (traces show scar tissue) or detritivores (traces lack scar tissue) (Beck & Labandeira, 1998; Zherikhin, 2002b). The insect origin problem also applies because other arthropods (e.g. woodlice and millipedes), molluscs (e.g. slugs and snails) and also vertebrates can produce similar traces. It is often difficult to determine the originator because the morphology is rarely diagnostic (Zherikhin, 2002b).

Leaf chewing is often rare before the Upper Cretaceous, which has many examples of damage to angiosperm leaves. However, there are some examples from the Late Carboniferous (e.g. Labandeira, 1998; Castro, 1997) and the Permian (Beck & Labandeira, 1998). Many examples are known from the Cretaceous to the Cenozoic (Labandeira *et al.*, 1994; Wilf & Labandeira, 1999), including from both amber and non-amber deposits (Figs. 237, 239). The feeding trace *Phagophytichnus ekowskii* was recorded from a cycadopsid leaf, from the Lika mudstone (Upper Kasimovian–Gzhelian) of Croatia as the oldest plant–insect interaction by Jarzembowski (2012), who proposed an orthopteroid producer of the damage.

Leaf mines
Leaf mines are commonly observed today, with the major culprits being microlepidopterans, beetles, flies and sawflies. Fossils are also fairly common; the majority show the same diagnostic properties of those observed in modern mines, and therefore have been attributed to extant groups (Zherikhin, 2002b; Winkler *et al.*, 2010). The oldest definitive leaf mine trace is from the Upper Jurassic/Lower Cretaceous. There have been some Paleozoic examples suggested (Müller, 1982), but these remain doubtful (Beck & Labandeira, 1998), with the oldest definitive leaf mine being from the Jurassic/earliest Cretaceous of Queensland (Rozefelds, 1988). The most common examples have been found within the Upper Cretaceous (e.g. Labandeira *et al.*, 1994, 1995).

Leaf galls
Galls are tumours found on leaves, stems, roots and buds of a plant that are produced by an insect parasite. Extant gall producers are hemipterans, beetles, lepidopterans, dipterans and hymenopterans, although non-insects such as mites, bacteria and fungi can also produce them. Galls are often quite distinctive structures that can be used to identify the producer to species level, but in the fossil record species identification is extremely tentative. In some cases they have been misidentified as seeds rather than galls (e.g. Stull *et al.*, 2013). Fossil galls attributed to insects date back to the Paleozoic, with numerous fossils described in recent years (see Labandeira, 2006ab; Stull *et al.*, 2013 for reviews). Present day insects have been attributed to the galls of Pliocene and Quaternary age due to the identical morphologies of the fossil and recent galls.

Plant sucking
Hemipterans are the most common extant insects with mouthparts adapted for piercing and sucking plant juices. The direct evidence of such behaviour in the fossil record is difficult to decipher because it is very hard to detect. Plant sucking damage has therefore received little attention and has only been mentioned briefly in some papers (Labandeira & Phillips, 1996; Labandeira *et al.*, 1998; Wilf & Labandeira, 1999). The earliest potential evidence of plant sucking by insects is damage to Devonian liverworts (Labandeira *et al.*, 2014).

Animal remains

In the fossil record there is evidence of insect feeding on dung and also feeding on and exploiting the remains of animals. This behaviour is present in extant insects, mainly in flies and beetles.

Dung feeding

Today, beetles and flies are the most common feeders on vertebrate dung and because dung is preserved in the fossil record (as coprolites), so too is the evidence of insects feeding on it. The earliest is from the Upper Cretaceous, where dinosaur dung has been found in burrows (Chin & Gill, 1996), most likely representing a dung beetle nest. Numerous other dung beetle nests and dung balls have been found throughout the Cenozoic in South America (Genise & Bown, 1994). In fact, fossil brood balls of dung beetles (Scarabaeinae) are one of the most common trace fossils of South American Cenozoic palaeosols (Cantil *et al.*, 2013; Sanchez *et al.*, 2013). Dung feeding can also be inferred by investigating the coprolites of the dung feeders themselves (e.g. Vršanský *et al.*, 2013).

Feeding and exploitation of animal remains

These trace fossils are uncommon and are mainly represented by traces on vertebrate bones. These traces have been interpreted as connections to pupal chambers (Martin & West, 1995) or breeding traces (Zherikhin, 2002b). The traces have been attributed to insects such as dermestid beetles and termites, and their burrows have been found on dinosaur bones from the Jurassic and Cretaceous (Saneyoshi *et al.*, 2011; Xing *et al.*, 2013), and mammal bones from the Tertiary and Quaternary (Pomi & Toni, 2011; Holden *et al.*, 2013). The producers proposed for some of these traces have been questioned, because dermestid beetles construct pupation chambers in soil not bone, and therefore the bone structures may have been created by other invertebrates (Zherikhin, 2002b).

Coprolites

Coprolites (fossil faeces) are often associated with trace fossils, e.g. in burrows, plant tissues and palaeosols (Baxendale, 1979; Zhou & Zhang, 1989; Rozefelds & De Baar, 1991). It is difficult to identify insect coprolites, and only a few, e.g. from termites have been identified (Rozefelds & De Baar, 1991). Klavins *et al.* (2005) proposed a beetle as the producer of coprolites found in a Mid-Triassic cycad pollen cone. Sometimes the remains of foodstuffs are preserved within the coprolites, and some, such as from the Cretaceous of Germany have been identified as hymenopteran (Kampmann, 1983). However, the morphology of extant insect coprolites is understudied (Frost, 1928; Ladle & Griffiths, 1980) making the interpretation of fossils difficult. In rare cases, an insect can be preserved in the process of defecating (e.g. Vršanský *et al.*, 2013) and so producer and coprolite are preserved together (Fig. 214). It is also possible to investigate the coprolites in detail to try and understand more about the palaeoecology of the palaeoecosystem. For example, Vršanský *et al.* (2013) examined cockroach (Blattulidae) coprolites in Lebanese amber using synchrotron X-ray tomography and concluded that cockroaches were probably the main recyclers of the huge amounts of dung produced by the contemporary herbivorous dinosaurs.

237

Probable insect damage to a leaf from the Tertiary of British Columbia, Canada. RCDP

238

239

Weevil pupation chamber (Coleoptera) from the Tertiary Weipa Bauxite of northern Queensland, Australia. RCDP

Partially eaten leaf and coprolites in Miocene Mexican amber. PCAD

How long does an insect species exist?

Hopefully, among other things, this book has raised the obvious question: *How long does an insect species exist?* Clearly, the answer is not particularly straight forward and there are no studies to date that have provided a reliable answer based on an analysis of robust data. One major problem is that the biological species concept (contentious in itself, see Zakharov, 2013), which defines a species as *members of populations that actually or potentially interbreed in nature to produce fertile offspring* cannot be applied to fossils. Indeed, this definition is often problematic for extant species, especially with the new discoveries of cryptic species complexes using molecular methods. Identification of fossil species relies solely on morphological features; even very young sub-fossils in copal appear not to contain any insect DNA (Penney *et al.*, 2013b). An early species longevity estimate of 1–2 million years for insects has been hinted at in the literature, but this is clearly an underestimate, especially given that the majority of Quaternary insect sub-fossils appear to belong to extant forms. More recent estimates range from 3–10 million years. Estimates beyond these are most probably based on inaccurate comparisons of fossil specimens with extant species or incorrect age determination of the fossils. For example, some fossils previously identified as extant species in Baltic amber are actually preserved in sub-Recent Madagascan copal, such as the cockroach *Euthyrrhapha pacifica* (Polyphagidae) (Grimaldi *et al.*, 1994). In other instances, the fossils were fakes, such as the so-called piltdown fly *Fannia scalaris* (Faniidae) identified in Baltic amber, which actually turned out to have been a modern specimen artificially inserted into the fossil resin, but nonetheless attained fame as an example of species stasis in the fossil record (Grimaldi *et al.*, 1994).

Nonetheless, fossils of several putatively extant species are currently accepted (Hörnschemeyer *et al.*, 2010: table 3). For example, *Bohartilla megalognatha* (Strepsiptera: Bohartillidae), *Lorelus wolcotti* and *Micromalthus debilis* (Coleoptera: Tenebrionidae, Micromalthidae) and *Ochrotrichia aldama* (Trichoptera: Hydroptilidae) in Miocene Dominican amber; *Belaphotroctes ghesquiere* (Psocodea: Liposcelidae), *Paleogryon muesebecki*, *Alaptus psocidivorus* and *A. globosicornis* (Hymenoptera: Scelionidae, Mymaridae) in Miocene Mexican amber; and *Heptagenia (Kageronia) fuscogrisea* (Ephemeroptera: Heptageniidae), *Nemadus colonoides* (Coleoptera: Leiodidae), *Buchonomyia thienemanni* (Diptera: Chironomidae) and *Mymaromma anomala* and *Palaeomyrmar duisburgi* (Hymenoptera: Mymarommatidae) in Eocene Baltic amber. In addition, a handful of specimens in Tertiary sediments, e.g. from Florissant, USA (Coleoptera: Chrysomelidae: possibly *Plateumaris nitida*; Diptera: Nemestrinidae: possibly *Neorhynchocephalus volaticus*), British Columbia, Canada (Hemiptera: Gerridae: *Limnoporus rufoscutellatus* species group), China (20 different species, see Zhang *et al.*, 1994) and Siberia, Russia (Coleoptera: Helophoridae: *Helophorus* (*Gephelophorus*) *sibiricus*, Fikáček *et al.*, 2011) have also been tentatively referred to extant species (Fig. 240).

Hörnschemeyer *et al.* (2010) suggested that a reanalysis of some of the fossils assigned to these extant taxa may demonstrate that the original identifications were incorrect. Nonetheless, given the foregoing, it is possible that some extant insect species appeared during the Miocene and Pliocene, with some possibly even during the Eocene.

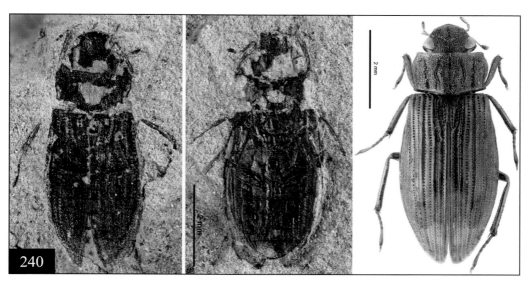

Fossil and extant examples of the hydrophiloid beetle *Helophorus* (*Gephelophorus*) *sibiricus* (Coleoptera: Helophoridae). Fossils (part and counterpart) from the early Miocene (16–23 Ma) deposits of Kartashevo (Siberia, Russia). Reproduced from Fikáček *et al*. (2011) with permission. PIN

Although some insect genera occur in both Cretaceous and Tertiary deposits, we are unaware of any shared species. Thus, an age of around 5–20 million years for insect species longevity may be a reasonable expectation, although presumably it will vary for different groups. Also, given that insects are such a diverse group, it is not unreasonable to expect that some species alive today will turn out to be so-called 'living fossils'. Presumably, molecular clock studies of extant taxa will help further refine the species longevity issue in the future.

How to become a palaeoentomologist

The desire to be a palaeoentomologist is not a particularly common career choice, which is probably a good thing as advertized job vacancies in this line of work are very few and far between. Nonetheless, the study of fossil insects can be particularly rewarding for those who choose (and who are lucky enough) to do it. However, there are several problems associated with studying fossil insects in general. First, an immense and broad knowledge and practical experience of living insects from all over the world is required. This knowledge is important because the distribution of fossils in the past is not necessarily the same as that at present. For example, the closest relative of a fossil in Baltic amber, may today be found in South Africa, Madagascar or even South America; the closest relative of a fossil in Dominican amber may be found in the extant fauna of Australia. Practical experience is necessary because many insect fossils consist of only fragmentary remains. In addition, the morphological features that are used in keys to identify living insects may be obscured due to the manner in which the fossil is preserved. It follows then, that keys for living insects (especially regional 'geographic') which often focus on a limited number of morphological features (e.g. genitalia) are of limited value when considering a newly discovered fossil. Furthermore, there is always the chance that the fossil may represent a totally new kind of insect, even at the level of order. Thus, identifying fossil insects often consists of time consuming and sometimes frustrating detective work. This often requires access to specialist scientific papers, some of which may be very old and published in obscure journals, making them very difficult to obtain. Hence, a palaeoentomologist must have excellent library facilities at their disposal. They should also preferably have access to a good collection of pinned extant insects from around the world, in order to make careful comparisons of morphologial features that may be visible in the fossils but not covered in the relevant literature. Hence, access to a good museum entomology collection is also highly desirable.

Finally, and foremost to any palaeoentomological investigation, is access to the fossils themselves. Although many fossil insects are widely available for purchase online, few of these will have significant scientific potential, although it is possible to pick up the odd gem now and then. There are also a considerable number of fakes on the market; the provenence (exact source locality) of the specimens can also be questionable for various reasons, including the fact that the seller should not actually be selling it due to various laws in the country of origin! In some sites it is possible to collect fossil insects directly without any restrictions, but more often these days, such sites are receiving legislative protection that prohibits collection or export of specimens from the host country. Also, unlike modern insects, where a scientist can visit a site and sample thousands of individuals in a matter of hours, many fossil insect species are known from only a single, or just a few specimens, which are usually kept under secure lock and key in the collections of natural history museums. In some instances, even highly experienced and respected researchers can have great difficulty gaining access to specimens for study and research.

Museums are highly unlikely to send specimens to private addresses, hence most palaeoentomologists work at research institutes, usually affiliated with universities or museums. Such positions usually (but not always) require at least a university degree-level qualification, but also a post-graduate degree (MSc or PhD). However, in some cases it is possible to get honorary research status at such institutions without these qualifications, but such positions usually need to be justified on the merits of the individual and their previous research achievements. Some museums provide opportunities for volunteers and this may be another way to gain access to specimens for research purposes.

Unless you have decided that you want to be a palaeoentomologist at the outset (and most palaeoentomologists do not do this) it can be rather tricky to develop the skill sets and knowledge required in order to have a complete understanding of the topic. This is because it covers two broad areas: Earth Sciences (in terms of the geological/palaeontological knowledge) and Life Sciences (in terms of entomological/ecological etc. knowledge). Indeed, these two disciplines are considered so disparate by most universities that they often fall under the auspices of different faculties, often with very little chance for overlap, although sometimes it is possible to do joint geology/biology degrees. Thus, palaeoentomologists often tend to have an excellent knowledge of one of these main areas and sort of stumble around a bit in the other, learning as they go along. You may be lucky to find a place on a MSc palaeobiology course that may help fill in the gaps that remain from undergraduate studies, but even this is trying to cram in a lot at rather a late stage of the learning process. Those individuals who already have a good background knowledge of one of these areas prior to attending university, will, most probably, make a better palaeoentomologist in the long run. However, having the correct qualification is usually not enough. Experience of palaeontological collections and research through volunteering in museums etc. is often seen as highly desirable. This is particularly true with regard to getting paid employment within a museum and would not go against you in any applications for further postgraduate research positions such as PhDs. Even having an advanced degree, such as a doctorate, is often not enough to secure future paid employment. It is important to publish good research papers as you progress through your research, and it is equally important to make contacts with other, more experienced researchers with similar interests, who may act as potential employers in the future.

Some entomologists are co-opted into palaeoentomology later in their careers, by palaeontologists who want their fossils identified. Usually, such scientists have already gained an excellent knowledge of the extant fauna of their particular group of interest. These days, there are many opportunities for self-funded PhD projects, so even if PhD positions are not advertized it may still be worth contacting potential supervisors, assuming you have the financial means to support yourself for at least 3–4 years.

The foregoing is not meant as a deterrent to potential students of palaeoentomology (one aim of this book is to encourage future palaeoentomologists!), but is intended to highlight some of the difficulties and practicalities of choosing this particular branch of science. As mentioned earlier, and as we hope to have conveyed throughout this book, palaeoentomology can be extremely rewarding, thought provoking and inspirational. Both authors, who have experienced various stumbling blocks along the way as a result of some of the above, are still more than happy with the knowledge that fossil insects will no doubt fascinate and occupy them until they are physically or mentally no longer able to research them.

Literature cited in the text

Alonso, J., Arillo, A., Barrón, E., Corral, J.C., Grimalt, J., López, J.F., López, R., Martínez-Delclòs, X., Ortuño, V., Peñalver, E. & Trincao P.R. 2000. A new fossil resin with biological inclusions in Aptian deposits from the Sierra de Cantabria (Alava, northern Spain, Basque-Cantabrian Basin). Journal of Paleontology, 74: 158–178.

Andersen, N.M. & Poinar, G.O. Jr. 1992. Phylogeny and classification of an extinct water strider genus (Hemiptera: Gerridae) from Dominican amber, with evidence of mate guarding in a fossil insect. Zeitschrift fur Zoologische Systematik and Evolutionforschung, 30: 256–267.

Anderson, J.M., Kohring, R. & Schlüter, T. 1998. Was insect biodiversity in the Late Triassic akin to today? A case study from the Molteno Formation. Entomologia Generalis, 23: 1–13.

Anderson, K.B. 1997. The natures and fate of natural resins in the geosphere – VII. A radiocarbon (14C) age scale for description of immature natural resins: An invitation to scientific debate. Organic Geochemistry, 25: 251–253.

Anderson, S.R. 2004. Insect meals from a leptodactylid frog (Amphibia: Leptodactylidae) in Dominican amber (Miocene, 23 Ma). Entomological News, 115: 55–57.

Ansorge, J. 1991. Zur Sedimentologie und Paläontologie des unterkretazischen Plattenkalkaufschlusses "La Cabrua" (Sierra deI Montsec; Provinz Lerida/NE - Spanien) unter besonderer Berücksichtigung der fossilen Insekten. Unpublished Diploma thesis, University of Greifswald.

Ansorge, J. 2003. Insects from the Lower Toarcian of Middle Europe and England. Acta Zoological Cracoviensia, 46(suppl.–Fossil Insects): 291–310.

Archibald, S.B., Greenwood, D.R., Smith, R.Y., Mathewes, R.W. & Basinger, J.F. 2011. Great Canadian Lagerstätten 1. Early Eocene Lagerstätten of the Okanagan Highlands (British Columbia and Washington State). Geoscience Canada, 38: 155–164.

Archibald, S.B., Greenwood, D.R. & Mathewes, R.W. 2013a. Seasonality, montane beta diversity, and Eocene insects: Testing Janzen's dispersal hypothesis in an equable world. Palaeogeography, Palaeoclimatology, Palaeoecology, 371: 1–8.

Archibald, S.B., Mathewes, R.W. & Greenwood, D.R. 2013b. The Eocene apex of panorpoid scorpionfly family diversity. Journal of Paleontology, 87: 677–695.

Arillo, A. 2007. Paleoethology: Fossilized behaviors in amber. Geologica Acta, 5: 57–64.

Arillo, A. & Ortuño, V.M. 1997. The fossil Acrididae from the Oligocene of Izarra (Alava, Spain). The antiquity of gregarious behavior (Orthoptera: Caelifera). Geobios, 30: 231–234.

Aristov, D.S. 2004. Grylloblattids of the Family Chaulioditidae (= Tomiidae syn. nov.) (Insecta: Grylloblattida) from the Upper Permian of the Orenburg Region. Paleontological Journal, 38: 146–149.

Aristov, D.S., Bashkuev, A.S., Golubeva, V.K., Gorochov, A.V., Karasev, E.V., Kopylov, D.S., Ponomarenko, A.G., Rasnitsyn, A.P., Rasnitsyn, D.A., Sinitshenkova, N.D., Sukatsheva, I.D. & Vassilenko, D.V. 2013. Fossil insects of the Middle and Upper Permian of European Russia. Paleontological Journal, 47: 641–832.

Aspöck, U., Haring, E. & Aspöck, H. 2012. They phylogeny of the Neuropterida: Long lasting and current controversies and challenges (Insecta: Endopterygota). Arthropod Systematics & Phylogeny, 70: 119–129.

Austin, J.J., Ross, A.J., Smith, A.B., Fortey, R.A. & Thomas, R.H. 1997. Problems of reproducibility—does geologically ancient DNA survive in amber-preserved insects. Proceedings of the Royal Society B, 264: 467–474.

Azar, D. 2007. A new method for extracting plant and insect fossils from Lebanese amber. Palaeontology, 40: 1027–1029.

Azar, D., Nel, A. & Waller, A. 2009. Two new Ptiloneuridae from Colombian copal (Psocodea: Psocomorpha). Denisia, 26: 21–28.

Azar, D., Gèze, R. & Acra, F. 2010. Lebanese amber. Pp. 271–298 in: Penney, D. (Ed.) 2010. Biodiversity of fossils in amber from the major world deposits. Siri Scientific Press, Manchester.

Bannister, J.M., Conran, J.G. & Lee, D.E. 2012. Lauraceae from rainforest surrounding an early Miocene maar lake, Otago, southern New Zealand. Review of Palaeobotany and Palynology, 178: 13–34.

Barden, P. & Grimaldi, D. 2012. Rediscovery of the bizarre Cretaceous ant Haidomyrmex Dlussky (Hymenoptera: Formicidae), with two new species. American Museum Novitates, 3755: 1–16.

Barling, N., Heads, S.W. & Martill, D.M. 2013. A new parasitoid wasp (Hymenoptera: Chalcidoidea) from the Lower Cretaceous Crato Formation of Brazil: The first Mesozoic Pteromalidae. Cretaceous Research, http://dx.doi.org/10.1016/j.cretres.2013.05.001.

Baroni-Urbani, C. 1995. Invasion and extinction in the West Indian ant fauna revised: The example of Pheidole (Amber collection Stuttgart: Hymenoptera, Formicidae. VIII: Myrmicinae, partim). Stuttgarter Beiträge fur Naturkunde (B), 222: 1–29.

Bashkuev, A., Sell, J., Aristov, D., Ponomarenko, A., Sinitshenkova, N. & Mahler, H. 2012. Insects from the Buntsandstein of Lower Franconia and Thuringia. Palaeontologische Zeitschrift, 86: 175–185. (published online in 2011)

Batelka, J., Engel, M.S., Falin, Z.H. & Prokop, J. 2011. Two new ripidiine species in Dominican amber with evidence of aggregative behaviour of males "frozen" in the fossil record (Coleoptera: Ripiphoridae). European Journal of Entomology, 108: 275–286.

Baxendale, R.W. 1979. Plant-bearing coprolites from North American Pennsylvanian coal balls. Palaeontology, 22: 537–548.

Beattie, R. 2007. The geological setting and palaeoenvironmental and palaeoecological reconstructions of the Upper Permian insect beds at Belmont, New South Wales, Australia. African Invertebrates, 48: 41–57.

Beattie, R. & Avery, S. 2012. Palaeoecology and palaeoenvironment of the Upper Jurassic Talbragar Fossil Fish Bed, Gulgong, New South Wales, Australia. Alcheringa, 36: 453–468.

Beattie, R. & Nel, A. 2012. A new dragonfly, *Austroprotolindenia jurassica* (Odonata: Anisoptera), from the Upper Jurassic of Australia. Alcheringa, 36: 189–193.

Beccaloni, G.W. & Eggleton, P. 2011. Order Blattodea Brunner von Wattenwyl, 1882. In: Zhang, Z.-Q. (Ed.) Animal biodiversity: An outline of higher-level classification and survey of taxonomic richness. Zootaxa, 3148: 199–200.

Bechly, G. & Wolf-Schwenninger, K. 2011. A new fossil genus and species of snakefly (Raphidioptera: Mesoraphidiidae) from Lower Cretaceous Lebanon amber, with a discussion on snakefly phylogeny and fossil history. Insect Systematics & Evolution, 42: 221–236.

Beck, A.L. & Labandeira, C.C. 1998. Early Permian insect folivory on a gigantopterid-dominated riparian flora from north-central Texas. Palaeogeography, Palaeoclimatology, Palaeoecology, 142: 139–173.

Beckemeyer, R.J. 2000. The Permian insect fossils of Elmo, Kansas. The Kansas School Naturalist, 46: 3–15.

Beckemeyer, R.J. & Hall, J.D. 2007. The entomofauna of the Lower Permian fossil insect beds of Kansas and Oklahoma, USA. African Invertebrates, 48: 23–39.

Benner, J.S., Knecht, R.J. & Engel, M.S. 2013. Comment on Marden (2013): "Reanalysis and experimental evidence indicate that the earliest trace fossil of a winged insect was a surface skimming neopteran". Evolution, 67: 2142–2149.

Bennike, O. & Böcher, J. 1990. Forest-tundra neighbouring the North Pole: Plant and insect remains from the Plio-Pleistocene Kap København Formation, North Greenland. Arctic, 43: 331–338.

Benton, M.J. & Newell, A.J. 2014. Impacts of global warming on Permo-Triassic terrestrial ecosystems. Gondwana Research, 25: 1308–1337.

Béthoux, O. 2007. Cladotypic taxonomy applied: Titanopterans are orthopterans. Arthropod Systematics & Phylogeny, 65: 135–156.

Béthoux, O. 2008a. Groundplan, nomenclature, homology, phylogeny, and the question of the insect wing venation pattern. Alavesia, 2: 219–232.

Béthoux, O. 2008b. The insect fauna from the Permian of Lodève (Hérault, France): State of the art and perspectives. Journal of Iberian Geology, 34: 109–113.

Béthoux, O. 2009. The earliest beetle identified. Journal of Paleontology, 83: 931–937.

Béthoux, O. & Nel, A. 2005. Some Palaeozoic 'Protorthoptera' are 'ancestral' orthopteroids: Major wing braces as clues to a new split among the 'Protorthoptera' (Insecta). Journal of Systematic Palaeontology, 2: 285–309.

Béthoux, O. & Wieland, F. 2009. Evidence for Carboniferous origin of the order Mantodea (Insecta: Dictyoptera) gained from forewing morphology. Zoological Journal of the Linnean Society, 156: 79–113.

Béthoux, O., McBride, J. & Maul, C. 2004a. Surface laser scanning of fossil insects. Palaeontology, 47: 12–19.

Béthoux, O., Nel, A. & Lapeyrie, J. 2004b. The extinct order Caloneurodea (Insecta: Pterygota: Panorthoptera): Wing venation, systematics and phylogenetic relationships. Annales Zoologici, 54: 289–318.

Béthoux, O., Galtier, J. & Nel, A. 2004c. Earliest evidence of insect endophytic oviposition. Palaios, 19: 408–413.

Béthoux, O., Beattie, R.G. & Nel, A. 2007. Wing venation and relationships of the order Glosselytrodea (Insecta). Alcheringa, 31: 285–296.

Béthoux, O., Cui, Y., Kondratieff, B., Stark, B. & Ren, D. 2011. At last, a Pennsylvanian stem-stonefly (Plecoptera) discovered. BMC Evolutionary Biology, 2011, 11:248 doi:10.1186/1471-2148-11-248.

Béthoux, O., Gu, J.-J. & Ren, D. 2012. A new Upper Carboniferous stem-orthopteran (Insecta) from Ningxia (China). Insect Science, 19: 153–158.

Beutel, R.G., Friedrich, F., Ge, S.-Q. & Yang, X.-K. 2014. Insect morphology and phylogeny. A textbook for students of entomology. Walter de Gruyter, Berlin.

Bisulca, C., Nascimbene, P.C., Elkin, L. & Grimaldi, D.A. 2012. Variation in the deterioration of fossil resins and implications for the conservation of fossils in amber. American Museum Novitates, 3734: 1–19.

Blagoderov, V.A., Lukashevich, E.D. & Mostovski, M.B. 2002. Order Diptera Linné, 1758, the true flies. Pp. 227–240 in: Rasnitsyn, A.P. & Quicke, D.L.J. (Eds.) 2002. History of insects. Kluwer Academic Publishers, Dordrecht.

Blagoderov, V., Grimaldi, D.A. & Fraser, N.C. 2007. How time flies for flies: Diverse Diptera from the Triassic of Virginia and early radiation of the order. American Museum Novitates, 3572: 1–39.

Blanke, A., Koch, M., Wipfler, B., Wilde, F. & Misof, B. 2014. Head morphology of *Tricholepidion gertschi* indicates monophyletic Zygentoma. Frontiers in Zoology, 11:(1):16. DOI:10.1186/1742-9994-11-16.

Bolton, H. 1917. On some insects from the British Coal Measures. Quarterly Journal of the Geological Society, 72: 43–62.

Bolton, H. 1921. A monograph of the fossil insects of the British Coal Measures. The Palaeontographical Society, London.

Bonde, N., Andersen, S., Hald, N. & Jakobsen, S.L. 2008. Danekræ – Danmarks bedste fossiler. Gyldendal Fakta, Denmark.

Boucot, A.J. 1990. Palaeobiology of behaviour and co-evolution. Elsevier, Amsterdam.

Boucot, A.J. & Poinar, G.O. Jr. 2010. Fossil behavior compendium. CRC Press, Boca Raton.

Braddy, S.J. & Briggs, D.E.G. 2002. New Lower Permian nonmarine arthropod trace fossils from New Mexico and South Africa. Journal of Paleontology, 76: 546–557.

Bradler, S. & Buckley, T.R. 2010. Stick insect on unsafe ground: Does a fossil from the early Eocene of France really link Mesozoic taxa with the extant crown group of Phasmatodea? Systematic Entomology, 36: 218–222. (published online ahead of print)

Bradley, T.J., Briscoe, A.D., Brady, S.G., Contreras, H.L., Danforth, B.N., Dudley, R., Grimaldi, D., Harrison, J.F., Kaiser, J.A., Merlin, C., Reppert, S.M., VandenBrooks, J.M. & Yanoviak, S.P. 2009. Episodes in insect evolution. Integrative and Comparative Biology, 49: 590–606.

Brandao, C.R.F., Baroni-Urbani, C.,Wagensberg, J. & Yamamoto, C.I. 1999. New *Technomyrmex* in Dominican amber (Hymenoptera: Formicidae), with a reappraisal of the Dolichoderinae phylogeny. Entomologica scandinavica, 29: 411–428.

Brasero, N., Nel, A. & Michez, D. 2009. Insects from the Early Eocene amber of Oise (France): Diversity and palaeontological significance. Denisia, 26: 41–52.

Brauckmann, C., Gallego, O.F., Hauschke, N., Martins-Neto, R.G., Groening, E., Ilger, J.-M. & Lara, M.B. 2010. First Late Triassic record of a paleoentomofauna from South America (Malargüe Basin, Mendoza Province, Argentina). Acta Geologica Sinica, 84: 915–924.

Briggs, J.C. 1995. Global biogeography. Elsevier, Amsterdam.

Brock, P.D. & Marshall, J. 2011. Order Phasmida Leach, 1815. In: Zhang, Z.-Q. (Ed.) Animal biodiversity: An outline of higher level classification and survey of taxonomic richness. Zootaxa, 3148: 198.

Brongniart, C. 1884. Sur un gigantesque Néurorthoptère, provenant des terrains houillers de Commentry (Allier). Comptes Rendus Hebdomadaires des Seances de l'Academie des Sciences, 98: 832–833.

Brongniart, C. 1893. Recherches pour servir à l'histoire des insectes fossiles des temps primaires précédées d'une étude sur la nervation des ailes des insectes. Bulletin de la Société d'Industrie Minérale de Saint-Etienne, 7: 124–615.

Brothers, D. 1992. The first Mesozoic Vespidae from the Southern Hemisphere, Botswana. Journal of Hymenoptera Research, 1: 119–124.

Brothers, D.J. & Rasnitsyn, A.P. 2003. Diversity of Hymenoptera and other insects in the Late Cretaceous (Turonian) deposits at Orapa, Botswana: A preliminary review. African Entomology, 11: 221–226.

Brown, B.V. 1997. Systematics and fossil evidence of host-parasitoid relationships of *Calamiscus* Borgmeier (Diptera: Phoridae). Journal of Natural History, 31: 1253–1259.

Brown, B.V. 1999. Re-evaluation of the fossil Phoridae (Diptera). Journal of Natural History, 33: 1561–1573.

Brues, C.T. 1936. Evidences of insect activity preserved in fossil wood. Journal of Paleontology, 10: 637–643.

Burleigh, R. & Whalley, P. 1983. On the relative geological ages of amber and copal. Journal of Natural History, 17: 919–921.

Burnham, L. 1978. Survey of social insects in the fossil record. Psyche, 85: 85–133.

Cai, C.-Y., Yan, E.V., Beattie, R., Wang, B. & Huang, D.-Y. 2013. First rove beetles from the Jurassic Talbragar Fish Bed of Australia (Coleoptera: Staphylinidae). Journal of Paleontology, 87: 650–656.

Cantil, L.F., Sanchez, M.V., Bellosi, E.S., Gonzalez, M.G., Sarzetti, L.C. & Genise, J.F. 2013. *Coprinisphaera akatanka* isp. nov.: The first fossil brood ball attributable to necrophagous dung beetles associated with an Early Pleistocene environmental stress in the Pampean region (Argentina). Palaeogeography, Palaeoclimatology, Palaeoecology, 386: 541–554.

Carpenter, F.M. 1992. Superclass Hexapoda. Volume 3 of Part R, Arthropoda 4; Treatise on invertebrate paleontology. Geological Society of America, Boulder, Colorado.

Carpenter, F.M. 1997. Insecta. Pp. 184–193 in: Shabica, C.W. & Hay, A.A. (Eds.) Richardson's guide to the fossil fauna of Mazon Creek. Northeastern Illinois University Press, Chicago.

Castro, M.P. 1997. Huellas de actividad biológica sobre plantas del Estafaniense Superior de la Magdalena (León, España). Revista Española de Paleontología, 12: 52–66.

Chaboo, C.S., Engel, M.S. & Chamorro-Lacayo, M.L. 2009. Maternally inherited architecture in Tertiary leaf beetles: Paleoichnology of cryptocephaline fecal cases in Dominican and Baltic amber. Naturwissenschaften, 96: 1121–1126.

Chin, K. & Gill, B.D. 1996. Dinosaurs, dung beetles, and conifers: Participants in a Cretaceous food web. Palaios, 11: 280–285.

Cockerell, T.D.A. 1907. Some fossil arthropods from Florissant, Colorado. Bulletin of the American Museum of Natural History, 23: 605–616.

Cockerell, T.D.A. 1908. New fossil insects from Florissant, Colorado. Annals of the Entomological Society of America, 2: 251–258.

Cockerell, T.D.A. 1909. Fossil insects from Florissant, Colorado. Bulletin of the American Museum of Natural History, 26: 67–76.

Cockerell, T.D.A. 1914. New and little known insects from the Miocene of Florissant, Colorado. Journal of Geology, 22: 714–724.

Coleman, C.O. 2003. "Digital inking": How to make perfect line drawings on computers. Organisms, Diversity & Evolution, Electronic Supplement, 14: 1–14.

Compton, S.G., Ball, A.D., Collinson, M.E., Hayes, P., Rasnitsyn, A.P. & Ross, A.J. 2010. Ancient fig wasps indicate at least 34 Myr of stasis in their mutualism with fig trees. Biology Letters, 6: 838–842.

Comstock, J.H. 1918. The wings of insects. Comstock Publishing Company, Ithaca, New York.

Coope, G.R. 2004. Several million years of stability among insect species because of, or in spite of, Ice Age climatic instability. Philosphical Transactions of the Royal Society of London, Series B, 359: 209–214.

Coram, R.A. & Jepson, J.E. 2012. Fossil insects of the Purbeck Limestone Group of southern England: Palaeoentomology from the dawn of the Cretaceous. Monograph Series, Volume 3. Siri Scientific Press, Manchester.

Corral, J.C., López, R. & Alonso, J. 1999. El ámbar Cretácico de Álava (Cuenca Vasco-Cantábrica, norte de España). Su colecta y preparación. Estudios Museo Ciencias Naturales de Álava, 14 (Spec. No. 2): 7–21.

Crepet, W.L., Friis, E.M., Nixon, K.C., Lack, A.J. & Jarzembowski, E.A. 1991. Fossil evidence for the evolution of biotic pollination. Philosphical Transactions of the Royal Society of London, Series B, 333: 187–195.

Crowson, R.A. 1991. The relations of Coleoptera to Cycadales. Pp. 13–28 in: Zunino, M., Belles, X. & Blas, M. (Eds.) Advances in coleopterology. European Association of Coleopterology, Barcelona.

Cui, Y., Béthoux, O. & Ren, D. 2011. Intraindividual variability in Sinonamuropteridae forewing venation (Grylloblattida; Late Carboniferous): Taxonomic and nomenclatural implications. Systematic Entomology, 36: 44–56.

Dalgleish, R.G., Palma, R.L., Price, R.D. & Smith, V.S. 2006. Fossil lice (Insecta: Phthiraptera) reconsidered. Systematic Entomology, 31: 648–651.

Damgaard, J., Moreira, F.F.F., Hayashi, M., Weir, T.A. & Zettel, H. 2012. Molecular phylogeny of the pond treaders (Insecta: Hemiptera: Heteroptera: Mesoveliidae), discussion of the fossil record and a checklist of species assigned to the family. Insect Systematics & Evolution, 43: 175–212.

Dammer, F., Weyda, F., Beneš, J., Šopko, V., Jandejsek, I. & Pflegerova, J. 2013. High resolution radiography of ambers with pixel detectors. Journal of Instrumentation, 8: C03024.

Davis, R.B., Minter, N.J. & Braddy, S.J. 2007. The neoichnology of terrestrial arthropods. Palaeogeography, Palaeoclimatology, Palaeoecology, 255: 284–307.

Davis, R.B., Baldauf, S.L. & Mayhew, P.J. 2010. Many hexapod groups originated earlier and withstood extinction events better than previously realized: Inferences from supertrees. Proceedings of the Royal Society B, 277: 1597–1606.

Delclòs, X., Nel, A., Azar, D., Bechly, G., Dunlop, J.A., Engel, M.S. & Heads, S.W. 2008. The enigmatic Mesozoic insect taxon Chresmodidae (Polyneoptera): New palaeobiological and phylogenetic data, with the description of a new species from the Lower Cretaceous of Brazil. Neues Jahrbuch für Geologie und Paläontologie, Abhandlungen, 247: 353–381.

De Meulemeester, T., Michez, D., Aytekin, A.M. & Danforth, B.N. 2012. Taxonomic affinity of halictid bee fossils (Hymenoptera: Anthophila) based on geometric morphometrics analyses of wing shape. Journal of Systematic Palaeontology, iFirst 2012: 1–10.

Dewulf, A., De Meulemeester, T., Dehon, M., Engel, M.S. & Michez, D. 2014. A new interpretation of the bee fossil Melitta willardi Cockerell (Hymenoptera: Melittidae) based on geometric morphometrics of the wing. ZooKeys, 389: 35–48.

Dikow, T. & Grimaldi, D.A. 2014. Robber flies in Cretaceous ambers (Insecta: Diptera: Asilidae). American Museum Novitates, 3799: 1–19.

Dlussky, G.M., Karl, H.-V., Brauckman, C., Gröning, E. & Reich, M. 2011. Two ants (Insecta: Hymenoptera: Formicidae: Formicinae) from the Late Pliocene of Willershausen, Germany, with a nomenclatural note on the genus Camponotites. Paläontologishe Zeitscrift, 85: 449–455.

Doludenko, M.P., Samulina, G.V. & Pononiarenko, A.G. 1990. Regional geologic structure and unique Late Jurassic occurrences of fauna and flora from Auhe (Karatau, Jurassic of Kazakhstan). USSR Academy of Sciences, Moscow.

Dunlop, J.A. 2010. Bitterfeld amber. Pp. 57–68 in: Penney, D. (Ed.) Biodiversity of fossils in amber from the major world deposits. Siri Scientific Press, Manchester.

Dunlop, J.A. & Penney, D. 2012. Fossil arachnids. Monograph Series, Volume 2. Siri Scientific Press, Manchester.

Dunlop, J.A., Penney, D., Daluge, N., Jager, P., McNeil, A., Bradley, R., Whithers, P.J. & Preziosi, R.F. 2011a. Computed tomography recovers data from historical amber: An example from huntsman spiders. Naturwissenschaften, 98: 519–527.

Dunlop, J.A., Wirth, S., Penney, D., McNeil, A., Bradley, R.S., Withers, P.J. & Preziosi, R.F. 2011b. A minute fossil phoretic mite recovered by X-ray computed tomography. Biology Letters, 8: 457–460. (published online ahead of print)

Dunlop, J.A., Kontschán, J. & Zwanzig, M. 2013. Fossil mesostigmatid mites (Mesostigmata: Gamasina, Microgyniina, Uropodina), associated with longhorn beetles (Coleoptera: Cerambycidae) in Baltic amber. Naturwissenschaften, 100: 337–344.

EDNA 2007 (accessed November 2013). Fossil Insect Database. http://edna.palass-hosting.org/

Ehrmann, R. 1999. Gottesanbeterinnen in Kopal und Bernstein (Insecta: Mantodea). Arthropoda, 7: 2–8.

Elias, S.A. 2009. Advances in Quaternary entomology. Elsevier, Amsterdam.

Eltz, T., Fritzsch, F., Pech, J.R., Zimmermann, Y., Ramrez, S.R., Quezada-Euan, J.J. & Bemb, B. 2011. Characterization of the orchid bee *Euglossa viridissima* (Apidae: Euglossini) and a novel cryptic sibling species, by morphological, chemical, and genetic characters. Zoological Journal of the Linnean Society, 163: 1064–1076.

Emmel, T.C., Minno, M.C. & Drummond, B.A. 1992. Florissant butterflies: A guide to the fossil and present-day species of central Colorado. Stanford University Press, California.

Engel, M.S. 2001. A monograph of the Baltic amber bees and the evolution of the Apoidea (Hymenoptera). Bulletin of the American Museum of Natural History, 259: 1–192.

Engel, M.S. 2002. The smallest snakefly (Raphidioptera: Mesoraphidiidae): A new species in Cretaceous amber from Myanmar, with a catalog of fossil snakeflies. American Museum Novitates, 3363: 1–22.

Engel, M.S. 2003. A new Eocene-Oligocene snakefly from Florissant, Colorado (Raphidioptera: Raphidiidae). Transactions of the Kansas Academy of Science, 106: 124–128.

Engel, M.S. 2005. A remarkable kalligrammatid lacewing from the Upper Jurassic of Kazakhstan (Neuroptera: Kalligrammatidae). Transactions of the Kansas Academy of Science, 108: 59–62.

Engel, M.S. 2008. A new apterous *Zorotypus* in Miocene amber from the Dominican Republic (Zoraptera: Zorotypidae). Acta Entomologica Slovenica, 16: 127–136.

Engel, M.S. 2009a. Gregarious behaviour in Cretaceous earwig nymphs (Insecta: Dermaptera) from southwestern France. Geodiversitas, 31: 129–135.

Engel, M.S. 2009b. A new termite bug in Miocene amber from the Dominican Republic (Hemiptera: Termitaphididae). ZooKeys, 45: 61–68.

Engel, M.S. 2011. A new snakefly from the Eocene Green River Formation (Raphidioptera: Raphidiidae). Transactions of the Kansas Academy of Science, 114: 77–87.

Engel, M.S. & Grimaldi, D.A. 2004. New light shed on the oldest insect. Nature, 427: 627–630.

Engel, M.S. & Grimaldi, D.A. 2007. The neuropterid fauna of Dominican and Mexican amber (Neuropterida: Megaloptera, Neuroptera). American Museum Novitates, 3587: 1–58.

Engel, M.S., Grimaldi, D.A., Singh, H. & Nascimbene, P.C. 2011. Webspinners in Early Eocene amber from western India (Insecta: Embiodea). ZooKeys, 148: 197–208.

Engel, M.S., McKellar, R.C., Gibb, S. & Chatterton, B.D.E. 2012. A new Cenomanian–Turonian (Late Cretaceous) insect assemblage from southeastern Morocco. Cretaceous Research, 35: 88–93.

Engel, M.S., Grimaldi, D.A. & Ortega-Blanco, J. 2013a. A stephanid wasp in Mid-Cretaceous Burmese amber (Hymenoptera: Stephanidae), with comments on the antiquity of the hymenopteran radiation. Journal of the Kansas Entomological Society, 86: 244–252.

Engel, M.S., Pan, A.D. & Jacobs, B.F. 2013b. A termite from the Late Oligocene of northern Ethiopia. Acta Palaeontologica Polonica, 58: 331–334.

Erwin, D.H. 1998. The end and the beginning: recoveries from mass extinctions. TREE, 13: 344–349.

Erwin, D.H. 2001. Lessons from the past: Biotic recoveries from mass extinctions. PNAS, 98: 5399–5403.

Evanoff, E. McIntosh, W.C. & Murphey, P.C. 2001. Stratigraphic summary and 40Ar/39Ar. geochronology of the Florissant Formation, Colorado. Pp. 1–16 in: Evanoff, E., Gregory-Wodzicki, K.M. & Johnson, K.R. (Eds.) Fossil flora and stratigraphy of the Florissant Formation, Colorado. Proceedings of the Denver Museum of Nature and Science, ser. 4(1).

Evenhuis, N.L. 1994. Catalogue of the fossil flies of the world (Insecta: Diptera). Backhuys Publishers, Leiden. (updated online version at: http://hbs.bishopmuseum.org/fossilcat/)

Fang, Shi-Wei, Zhang, Xiao, Yang, Qiang, Guan, Xin-Yang, Gao, Tai-Ping, Ren, Dong 2010. Mimicry and extinction mechanism of kalligrammatid lacewings during [the] Mesozoic (Neuroptera: Kalligrammatidae). Acta Zootaxonomica Sinica, 35: 165–172.

Fikáček, M., Prokin, A. & Angus, R.B. 2011. A long-living species of the hydrophiloid beetles: *Helophorus sibiricus* from the early Miocene deposits of Kartashevo (Siberia, Russia). ZooKeys, 130: 239–254.

Fikáček, M., Prokin, A., Yan, E., Yue, Y., Wang, B., Ren, D. & Beattie, R. 2014. Modern hydrophilid clades present and widespread in the Late Jurassic and Early Cretaceous (Coleoptera: Hydrophiloidea: Hydrophilidae). Zoological Journal of the Linnean Society, 170: 710–734.

Fraser, N.C., Grimaldi, D.A., Olsen, P.E. & Axsmith, B. 1996. A Triassic Lagerstätte from eastern North America. Nature, 380: 615–619.

Frickhinger, K.A. 1999. Die Fossilien von Solnhofen 2. Goldschneck-Verlag, Germany.

Frost, S.W. 1928. Insect scatology. Annals of the Entomological Society of America, 21: 36–46.

Gall, J-C. 1985. Fluvial depositional environment evolving into deltaic setting with marine influences in the Buntsand-stein of Northern Vosges (France). Pp. 449–477 in: Mader, D. (Ed.) Aspects of fluvial sedimentation in the Lower Triassic Buntsandstein of Europe. Lecture notes in Earth sciences 4. Springer, Berlin.

Gall, J.-C. & Grauvogel-Stamm, L. 2005. The early Middle Triassic 'Grès à Voltzia' Formation of eastern France: A model of environmental refugium. Comptes Rendus Palevol, 4: 637–652.

Gao, T., Shih, C., Rasnitsyn, A.P. & Ren, D. 2013a. *Hoplitolyda duolunica* gen. et sp. nov. (Insecta: Hymenoptera: Prae-siricidae), the hitherto largest sawfly from the Mesozoic of China. PLoS ONE, 8(5): e62420.

Gao, T., Shih, C., Rasnitsyn, A.P., Xu, X., Wang, S. & Ren, D. 2013b. New transitional fleas from China highlighting diversity of Early Cretaceous ectoparasitic insects. Current Biology, 23: 1261–1266.

Garrouste, R., Clément, G., Nel, P., Engel, M.S., Grandcolas, P., D'Haese, C., Lagebro, L., Denayer, J., Gueriau, P., Lafaite, P., Olive, S., Prestianni, C. & Nel, A. 2012. A complete insect from the Late Devonian period. Nature, 488(7409): 82–85.

Garwood, R.J. & Sutton, M.D. 2010. X-ray micro-tomography of Carboniferous stem-Dictyoptera: New insights into early insects. Biology Letters, 6: 699–702.

Garwood, R., Ross, A., Sotty, D., Chabard, D., Charbonnier, S., Sutton, M. & Withers, P.J. 2012. Tomographic recon-struction of neopterous Carboniferous insect nymphs. PLoS ONE, 7(9): e45779.

Gaunt, M.W. & Miles, M.A. 2002. An insect molecular clock dates the origin of the insects and accords with palaeonto-logical and biogeographic landmarks. Molecular Biology and Evolution, 19: 748–761.

Genise, J.F. 1999. Fossil bee cells from the Asencio Formation (Late Cretaceous–Early Tertiary) of Uruguay, South America. Proceedings of the first palaeoentomological conference, Moscow, 1998. Bratislava: Amba Projects, 27–32.

Genise, J.F. 2000. The ichnofamily Celliformidae for *Celliforma* and allied ichnogenera. Ichnos, 7: 267–282.

Genise, J.F. & Bown, T.M. 1994. New Miocene scarabeid and hymenopterous nests and early Miocene (Santacrucian) paleoenvironments, Patagonian Argentina. Ichnos, 3: 107–117.

Genise, J.F. & Bown, T.M. 1996. *Uruguay* Roselli 1938 and *Rosellichnus*, n. ichnogenus: Two ichnogenera for clusters of fossil bee cells. Ichnos, 4: 199–217.

Genise, J.F. & Hazeldine, P.L. 1998. 3D reconstruction of insect trace fossils: *Ellipsoideichnus meyeri* Roselli. Ichnos, 5: 167–175.

Genise, J.F., Alonso-Zarza, A.M., Verde, M. & Melenndez, A. 2013a. Insect trace fossils in aeolian deposits and calcretes from the Canary Islands: Their ichnotaxonomy, producers, and palaeoenvironmental significance. Palaeogeography, Palaeoclimatology, Palaeoecology, 377: 110–124.

Genise, J.F., Melchor, R.N., Sanchez, M.V. & Gonzalez, M.G. 2013b. *Attaichnus kuenzelii* revisited: A Miocene record of fungus-growing ants from Argentina. Palaeogeography, Palaeoclimatology, Palaeoecology, 386: 349–363.

Gersdorf, E. & Hiltermann, H. 1968. Beiheft zu den Berichten der Naturhistorischen Gesellschaft zu Hannover, 6: 1–94.

Gordh, G. & Headrick, D. 2011. A dictionary of entomology 2nd edition. CAB International, Wallingford.

Gorochov, A.V. 2007. The first representative of the suborder Mesotitanina from the Paleozoic and notes on the system and evolution of the order Titanoptera (Insecta: Polyneoptera). Paleontological Journal, 41: 621–625.

Gorochov, A.V. 2013. No evidence for Paleozoic origin of mantises (Dictyoptera: Mantina). Zoosystematica Rossica, 22: 6–14.

Gorochov, A.V. & Rasnitsyn, A.P. 2002. Superorder Gryllidea Laicharting, 1781 (= Orthopteroidea Handlirsch, 1903). Pp. 294–301 in: Rasnitsyn, A.P. & Quicke, D.L.J. (Eds.) History of insects. Kluwer Academic Publishers.

Grande, L. 2013. The lost world of Fossil Lake: Snapshots from deep time. The University of Chicago Press, Chicago.

Greenwalt, D.E., Goreva, Y.S., Siljeström, S.M., Rose, T. & Harbach, R.E. 2013. Hemoglobin-derived porphyrins pre-served in a Middle Eocene blood-engorged mosquito. PNAS Early Edition, doi/10.1073/pnas.1310885110.

Grimaldi, D.A. 1991. Mycetobiine woodgnats (Diptera: Anisopodidae) from the Oligo-Miocene amber of the Dominican Republic, and Old World affinities. American Museum Novitates, 3014: 1–24.

Grimaldi, D.A. 1999. The co-radiation of pollinating insects and angiosperms in the Cretaceous. Annals of the Missouri Botanical Gardens, 86: 373–406.

Grimaldi, D. (Ed.) 2000. Studies on fossils in amber, with particular reference to the Cretaceous of New Jersey. Backhuys Publishers, Leiden.

Grimaldi, D. 2003. A revision of Cretaceous mantises and their relationships, including new taxa (Insecta: Dictyoptera: Mantodea). American Museum Novitates, 3412: 1–47.

Grimaldi, D.A. 2010. 400 million years on six legs: On the origin and early evolution of Hexapoda. Arthropod Structure & Development, 39: 191–203.

Grimaldi, D.A. & Engel, M.S. 2005. Evolution of the insects. Cambridge University Press, New York.

Grimaldi, D.A. & Nascimbene, P.C. 2010. Raritan (New Jersey) amber. Pp. 167–191 in: Penney, D. (Ed.) Biodiversity of fossils in amber from the major world deposits. Siri Scientific Press, Manchester.

Grimaldi, D.A., Shedrinsky, A., Ross, A.J. & Baer, N.S. 1994. Forgeries of fossils in 'amber': History, identification and case studies. Curator, 37: 251–274.

Grimaldi, D.A., Shmakov, A. & Fraser, N. 2004. Mesozoic thrips and early evolution of the order Thysanoptera (Insecta). Journal of Paleontology, 78: 941–952.

Gu, J.-J., Montealegre-Z, F., Robert, D., Engel, M.S., Qiao, G.-X. & Ren, D. 2012. Wing stridulation in a Jurassic katydid (Insecta: Orthoptera) produced low-pitched musical calls to attract females. PNAS, 109: 3868–3873.

Haas, F., Waloszek, D. & Hartenberger, R. 2003. *Devonohexapodus bocksbergensis*, a new marine hexapod from the Lower Devonian Hunsrück Slates, and the origin of Atelocerata and Hexapoda. Organisms Diversity & Evolution, 3: 39–54.

Hagstrom, J. & Mehlqvist, K. 2012. The dawn of terrestrial ecosystems on Baltica: First report on land plant remains and arthropod coprolites from the Upper Silurian of Gotland, Sweden. Palaeogeography, Palaeoclimatology, Palaeoecology, 317–318: 162–170.

Hand, S., Archer, M., Bickel, D., Creaser, P., Dettmann, M., Godthelp, H., Jones, A., Norris, B. & Wicks, D. 2010. Australian amber. Pp. 69–79 in: Penney, D. (Ed.) Biodiversity of fossils in amber from the major world deposits. Siri Scientific Press, Manchester.

Hall, J.P.W., Robbins, R.K. & Harvey, D.J. 2004. Extinction and biogeography in the Caribbean, new evidence from a fossil riodinid butterfly in Dominican amber. Proceedings of the Royal Society of London B, 271: 789–801.

Haug, J.T., Müller, C.H.G. & Sombke, A. 2013. A centipede nymph in Baltic amber and a new approach to document amber fossils. Organisms Diversity & Evolution, 13: 425–432.

Hasiotis, S.T. & Demko, T.M. 1996. Terrestrial and freshwater trace fossils, Upper Jurassic Morrison Formation, Colorado Plateau. In: Morales, M. (Ed.) The continental Jurassic. Bulletin of the Museum of Northern Arizona, 60: 355–370.

Háva, J. & Wappler, T. 2014. A new genus and species of Dermestidae (Coleoptera) from the Eckfeld Maar crater (Middle Eocene, Germany). Bulletin of Geosciences, 89: 67–74.

Heads, S.W. 2008. The first fossil Proscopiidae (Insecta: Orthoptera: Eumastacoidea) with comments on the historical biogeography and evolution of the family. Palaeontology, 51: 499–507.

Heads, S.W. & Wang, Y. 2013. First fossil record of *Melanoplus differentialis* (Orthoptera: Acrididae: Melanoplinae). Entomological News, 123: 33–37.

Heads, S.W., Martill, D.M. & Loveridge, R.F. 2005. An exceptionally preserved antlion (Insecta: Neuroptera) with colour pattern preservation from the Cretaceous of Brazil. Palaeontology, 48: 1409–1417.

Henning, J.T., Smith, D.A., Nofio, C.R. & Meyer, H.R. 2012. Depositional setting and fossil insect preservation: A study of the Late Eocene Florissant Formation, Colorado. Palaios, 7: 481–488.

Hiltermann, H. 1968. Gehäuse von Insekten-Larven, insbesondere von Chironomiden, in Quartären Sedimenten. Mitteilungen aus dem Geologischen Institut der TU Hannover, 8: 34–53.

Hiltermann, H. & Gersdorf, E. 1967. Bericht der Naturhistorischen Gesellschaft zu Hannover, 111: 1–120.

Hiltermann, H. & Zobel, B. 1969. Bericht der Naturhistorischen Gesellschaft zu Hannover, 113: 1–108.

Hinojosa-Díaz, I.A. & Engel, M.S. 2007. A new fossil orchid bee in Colombian copal (Hymenoptera: Apidae). American Museum Novitates, 3589: 1–7.

Hoffeins, H.W. 2001. On the preparation and conservation of amber inclusions in artificial resin. Polish Journal of Entomology, 70: 215–219.

Hoffeins, C. & Hoffeins, H.W. 2013. Diptera in Baltic amber – the most frequent order within arthropod inclusions. Abstracts of the 6th International Congress on Fossil Insects, Arthropods and Amber, Byblos, Lebanon, 2013: 43–44.

Holden, A.R., Harris, J.M. & Timm, R.M. 2013. Paleoecological and taphonomic implications of insect-damaged Pleistocene vertebrate remains from Rancho La Brea, southern California. PLoS ONE, 8(7): e67119.

Holden, A.R., Koch, J.B., Griswold, T., Erwin, D.M. & Hall, J. 2014. Leafcutter bee nests and pupae from the Rancho La Brea tar pits of southern California: Implications for understanding the paleoenvironment of the Late Pleistocene. PLoS ONE, 9(4): e94724.

Holzenthal, R.W., Morse, J.C. & Kjer, K.M. 2011. Order Trichoptera Kirby, 1813. In: Zhang, Z.-Q. (Ed.), Animal diversity: An outline of higer-level classification and survey of taxonomic richness. Zootaxa, 3148: 209–211.

Hong, Y. 2002. Atlas of amber insects of China. Henan Scientific and Technological Publishing House, Henan. (in Chinese with English summary)

Hong, Y. 1985. Fossil insects, scorpionids and araneids in the diatoms of Shanwang. Geological Publishing House, Beijing. (in Chinese with English summary)

Hörnschemeyer, T. 1999. Fossil insects from the Lower Permian of Nierdermoschel (Germany). Proceedings of the First Palaeoentomological Conference, Moscow, 1998. Bratislava: Amba Projects, 57–59.

Hörnschemeyer, T. & Stapf, H. 2001. Review of Blattinopsidae (Protorthoptera) with description of new species from the Lower Permian of Niedermoschel (Germany). Neues Jahrbuch für Geologie und Paläontologie, Abhandlungen, 221: 81–109.

Hörnschemeyer, T., Wedmann, S. & Poinar, G.O. Jr. 2010. How long can insect species exist? Evidence from extant and fossil *Micromalthus* beetles (Insecta: Coleoptera). Zoological Journal of the Linnean Society, 158: 300–311.

Hörnschemeyer, T., Haug, J.T., Bethoux, O., Beutel, R.G., Charbonnier, S., Hegna, T.A., Koch, M., Rust, J., Wedmann, S., Bradler, S. & Willmann, R. 2013. Is *Strudiella* a Devonian insect? Nature, 494(7437): E3–4; discussion E4–5.

Huang, D.-y., Nel, A., Lin, Q.-b. & Dong, F.-b. 2007. The first Glosselytrodea (Insecta) from the latest Middle Permian of Anhui Province, China. Bulletin de la Societe Entomologique de France, 112: 179–182.

Huang, D.-y., Engel, M.S., Cai, C., Wu, H. & Nel, A. 2012. Diverse transitional giant fleas from the Mesozoic era of China. Nature, 483: 201–204.

Huang, D.-y., Nel, A., Cai, C., Lin, Q. & Engel, M.S. 2013. Amphibious flies and paedomorphism in the Jurassic period. Nature, 495: 94–97.

Huber, J.T. & Greenwalt, D. 2011. Compression fossil Mymaridae (Hymenoptera) from Kishenehn oil shales, with description of two new genera and review of Tertiary amber genera. In Shcherbakov, D.E., Engel, M.S. & Sharkey, M.J (Eds.) Advances in the systematics of fossil and modern insects: Honouring Alexandr Rasnitsyn. ZooKeys, 130: 473–494.

Ingrisch, S. 2011. Order Orthoptera Oliver, 1789. In: Zhang, Z.-Q. (Ed.) Animal biodiversity: An outline of higher-level classification and survey of taxonomic richness. Zootaxa, 3148: 195–197.

Ivanov, V.D. 2006. Larvae of caddisflies (Insecta: Trichoptera) from the Mesozoic of Siberia. Paleontological Journal, 40: 178–189.

Janssens, F. & Christiansen, K.A. 2011. Class Collembola Lubbock, 1870. In: Zhang, Z.-Q. (Ed.) Animal biodiversity: An outline of higher-level classification and survey of taxonomic richness. Zootaxa, 3148: 192–194.

Jarzembowski, E.A. 1987. The occurrence and diversity of Coal Measure insects. Journal of the Geological Society, 144: 507–511.

Jarzembowski, E.A. 2003. Palaeoentomology: Towards the bigger picture. Acta Zoological Cracoviensia, 46(suppl.–Fossil Insects): 25–36.

Jarzembowski, E.A. 2011. Insects (excluding cockroaches), Pp. 138–174 in: Batten, D.J. (Ed.) English Wealden fossils. The Palaeontological Association, UK.

Jarzembowski, E.A. 2012. The oldest plant-insect interaction in Croatia: Carboniferous evidence. Geologia Croatica, 65: 387–392.

Jarzembowski, E.A. & Ross, A.J. 1996. Insect origination and extinction in the Phanerozoic. In: Hart, M.B. (Ed.) Biotic recovery from mass extinction events. Geological Society Special Publications, 102: 65–78.

Jell, P.A. 2004. The fossil insects of Australia. Memoirs of the Queensland Museum, 50: 1–124.

Jell, P.A. & Duncan, P.M. 1986. Invertebrates, mainly insects, from the freshwater, Lower Cretaceous, Koonwarra Fossil Bed (Korumburra Group), South Gippsland, Victoria. Memoir of the Association of Australasian Palaeontologists, 3: 111–205.

Jepson, J.E. & Jarzembowski, E.A. 2008. Two new species of snakefly (Insecta: Raphidioptera) from the Lower Cretaceous of England and Spain with a review of other fossil raphidiopterans from the Jurassic/Cretaceous transition. Alavesia, 2: 193–201.

Joachim, C. 2010. Biodiversität und Palökologie fossiler Insekten des Randecker Maar (Unter-Miozän, SW-Deutschland). Documenta Naturae, 179: 1–116.

Johnson, C., Agosti, D., Delabie, J.H., Dumpert, K., Williams, D.J., Von Tschirnhaus, M. & Maschwitz, U. 2001. *Acropyga* and *Azteca* ants (Hymenoptera: Formicidae) with scale insects (Sternorrhyncha: Coccoidea): 20 million years of intimate symbiosis. American Museum Novitates, 3335: 1–18.

Kaddumi, H.F. 2007. Amber of Jordan: The oldest prehistoric insects in fossilized resin (3rd edition). Published by the author, Jordan.

Kalugina, N.S. 1993. Chaoborids and non-biting midges from the Mesozoic of eastern Transbaikalia (Diptera: Chaoboridae and Chironomidae). Pp. 117–139 in: Ponomarenko, A.G. (Ed.) Mesozoic insects and ostracods of Asia. Trudy Paleontologicheskogo Instituta Akademii Nauk SSSR, Moscow.

Kampmann, H. 1983. Ein Insekten-Exkrement aus Sporen aus dem unterkretazischen Saurlager von Nehden (Sauerland, Westfalen). Paläontologische Zeitschrift, 57: 75–77.

Kaulfuss, U., Wappler, T., Heiss, E. & Larivière, M.-C. 2011. *Aneurus* sp. from the early Miocene Foulden Maar, New Zealand: the first Southern Hemisphere record of fossil Aradidae (Insecta: Hemiptera: Heteroptera). Journal of the Royal Society of New Zealand, 41: 279–285.

Kaulfuss, U., Lee, D.E., Bannister, J.M., Lindqvist, J.K., Conran, J.G., Mildenhall, D.C., Kennedy, E.M., Perrichot, V., Maraun, M. & Schmidt, A. 2013. Foulden Maar and South Island amber (New Zealand) – two exceptional windows into Southern Hemisphere Cenozoic terrestrial ecosystems. Pp. 84–89 in: Reitner *et al.* (Eds.) Palaeobiology and geobiology of fossil Lagerstätten through Earth history. (talk abstract)

Kerp, H. & Bomfleur, B. 2011. Photography of plant fossils – New techniques, old tricks. Review of Palaeobotany and Palynology, 166: 117–151.

Kiecksee, A.P., Kaulfuss, U., Lee, D.E., Sadowski, E.-M., Schmidt, A. & Maraun, M. 2013. Diversity of mites from New Zealand amber. Pp. 86–87 in: Reitner *et al.* (Eds.) Palaeobiology and geobiology of fossil Lagerstätten through Earth history. (poster abstract)

Kinzelbach, R. Von & Lutz, H. 1985. Stylopid larva from the Eocene – a spotlight on the phylogeny of the stylopids (Strepsiptera). Annals of the Entomological Society of America, 78: 600–602.

Kinzelbach, R. Von & Pohl, H. 1994. The fossil Strepsiptera (Insecta: Strepsiptera). Annals of the Entomological Society of America, 87: 59–70.

Kirejtshuk, A.G. & Nel, A. 2013. Skleroptera, a new order of holometabolous insects (Insecta) from the Carboniferous. Zoosystematica Rossica, 22: 247–257.

Kirejtshuk, A.G., Poschmann, M. Prokop, J., Garrouste, R. & Nel, A. 2013. Evolution of the elytral venation and structural adaptations in the oldest Palaeozoic beetles (Insecta: Coleoptera: Tshekardocoleidae). Journal of Systematic Palaeontology, doi: 10.1080/14772019.2013.821530.

Kistner, D.H. 1998. New species of termitophylous Trichopseniinae (Coleoptera: Staphylinidae) found with *Mastotermes darwiniensis* in Australia and in Dominican amber. Sociobiology, 31: 51–76.

Klavins, S.D., Kellogg, D.W., Krings, M., Taylor, E.L. & Taylor, T.N. 2005. Coprolites in a Middle Triassic cycad pollen cone: Evidence for insect pollination in early cycads? Evolutionary Ecology Research, 7: 479–488.

Klopfstein, S., Wilhelmsen, L., Heraty, J.M., Sharkey, M. & Ronquist, F. 2013. The hymenopteran tree of life: Evidence from protein-coding genes and objectively aligned ribosomal data. PLoS ONE, 8(8): e69344.

Kluge, N.J. 2013. Ephemeroptera of the world. Online at: http://www.insecta.bio.spbu.ru/z/Eph-spp/Contents.htm.

Knecht, R.J., Engel, M.S. & Benner, J.S. 2011. Late Carboniferous paleoichnology reveals the oldest full-body impression of a flying insect. PNAS, 108: 6515–6519.

Kogan, M. & Poinar, G.O. Jr. 2010. New fossil *Stylops* (Strepsiptera: Stylopidae) from Dominican amber. Neotropical Entomology, 39: 227–234.

Koteja, J. & Poinar, G.O. Jr. 2005. Scale insects (Coccinea) associated with mites (Acari) in the fossil record. Polskie Pismo Entomologiczne, 74: 287–298.

Kozlov, M.V. 1988. Palaeontological data and the problems of phylogeny of the order Papilionida. Pp. 16–69 in: Ponomarenko, A.G. (Ed.) 1988. Cretaceous biocoenotic crisis and evolution of the insects. Nauka, Moscow.

Krasnov, B.R. 2008. Functional and evolutionary ecology of fleas: A model for ecological parasitology. Cambridge University Press, Cambridge.

Krassilov, V.A. 2007. Mines and galls on fossil leaves from the Late Cretaceous of southern Negev, Israel. African Invertebrates, 48: 13–22.

Krassilov, V.A. & Rasnitsyn, A.P. 1999. Plant remains from the guts of fossil insects: Evolutionary and paleoecological inferences. Proceedings of the First Palaeoentomological Conference, Moscow, 1998. Bratislava: Amba Projects, 65–72.

Krassilov, V.A., Rasnitsyn, A.P. & Afonin, S.A. 2007. Pollen eaters and pollen morphology: Co-evolution through the Permian and Mesozoic. African Invertebrates, 48: 3–11.

Krishna, K., Grimaldi, D.A., Krishna, V. & Engel, M.S. 2013. Treatise on the Isoptera of the world. Bulletin of the American Museum of Natural History, 377: 1–2704.

Križnar, M. 2013. Fossil insect sites in Slovenia. Acta Entomologica Slovenica, 21: 59–64.

Krzemińska, E. & Krzemiński, W. 2009. Monograph of fossil Trichoceridae (Diptera) over 180 million years of evolution. Polish Academy of Sciences, Kraków.

Krzemiński, W. & Krzemińska, E. 2003. Triassic Diptera: descriptions, revisions and phylogenetic relations. Acta Zoological Cracoviensia, 46(suppl.–Fossil Insects): 153–184.

Krzemiński, W., Krzemińska, E., Kubisz, D., Mazur, M. & Pawlowski, J. 1997. Preliminary report on a Pliocene fauna from western Hungary. Studia Naturalia, 10: 177–191.

Kühl, G. & Rust, J. 2009. *Devonohexapodus bocksbergensis* is a synonym of *Wingertshellicus backesi* (Euarthropoda) – no evidence for marine hexapods living in the Devonian Hunsrück Sea. Organisms Diversity & Evolution, 9: 215–231.

Kukalová J. 1964. Permian Insects of Moravia. Part II. Liomopteridea. Sbornik Geologickych Ved, Paleontologie, 3: 39–118.

Kukalová-Peck, J. & Brauckmann, C. 1992. Most Paleozoic Protorthoptera are ancestral hemipteroids: major wing braces as clues to a new phylogeny of Neoptera (Insecta). Canadian Journal of Zoology, 70: 2452–2473.

Kukalová-Peck J. & Willmann R. 1990. Lower Permian 'mecopteroid-like' insects from Central Europe (Endopterygota). Canadian Journal of Earth Sciences, 27: 459–468.

Labandeira, C.C. 1998. Early history of arthropod and vascular plant associations. Annual Review of Earth and Planetary Sciences, 26: 329–377.

Labandeira, C.C. 2000. The paleobiology of pollination and its precursors. In: Gastaldo, R.A. & DiMichele, W.A. (Eds.) Phanerozoic terrestrial ecosystems. Paleontological Society Papers, 6: 233–269.

Labandeira, C.C. 2002. Paleobiology of predators, parasitoids, and parasites: Death and accommodation in the fossil record of continental invertebrates. In: Kowalewski, M. & Kelley, P.H. (Eds.) The fossil record of predation. Paleontological Society Papers, 8: 211–249.

Labandeira, C.C. 2005. The fossil record of insect extinction: New approaches and future directions. Amererican Entomologist, 51: 14–29.

Labandeira, C.C. 2006a. The four phases of plant–arthropod associations in deep time. Geologica Acta, 4: 409–438.

Labandeira, C.C. 2006b. Silurian to Triassic plant and insect clades and their associations: New data, a review, and interpretations. Arthropod Systematics & Phylogeny, 64: 53–94.

Labandeira, C.C. & Currano, E.D. 2013. The fossil record of plant-insect dynamics. Annual Review of Earth and Planetary Sciences, 41: 287–311.

Labandeira, C.C. & Phillips, T.L. 1996. Insect fluid-feeding on Upper Pennsylvanian tree ferns (Palaeodictyoptera, Marattiales) and the early history of the piercing-and-sucking functional feeding group. Annals of the Entomological Society of America, 89: 157–183.

Labandeira, C.C. & Sepkoski, J.J. Jr. 1993. Insect diversity in the fossil record. Science, 261: 310–315.

Labandeira, C.C., Beall, B.S. & Hueber, F.M. 1988. Early insect diversification: Evidence from a Lower Devonian bristletail from Québec. Science, 242: 913–916.

Labandeira, C.C., Dilcher, D.L., Davis, D.R. & Wagner, D.I. 1994. Ninety-seven million years of angiosperm–insect association: Paleobiological insight into the meaning of co-evolution. PNAS, 9: 12278–12282.

Labandeira, C.C., Phillips, T.L. & Norton, R.A. 1997. Oribatid mites and the decomposition of plant tissues in Paleozoic coal-swamp forests. Palaios, 12: 319–353.

Labandeira, C.C., Johnson, K.C. & Wilf, P. 2002. Impact of the terminal Cretaceous event on plant insect associations. PNAS, 99: 2061–2066.

Labandeira, C.C., Tremblay, S.L., Bartowski, K.E. & VanAller Hernick, L. 2014. Middle Devonian liverwort herbivory and antiherbivore defence. New Phytologist, 202: 247-258.

Ladle, M. & Griffiths, B.S. 1980. A study on the feces of some chalk stream invertebrates. Hydrobiologia, 74: 161–171.

Lambkin, K.J. 2014. 'Psychopsoid Neuroptera' ('Psychopsidae', 'Osmylopsycopidae') from the Queensland Triassic [online]. The Australian Entomologist, 41: 57–76.

LaPolla, J.S. 2005. Ancient trophophoresy: a fossil *Agropyga* (Hymenoptera: Formicidae) in Dominican amber. Transactions of the American Entomological Society, 131: 21–28.

LaPolla, J.S., Dlussky, G.M. & Perrichot, V. 2013. Ants and the fossil record. Annual Review of Entomology, 58: 609–630.

Lara, M.B. & Lukashevich, E.D. 2013. The first Triassic dipteran (Insecta) from South America, with review of Hennigmatidae. Zootaxa, 3710: 81–92.

Lara, M.B., Gallego, O.F. & Tassi, L.V. 2012. Mesozoic coleopteran faunas from Argentina: Geological context, diversity, taphonomic observations, and comparison with other fossil insect records. Psyche, 2012: doi:10.1155/2012/242563.

Lara, M.B., Rasnitsyn, A.P. & Zavattieri, A.M. 2014. *Potrerilloxyela menendezi* gen. et sp. nov. from the Late Triassic of Argentina: The oldest representative of Xyelidae (Hymenoptera: Symphyta) for the Americas. Paleontological Journal, 48(2): 81–89.

Larocque-Tobler, I. 2014. The Polish sub-fossil chironomids. Palaeontologia Electronica, 17 (1;3A): 28 pp.

Larsson, S.G. 1978. Baltic amber – A palaeobiological study. Entomonograph, 1: 1–192.

Leakey, L.S.B. 1952. Lower Miocene invertebrates from Kenya. Nature, 169: 624–625.

Lehane, J.R. & Ekdale, A.A. 2013. Pitfalls, traps, and webs in ichnology: Traces and trace fossils of an understudied behavioral strategy. Palaeogeography, Palaeoclimatology, Palaeoecology, 375: 59–69.

Lewis, R.E. & Grimaldi, D.A. 1997. A pulicid flea in Miocene amber from the Dominican Republic (Insecta: Siphonaptera: Pulicidae). American Museum Novitates, 3205: 1–9.

Li, S., Shih, C., Wang, C., Pang, H. & Ren, D. 2013. Forever love: The hitherto earliest record of copulating insects from the Middle Jurassic of China. PLoS ONE, 8(11): e78188.

Li, Y., Béthoux, O., Pang, H. & Ren, D. 2013. Early Pennsylvanian Odonatoptera from the Xiaheyan locality (Ningxia, China): New material, taxa, and perspectives. Fossil Record, 16: 117–139.

Liu, X., Wang, Y., Shih, C., Ren, D. & Yang, D. 2012. Early evolution and historical biogeography of fishflies (Megaloptera: Chauliodinae): Implications from a phylogeny combining fossil and extant taxa. PLoS ONE, 7(7): e40345.

Liu, X., Hayashi, F. & Yang, D. 2014. Phylogeny of the family Sialidae (Insecta: Megaloptera) inferred from morphological data, with implications for generic classification and historical biogeography. Cladistics, doi: 10.1111/cla.12071.

Lovisolo, O. & Rösler, O. 2003. Searching for palaeontological evidence of viruses that multiply in Insecta and Acarina. Acta Zoological Cracoviensia, 46(suppl.–Fossil Insects): 37–50.

Lubkin, S.H. 2003. *Paracupes svitkoi* (Coleoptera: Cupedidae), a new species from the Cretaceous of New Jersey. Acta Zoological Cracoviensia, 46(suppl.–Fossil Insects): 189–194.

Lukashevich, E.D. & Mostovski, M. 2003. Hematophagous insects in the fossil record. Paleontological Journal, 37: 153–161.

Lutz, H. 1990. Systematische und paläökologische Untersuchungen an Insekten aus dem Mittel-Eozän der Grube Messel bei Darmstadt. Courier Forschungsinstitut Senckenberg, 124: 1–165.

Lyubarsky, G. Yu & Perkovsky, E.E. 2012. The first Eocene species of the genus *Cryptophagus* (Coleoptera: Clavicornia: Cryptophagidae). Vestnik Zoologii, 46: e-36–e-40.

MacLeod, N. 2013. The great extinctions: What causes them and how they shape life. The Natural History Museum, London.

Makarkin, V.N. & Archibald, S.B. 2014. A revision of the late Eocene snakeflies (Raphidioptera) of the Florissant Formation, Colorado, with special reference to the wing venation of the Raphidiomorpha. Zootaxa, 3784: 401–444.

Makarkin, V.N., Ren, D. & Yang, Q. 2009. Two new species of Kalligrammatidae (Neuroptera) from the Jurassic of China, with comments on venational homologies. Annals of the Entomological Society of America, 102: 964–969.

Malm, T., Johanson, K.A. & Wahlberg, N. 2013. The evolutionary history of Trichoptera (Insecta): A case of successful adaptation to life in freshwater. Systematic Entomology, 38: 459–473.

Mangano, M.G., Buatois, L.A., Maples, C.G. & Lanier, W.P. 1997. *Tonganoxichnus* a new insect trace from the Upper Carboniferous of eastern Kansas. Lethaia, 30: 113–125.

Mangano, M.G., Labandeira, C.C., Kvale, E.P. & Buatois, L.A. 2001. The insect trace fossil *Tonganoxichnus* from the middle Pennsylvanian of Indiana: Paleobiologic and paleoenvironmental implications. Ichnos, 8(3–4): 165–175.

Marchal-Papier, F. 1998. Les insectes du Buntsandstein des Vosges (NE de la France). Biodiversité et contribution aux modalités de la crise biologique du Permo-Trias. Thèse, Université Louis Pasteur, Strasbourg.

Marden, J.H. 2013a. Reanalysis and experimental evidence indicate that the earliest trace fossil of a winged insect was a surface-skimming neopteran. Evolution, 67: 274–280.

Marden, J.H. 2013b. Reply to "Comment on Marden (2013) regarding the interpretation of the earliest trace fossil of a winged insect". Evolution, 67: 2150–2153.

Martill, D., Bechly, G. & Loveridge, R.F. (Eds.) 2007. The Crato fossil beds of Brazil: Window into an ancient world. Cambridge University Press, Cambridge.

Martin, F., Hájek, J. & Schmied, H. 2011. On the identity of the fossil aquatic beetles from the Tertiary localities in the southern part of the Upper Rhine Graben (Coleoptera: Hydrophilidae, Dytiscidae). ZooKeys, 78: 15–25.

Martin, L.D. & West, D.L. 1995. The recognition and use of dermestid (Insecta: Coleoptera) pupation chambers in paleoecology. Palaeogeography, Palaeoclimatology, Palaeoecology, 113(2–4): 303–310.

Martin, S.K. 2008. Hill River rediscovered: Early Jurassic insects of the Perth Basin, Western Australia. Alavesia, 2: 7–14.

Martínez-Delclos, X. & Martinell, J. 1993. Insect taphonomy experiments. Their application to the Cretaceous outcrops of the Lithographic Limestones from Spain. Darmstadter Beiträge zur Naturgeschichte, 2: 133–144.

Martínez-Delclòs, X., Briggs, D.E.G. & Peñalver, E. 2004. Taphonomy of insects in carbonates and amber. Palaeogeography, Palaeoclimatology, Palaeoecology, 203: 19–64.

Martins-Neto, R.G. 1991. Paleoarthropodologia aplicada. University of Guarulhos, Brazil.

Martins-Neto, R.G., Gallego, O.F. & Melchor, R.N. 2003. The Triassic insect fauna from South America (Brazil, Argentina and Chile): A checklist (except Blattoptera and Coleoptera) and descriptions of new taxa. Acta Zoologica Cracoviensia (suppl.-Fossil Insects), 46: 229–256.

Martins-Neto, R.G., Gallego, O.F., Brauckmann, C. & Cruz, J.L. 2007. A review of the South American Palaeozoic entomofauna part I: The Ischnoneuroidea and Cacurgoidea, with description of new taxa. African Invertebrates, 48: 87–101.

Martins-Neto, R.G., Gallego, O.F. & Zavattieri, A.M. 2008. The Triassic insect fauna from Argentina: Coleoptera, Hemiptera and Orthoptera from the Potrerillos Formation, south of cerro Cacheuta, Cuyana basin. Alavesia, 2: 47–58.

Martins-Neto, R.G., Oliveira Assis, C. de & Tassi, L.V. 2010. New Blattoptera from Early Cretaceous of Santana Formation (Araripe Basin, NE Brazil) and a review of *Arariplebatta* Mendes, 2000. Gaea, 6: 9–13.

Mashimo, Y., Matsumura, Y., Machida, R., Dallai, R., Gottardo, M., Yoshizawa, K., Friedrich, F., Wipfler, B. & Beutel, R.G. 2014. 100 years Zoraptera—a phantom in insect evolution and the history of its investigation. Insect Systematics & Evolution, doi: 10.1163/1876312X-45012110.

Massaferro, J., Larocque-Tobler, I., Brooks, S.J., Vandergoes, M. Dieffenbacher-Krall, A. & Moreno, P. 2014. Quantifying climate change in Huelmo mire (Chile, northwestern Patagonia) during the Last Glacial Termination using a newly developed chironomid-based temperature model. Palaeogeography, Palaeoclimatology, Palaeoecology, 399: 214–224.

Matthews, J.V. Jr. & Telka, A. 1997. Insect fossils from the Yukon. Pp. 911–962 in Danks, H.V. & Downes, J.A. (Eds.) Insects of the Yukon. Biological Survey of Canada (Terrestrial Arthropods), Ottawa.

Mayhew, P.J. 2007. Why are there so many insect species? Perspectives from fossils and phylogenies. Biological Reviews, 82: 425–454.

Mazur, M. & Kubisz, D. 2008. The sculpture of elytra in species from the family Dytiscidae (Insecta: Coleoptera) as a diagnostic feature for the identification of subfossil material. Folia Quaternaria, 78: 71–98.

Mazur, N., Nagel, M., Leppin, U., Bierbaum, G. & Rust, J. 2012. The extraction of fossil arthropods from Lower Eocene Cambay amber. Acta Palaeontologica Polonica, doi: http://dx.doi.org/10.4202/app.2012.0018. (online in 2012)

McKellar, R.C. & Engel, M.S. 2012. Hymenoptera in Canadian Cretaceous amber (Insecta). Cretaceous Research, 35: 258–279.

McKellar, R.C. & Wolfe, A.P. 2010. Canadian amber. Pp. 149–166 in: Penney, D. (Ed.) Biodiversity of fossils in amber from the major world deposits. Siri Scientific Press, Manchester.

McNamara, M.E. 2013. The taphonomy of colour in fossil insects and feathers. Palaeontology, 2013: 1–19.

McNamara, M.E., Briggs, D.E.G., Orr, P.J., Wedmann, S., Noh, H. & Cao, H. 2011. Fossilized biophotonic nanostructures reveal the original colors of 47-million-year-old moths. PLoS Biol, 9(11): e1001200.

McNamara, M.E., Briggs, D.E.G., Orr, P.J., Noh, H. & Cao, H. 2012a. The original colours of fossil beetles. Proceedings of the Royal Society, B., 279: 1114–1121.

McNamara, M.E., Briggs, D.E.G. & Orr, P.J. 2012b. The controls on the preservation of structural color in fossil insects. Palaios, 72: 443–454.

McNamara, M.E., Briggs, D.E.G., Orr, P.J., Gupta, N.S., Locatelli, E.R., Qiu, L., Yang, H., Wang, Z., Noh, H. & Cao, H. 2013. The fossil record of insect color illuminated by maturation experiments. Geology, doi: 10.1130/G33836.1.

Meischner, D. 2000. Der Pliozäne Teich von Willershausen am Harz. Pp. 223–228, 261 in: Meischner, D. (Ed.) Europäische Fossillagerstätten. European Palaeontological Association. Springer Verlag, Berlin.

Meyer, H.W. 2003. The fossils of Florissant. Smithsonian Institution, Washington, D.C.

Meyer, H.M. & Smith, D.M. (Eds.) 2008. Paleontology of the Upper Eocene Florissant Formation, Colorado. Geological Society of America Special Paper, 435.

Michez, D., Vanderplanck, M. & Engel, M.S. 2012. Fossil bees and their plant associates. Pp. 103–164 in: Patiny, S. (Ed.) Evolution of plant-pollinator relationships. Cambridge University Press, Cambridge.

Miller, S.E. 1997. Late Quaternary insects of Rancho la Brea, California, USA. Pp. 185–191 in: Studies in Quaternary Entomology – An inordinate fondness for insects. Quaternary Proceedings No. 5. John Wiley & Sons Ltd., Chichester.

Moisan, P., Labandeira, C.C., Matushkina, N.A., Wappler, T., Voigt, S. & Kerp, H. 2012. Lycopsid–arthropod associations and odonatopteran oviposition on Triassic herbaceous *Isoetites*. Palaeogeography, Palaeoclimatology, Palaeoecology, 344–345: 6–15.

Moretti, G. 1955. Sulla presenza dei foderi dei Tricotteri e dei Ditteri Tanytarsi sui fondi del Lago Maggiore. Memorie dell' Istituto Italiano di Idrobiologia, 8: 205–219.

Mound, L.A. 2011. Order Thysanoptera Haliday, 1836. In: Zhang, Z.-Q. (Ed.) Animal biodiversity: An outline of higher-level classification and survey of taxonomic richness. Zootaxa, 3148: 201–202.

Müller, A.H. 1981. Zur Ichnologie, Taxiologie und Ökologie fossiler Tiere. Freiberger Forschungsheft, 151: 5–49.

Müller, A.H. 1982. Über Hyponome fossiler und rezenter Insekten, erster Beitrag. Freiberger Forschungsheft C, 366: 7–27.

Na, Y., Sun, C., Li, T. & Li, Y. 2014. The insect oviposition firstly discovered on the Middle Jurassic Ginkgoales leaf from Inner Mongolia, China. Acta Geologica Sinica, 88: 18–28.

Nagel, P. 1997. New fossil paussids from Dominican amber with notes on the phylogenetic systematics of the paussine complex (Coleoptera: Carabidae). Systematic Entomology, 22: 345–362.

Nascimbene, P. & Silverstein, H. 2000. The preparation of fragile Cretaceous ambers for conservation and study of organismal inclusions. Pp. 93–102 in: Grimaldi, D.A. (Ed.) Studies on fossils in amber, with particular reference to the Cretaceous of New Jersey. Backhuys Publishers, Leiden.

Nel, A. & Brasero, N. 2010. Oise amber. Pp. 137–148 in: Penney, D. (Ed.) Biodiversity of fossils in amber from the major world deposits. Siri Scientific Press, Manchester.

Nel, A. & Paicheler, J.-C. 1993. Les Isoptera fossiles. État actuel des connaissances, implications paléoécologiques et paléoclimatologiques (Insecta, Dictyoptera). Cahiers de Paléontologie, CNRS Editions, Paris: 101–179.

Nel, A., Albouy, V., Caussanel, C. & Jamet, C. 1994. Réflexion paléo-entomologique sur la systématique des Dermaptères. Quatre nouveaux forficules fossiles de l'Oligocène de Provence (France) (Dermaptera). Bulletin de la Société Entomologique de France, 99: 253–299.

Nel, A., Béthoux, O., Bechly, G., Martinez-Delclos, X. & Papier, F. 2001. The Permo-Triassic Odonatoptera of the "protodonate" grade (Insecta: Odonatoptera). Annales Société Entomologique de France (N.S.), 37: 501–525.

Nel, A., Prokop, J. & Ross, A.J. 2008. New genus of leaf-mimicking katydids (Orthoptera: Tettigoniidae) from the Late Eocene–Early Oligocene of France and England. Comptes Rendus Palevol, 7: 211–216.

Nel, A., Fleck, G., Garrouste, R., Gand, G., Lapeyrie, J., Bybee, S.M. & Prokop, J. 2009. Revision of Permo-Carboniferous griffinflies (Insecta: Odonatoptera: Meganisoptera) based upon new species and redescription of selected poorly known taxa from Eurasia. Palaeontographica Abteilung A, 289(4–6): 89–121.

Nel, A., Roques, P., Nel, P., Prokin, A.A., Bourgoin, T., Prokop, J., Szwedo, J., Azar, D., Desutter-Grandcolas, L., Wappler, T., Garrouste, R., Coty, D., Huang, D., Engel, M.S. & Kirejtshuk, A.G. 2013. The earliest known holometabolous insects. Nature, 503(7475): 257–261.

Novokshonov, V.G. & Aristov, D.S. 2004. New taxa of hypoperlids (Insecta: Hypoperlida) from the Upper Permian of the Arkhangelsk Region. Paleontological Journal, 38: 60–66.

Novokshonov, V.G. & Zhuzhgova, L.V. 2004. Discussion of the system and phylogeny of the order Palaeomanteida (=Miomoptera) with description of new representatives of the genus *Permosialis* Mart. from the Late Permian of Kirov Region and Triassic of Kyrgyzstan. Paleontological Journal, 38(Suppl. 2): S173–S184.

Ohl, M. 2011. Aboard a spider – a complex developmental stratergy fossilized in amber. Naturwissenschaften, 98: 453–456.

Okuno, E., Mori, Y. & Nakamura, T. 2010. Paleoenvironment of medieval archaeological sites in Central Japan: Assemblage analysis and 14C dating of insect fossils. Radiocarbon, 52(2–3): 511–519.

Olmi, M. & Guglielmino, A. 2011. Revision of fossil species of *Dryinus* belonging to *lamellatus* group, with description of a new species (Hymenoptera: Dryinidae). ZooKeys, 130: 505–514.

Ortega-Blanco, J., Delclòs, X. & Engel, M.S. 2011. Diverse stigmaphronid wasps in Early Cretaceous amber from Spain (Hymenoptera: Ceraphronoidea: Stigmaphronidae). Cretaceous Research, 32: 762–773.

Panagiotakopulu, E. 1999. An examination of biological materials from coprolites from XVIII Dynasty Amarna, Egypt. Journal of Archaeological Science, 26: 547–551.

Papadopoulou, A., Anastasiou, I. & Vogler, A.P. 2010. Revisiting the insect mitochondrial molecular clock: The Mid-Aegean trench calibration. Molecular Biology & Evolution, 27: 1659–1672.

Papier, F., Grauvogel-Stamm, L. & Nel, A. 1994. *Subioblatta undulata* n.sp., une nouvelle blatte (Bubioblattidae Schneider) du Buntsandstein superieur (Anisien) des Vosges (France). Morphologie, systematique et affinites. Neues Jahrbuch für Geologie und Paläontologie, Montashefte, 5: 277–290.

Park, L.E. & Downing, K.F. 2001. Paleoecology of an exceptionally preserved arthropod fauna from lake deposits of the Miocene Barstow Formation, southern California, U.S.A. Palaios, 16: 175–184.

Parker, A.R. & McKenzie, D.R. 2003. The cause of 50 million-year-old colour. Proceedings of the Royal Society B, 270 (Suppl. 2): S151–S153.

Paulian, M.R. 1965. Decouverte d'une faune entomologique permienne à Madagascar. Comptes rendus de l'Académie des Sciences, Paris, 260: 4028–4030.

Peñalver, E. 1998. Estudio tafonómico y paleoecológico de los insectos del Mioceno de Rubielos de Mora (Teruel). Instituto de Estudios Turolenses Ed., Teruel.

Peñalver, E. 2002. Los insectos dípteros del Mioceno del Este de la Península Ibérica; Rubielos de Mora, Ribesalbes y Bicorp. Tafonomía y sistemática. Ph.D. thesis. Universitat de València, Valencia.

Peñalver, E. & Martínez-Delclòs, X. 1996. Niveles con concentraciones de insectos chironómidos en el Mioceno de Rubielos de Mora (Teruel) y Ribesalbes (Castellón): Consideraciones tafonómicas y paleoecológicas. Comunicaciones de la II Reunión de Tafonomía y Fosilización, Zaragoza: 305–310.

Peñalver, E. & Delclòs, X. 2004. Insects del Mioceno inferior de Ribesalbes (Castellón, España). Interacciones planta-insecto. Treballs del Museu de Geología de Barcelona, 12: 69–95.

Peñalver, E. & Delclòs, X. 2010. Spanish amber. Pp. 236–270 in: Penney, D. (Ed.) Biodiversity of fossils in amber from the major world deposits. Siri Scientific Press, Manchester.

Peñalver, E. & Engel, M.S. 2006. Two wasp families rare in the fossil record (Hymenoptera): Perilampidae and Megaspilidae from the Miocene of Spain. American Museum Novitates, 3540: 1–12.

Peñalver, E. & Grimaldi, D. 2006. New data on Miocene butterflies in Dominican amber (Lepidoptera: Riodinidae and Nymphalidae) with the description of a new nymphalid. American Museum Novitates, 3519: 1–17.

Peñalver, E., Nel, A. & Martínez-Delclòs, X. 1996. Insects del Mioceno inferior de Ribesalbes (Castellón, España). Paleoptera y Neoptera poli- y paraneoptera. Treballs del Museu de Geología de Barcelona, 5: 15–95.

Peñalver, E., Martínez-Delclòs, X. & Arillo, A. 1999. Yacimientos con insectos fósiles en España. Revista Española de Paleontologia, 14: 231–245.

Peñalver, E., Grimaldi, D.A. & Delclòs, X. 2006. Early Cretaceous spider web with its prey. Science, 312: 1761.

Peng, Y., Makarkin, V.N., Wang, X. & Ren, D. 2011. A new fossil silky lacewing genus (Neuroptera: Psychopsidae) from the Early Cretaceous Yixian Formation of China. ZooKeys, 130: 217–228.

Penney, D. 2005. Fossil blood droplets in Miocene Dominican amber yield clues to speed and direction of resin secretion. Palaeontology, 48: 925–927.

Penney, D. (Ed.) 2010a. Biodiversity of fossils in amber from the major world deposits. Siri Scientific Press, Manchester.

Penney, D. 2010b. Dominican amber. Pp. 22–41 in: Penney, D. (Ed.) Biodiversity of fossils in amber from the major world deposits. Siri Scientific Press, Manchester.

Penney, D. 2010c. The evolution of jumping spiders (Araneae: Salticidae): The palaeontological evidence. Peckhamia, 81.8: 1–3.

Penney, D. & Green, D.I. 2011. Fossils in amber: Remarkable snapshots of prehistoric forest life. Siri Scientific Press, Manchester.

Penney, D. & Langan, A.M. 2006. Comparing amber fossils across the Cenozoic. Biology Letters, 2: 266–270.

Penney, D. & Langan, A.M. 2010. Morphometric identification of fossils spiders: Comment. Paleontological Journal, 44: 644–648.

Penney, D. & Preziosi, R.F. 2013. Subfossils in copal: an undervalued scientific resource. Abstracts. International Amber Researcher Symposium, Gdansk, Poland, 38–41.

Penney, D. & Selden, P.A. 2011. Fossil spiders: The evolutionary history of a mega-diverse order. Monograph Series, Volume 1. Siri Scientific Press, Manchester.

Penney, D., McNeil, A., Green, D.I., Bradley, R., Jepson, J.E., Whithers, P.J. & Preziosi, R.F. 2012a. Ancient Ephemeroptera-Collembola symbiosis predicts contemporary phoretic associations. PLoS ONE, 7(10): e47651.

Penney, D., Green, D.I., Titchener, S.B, Titchener, B.G., Brown, T.A. & Preziosi, R.F. 2012b. An unusual palaeobiocoenosis of (sub)fossil spiders in Colombian copal. Bulletin of the British Arachnological Society, 15: 241–244.

Penney, D., Wadsworth, C., Green, D.I., Kennedy, S.L., Preziosi, R.F. & Brown, T.A. 2013a. Extraction of inclusions from (sub)fossil resins with description of a new species of stingless bee (Apidae: Meliponini) in Colombian copal. Paleontological Contributions, 7: 1–6.

Penney, D., Wadsworth, C., Fox, G., Kennedy, S.L., Preziosi, R.F. & Brown, T.A. 2013b. Absence of ancient DNA in sub fossil insect inclusions preserved in 'Anthropocene' Colombian copal. PLoS ONE, 8(9): e73150.

Pérez-de la Fuente, R., Delclòs, X., Peñalver, E., Speranza, M., Wierzchos, J., Ascaso, C. & Engel, M.S. 2012a. Early evolution and ecology of camouflage in insects. PNAS, 109(52): 21414–21419.

Pérez-de la Fuente, R., Peñalver, E., Delclòs, X. & Engel, M.S. 2012b. Snakefly diversity in Early Cretaceous amber from Spain (Neuropterida: Raphidioptera). ZooKeys, 204: 1–40.

Pérez-Gelabert, D.E. 2008. Arthropods of Hispaniola (Dominican Republic and Haiti): A checklist and bibliography. Zootaxa, 1831: 1–530.

Peris, D., Delclòs, X., Soriano, C. & Perrichot, V. 2014. The earliest occurrence and remarkable stasis of the family Bostrichidae (Coleoptera: Polyphaga) in Cretaceous Charentes amber. Palaeontologia Electronica, 17.1.14A.

Perkovsky, E., Zosimovich, V.Y. & Vlaskin, A.P. 2010. Rovno amber. Pp. 116–136 in: Penney, D. (Ed.) Biodiversity of fossils in amber from the major world deposits. Siri Scientific Press, Manchester.

Perrichot, V. & Girard, V. 2009. A unique piece of amber and the complexity of ancient forest ecosystems. Palaios, 24: 137–139.

Perrichot, V., Néraudeau, D. & Tafforeau, P. 2010. Charentese amber. Pp. 192–207 in: Penney, D. (Ed.) Biodiversity of fossils in amber from the major world deposits. Siri Scientific Press, Manchester.

Perrichot, V., Beaucournu, J.-C. & Velten, J. 2012. First extinct genus of a flea (Siphonaptera: Pulicidae) in Miocene amber from the Dominican Republic. Zootaxa, 3438: 54–61.

Peters, R.S., Meusemann, K., Petersen, M., Mayer, C., Wilbrandt, J., Ziesmann, T., Donath, A., Kjer, K.M., Aspöck, U., Aspöck, H., Aberer, A., Stamatakis, A., Friedrich, F., Hünefeld, F., Niehuis, O., Beutel, R.G. & Misof, B. 2014. The evolutionary history of holometabolous insects inferred from transcriptome-based phylogeny and comprehensive morphological data. BMC Evolutionary Biology, 14(1):52. doi: 10.1186/1471-2148-14-52.

Petrulevičius, J.F., Wappler, T., Nel, A. & Rust, J. 2011. The diversity of Odonata and their endophytic ovipositions from the Upper Oligocene Fossil-Lagerstätte of Rott (Rhineland, Germany). ZooKeys, 130: 67–89.

Pisani, D., Poling, L.L., Lyons-Weiler, M. & Hedges, S.B. 2004. The colonization of land by animals: Molecular phylogeny and divergence times among arthropods. BMC Biology, 2: 1doi:10.1186/1741-7007-2-1.

Plotnick, R. & Smith, D. 2012. Exceptionally preserved fossil insect ears from the Eocene Green River Formation. Journal of Paleontology, 86: 19–24.

Pohl, H. 2009. The oldest fossil strepsipteran larva (Insecta: Strepsiptera) from the Geisel Valley, Germany (Eocene). Insect Systematics & Evolution, 40: 333–347.

Pohl, H. & Beutel, R.G. 2013. The Strepsiptera-Odyssey: The history of the systematic placement of an enigmatic parasitic insect order. Entomologia, doi: 10.4081/entomologia.2013.e4.

Pohl, H. & Kinzelbach, R. 2001. First record of a female stylopid (Strepsiptera: ?Myrmecolacidae) parasite of a prionomyrmecine ant (Hymenoptera: Formicidae) in Baltic amber. Insect Systematics and Evolution, 32: 143–146.

Poinar, G.O. Jr. 1987. Fossil evidence of spider parasitism by Ichneumonidae. Journal of Arachnology, 14: 399–400.

Poinar, G.O. Jr. 1992a. Life in amber. Stanford University Press, California.

Poinar, G.O. Jr. 1992b. Fossil evidence of resin utilization by insects. Biotropica, 24: 466–468.

Poinar, G.O. Jr. 1999a. Extinction of tropical insect lineages in Dominican amber from Plio-Pleistocene cooling events. Russian Entomological Journal, 8: 1–4.

Poinar, G.O. Jr. 1999b. Paleochordodes protus n.g., n.sp. (Nematomorpha: Chordodidae), parasites of a fossil cockroach, with a critical examination of other fossil hairworms and helminths of extant cockroaches (Insecta: Blattaria). Invertebrate Biology, 118: 109–115.

Poinar, G.O. Jr. 2004. Evidence of parasitism by Strepsiptera in Dominican amber. Biocontrol, 49: 239–244.

Poinar, G.O. Jr. 2009. Description of an early Cretaceous termite (Isoptera: Kalotermitidae) and its associated intestinal protozoa, with comments on their co-evolution. Parasites & Vectors, 2: DOI: 10.1186/1756-3305-2-12.

Poinar, G.O. Jr. 2010. Palaeoecological perspectives in Dominican amber. Annales Société Entomologique de France (N.S.), 46: 23–52.

Poinar, G.O. Jr. 2011a. Panstrongylus hispaniolae sp. n. (Hemiptera: Reduviidae: Triatominae), a new fossil triatomine in Dominican amber, with evidence of gut flagellates. Palaeodiversity, 6: 1–8.

Poinar, G.O. Jr. 2011b. Vetufebrus ovatus n. gen., n. sp. (Haemospororida: Plasmodiidae) vectored by a streblid bat fly (Diptera: Streblidae) in Dominican amber. Parasites & Vectors, 4: 229.

Poinar, G.O. Jr. 2012. New fossil nematodes in Dominican and Baltic amber. Nematology, 14: 483–488.

Poinar, G.[O.] Jr. 2013. *Stenaspidiotus microptilus* n. gen., n. sp. (Coleoptera: Chrysomelidae: Chrysomelinae) in Dominican amber, with evidence of tachinid (Diptera: Tachinidae) oviposition. Historical Biology: An International Journal of Paleobiology, 25(1): 101–105.

Poinar, G.O. Jr. & Grimaldi, D.A. 1990. Fossil and extant macrochelid mites (Arari: Macrochelidae) phoretic on drosophilid flies (Diptera: Drosophilidae). Journal of the New York Entomological Society, 98: 88–92.

Poinar, G.O. Jr & Milki, R. 2001. Lebanese amber: The oldest insect ecosystem in fossilized resin. Oregon State University Press, Corvallis.

Poinar, G.O. Jr. & Miller, J.C. 2002. First fossil record of endoparasitism of adult ants (Formicidae: Hymenoptera) by Braconidae (Hymenoptera). Annals of the Entomological Society of America, 95: 41–43.

Poinar, G.O. Jr & Poinar, R. 1999. The amber forest: A reconstruction of a vanished world. Princeton University Press, New Jersey.

Poinar, G.O. Jr. & Telford, S.R. 2005. *Paleohaemoproteus burmacis* gen. n., sp. n. (Haemosporida: Plasmodiidae) from an Early Cretaceous biting midge (Diptera: Ceratopogonidae). Parasitology, 131: 79–84.

Poinar, G.O. Jr., Ćurčić, B.P.M. & Cokendolpher, J.C. 1998. Arthropod phoresy involving pseudoscorpions in the past and present. Acta Arachnologica, 47: 79–96.

Poinar, G.O. Jr., Marshall, C.J. & Buckley, R. 2007. One hundred million years of chemical warfare by insects. Journal of Chemical Ecology, 33: 1663–1669.

Pomi, L.H. & Tonni, E.P. 2011. Termite traces on bones from the Late Pleistocene of Argentina. Ichnos, 18: 166–171.

Ponomarenko, A.G. 1976. A new insect from the Cretaceous of Transbaikalia, a possible parasite of pterosaurians. Paleontological Journal, 10: 339–343.

Ponomarenko A.G. 1985. Fossil insects from the Tithonian "Solnhofener Plattenkalke" in the Museum of Natural History, Vienna. Annalen des Naturhistorischen Museums Wien A, 87: 135–144.

Poschmann, M. Schindler, T. & Uhl, D. 2010. Fossil-Lagerstätte Enspel – A short review of current knowledge, the fossil association, and a bibliography. Palaeobiodiversity and Palaeoenvironments, 90: 3–20.

Prokop, J. & Nel, A. 2009. Systematic position of *Triplosoba*, hitherto the oldest mayfly, from Upper Carboniferous of Commentry in Central France (Insecta: Palaeodictyopterida). Systematic Entomology, 34: 610–615.

Prokop, J. & Nel, A. 2011. New Middle Permian palaeopteran insects from Lodève Basin in southern France (Insecta: Ephemeroptera, Diaphanopterodea, Megasecoptera). ZooKeys, 130: 41–55.

Prokop, J., Nel, A. & Tenny, A. 2010. On the phylogenetic position of the palaeopteran Syntonopteroidea (Insecta: Ephemeroptera), with a new species from the Upper Carboniferous of England. Organisms Diversity & Evolution, 10: 331–340.

Prokop, J., Krzemiński, W., Krzemińska, E. & Wojciechowski, D. 2012. Paoliida, a putative stem-group of winged insects: Morphology of new taxa from the Upper Carboniferous of Poland. Acta Palaeontologica Polonica, 57: 161–173.

Prokop, J., Krzemiński, W., Krzemińska, E., Hörnschemeyer, T., Ilger, J.-M., Brauckmann, C., Grandcolas, P. & Nel, A. 2013. Late Palaeozoic Paoliida is the sister group of Dictyoptera (Insecta: Neoptera). Journal of Systematic Palaeontology, DOI: 10.1080/14772019.2013.823468.

Ramírez, S.R., Gavendeel, B., Singer, R.B., Marshall, C.R. & Pierce, N.E. 2007. Dating the origin of Orchidaceae from a fossil orchid with its pollinator. Nature, 448: 1042–1045.

Rasnitsyn, A.P. 1992. *Strashila incredibilis*, a new enigmatic mecopteroid insect with possible siphonapteran affinities from the Upper Jurassic of Siberia. Psyche, 99: 323–333.

Rasnitsyn, A.P. 2002a. Superorder Caloneurida Handlirsch, 1906. Pp. 105–111 in: Rasnitsyn, A.P. & Quicke, D.L.J. (Eds.) History of insects. Kluwer Academic Publishers, Dordrecht.

Rasnitsyn, A.P. 2002b. Superorder Vespidea Laicharting, 1781. Order Hymenoptera Linné, 1758 (=Vespida Laicharting, 1781). Pp. 242–254 in: Rasnitsyn, A.P. & Quicke, D.L.J. (Eds.) History of insects. Kluwer Academic Publishers, Dordrecht.

Rasnitsyn, A.P. 2004. Leposmatona, Caloneurida, Hypoperlida, Hemiptera, Palaeomanteida, Eoblattida. Important new insect fossils from Carrizo Arroyo and the Permo-Carboniferous faunal boundary. Carboniferous-Permian transition. New Mexico Museum of Natural History and Science Bulletin, 25: 215–246.

Rasnitsyn, A.P. & Aristov, D.S. 2013. Two new insects from the Upper Permian (Tatarian) of Belmont, New South Wales, Australia (Insecta: Hypoperlida: Anthracoptilidae = Permarrhaphidae; Grylloblattida: Sylvaphlebiidae). Paleontological Journal, 38: S158–S163.

Rasnitsyn, A.P. & Quicke, D.L.J. (Eds.) 2002. History of insects. Kluwer Academic Publishers, Dordrecht.

Rasnitsyn, A.P. & Zherikhin, V.V. 1999. First fossil chewing louse from the Lower Cretaceous of Baissa, Transbaikalia (Insecta: Pediculida = Phthiriaptera, Saurodectidae fam. n.). Russian Entomological Journal, 8: 253–255.

Rasnitsyn, A.P., Sukacheva, I.D. & Aristov, D.S. 2005. Permian insects of the Vorkuta Group in the Pechora Basin, and their stratigraphic implications. Paleontological Journal, 39: 404–416.

Rasser, M.W., Bechly, G., Böttcher, R., Ebner, M., Heizmann, E.P.J., Höltke, O., Joachim, C., Kern, A.K., Kovar-Eder, J., Nebelsick, J.H., Roth-Nebelsick, A., Schoch, R.R., Schweigert, G. & Ziegler, R. 2013. The Randeck Maar: Palaeoenvironment and habitat differentiation of a Miocene lacustrine system. Palaeogeography, Palaeoclimatology, Palaeoecology, 392: 426–453.

Rayner, R.J., Bamford, M.K., Brothers, D.J., Dippenaar-Schoeman, A.S., McKay, I.J., Oberprieler, R.G. & Waters, S.B. 1997. Cretaceous fossils from the Orapa diamond mine. Palaeontologica Africana, 33: 55–65.

Ren, D., Labandeira, C.C., Santiago-Blay, J.A., Rasnitsyn, A., Shih, C.K., Bashkuev, A., Logan, M.A., Hotton, C.L. & Dilcher, D. 2009. Probable pollination mode before angiosperms: Eurasian, long-proboscid scorpionflies. Science, 326(5954): 840–847.

Ren, D., Shih, C.-K., Gao, T.-P., Yao, Y.-Z. & Zhao, Y. 2010. Silent stories—insect fossil treasures from [the] dinosaur era of [the] northeastern China. Beijing, China: Science Press.

Richter, G. & Baszio, S. 2001. First proof of planctivory/insectivory in a fossil fish: *Thaumaturus intermedius* from the Eocene Lake Messel (FRG). Palaeogeography, Palaeoclimatology, Palaeoecology, 173: 75–85.

Riedel, A., dos Santos Rolo, T., Cecilia, A. & Van De Kamp, T. 2012. Sayrevilleinae Legalov, a newly recognised subfamily of fossil weevils (Coleoptera: Curculionoidea: Attelabidae) and the use of synchrotron microtomography to examine inclusions in amber. Zoological Journal of the Linnean Society, 165: 773–794.

Riek, E.F. 1970. Fossil history. Pp. 168–186 in: The insects of Australia. Melbourne University Press, Melbourne.

Riek, E.F. 1974a. A fossil insect from the Dwyka Series of Rhodesia. Palaeontologia Africana, 17: 15–17.

Riek, E.F. 1974b. Upper Triassic insects from the Molteno "Formations", South Africa. Palaeontologia Africana, 17: 19–31.

Riek, E.F. 1976. Neosecoptera, a new insect suborder based on specimens discovered in the Late Carboniferous of Tasmania. Alcheringa, 1: 227–234.

Riek, E.F. & Kukalova-Peck, J. 1984. A new interpretation of dragonfly wing venation based upon Early Upper Carboniferous fossils from Argentina (Insecta: Odonatoidea) and basic character states in pterygote wings. Canadian Journal of Zoology, 62: 1150–1166.

Ronquist, F., Kloppstein, S., Vilhelmsen, L., Schulmeister, S., Murray, D.L. & Rasnitsyn, A.P. 2012. A total-evidence approach to dating with fossils, applied to the early radiation of the Hymenoptera. Systematic Biology, 61: 973–999.

Ross, A.J. 2010. A review of the Carboniferous fossil insects from Scotland. Scottish Journal of Geology, 46: 157–168.

Ross, A.J. 2011. Cockroaches. Pp. 174–181 in: Batten, D.J. (Ed.) English Wealden fossils. The Palaeontological Association, UK.

Ross, A.J. 2012. Testing decreasing variability of cockroach forewings through time using four Recent species: *Blattella germanica, Polyphaga aegyptiaca, Shelfordella lateralis* and *Blaberus craniifer*, with implications for the study of fossil cockroach forewings. Insect Science, 19: 129–142.

Ross, A.J. & Sheridan, A. 2013. Amazing amber. National Museums Scotland, Edinburgh.

Ross, A.J., Jarzembowski, E.A. & Brooks, S.J. 2000. The Cretaceous and Cenozoic record of insects (Hexapoda) with regard to global change. Pp. 288–302 in: Culver, S.J. & Rawson, P.F. (Eds.) Biotic response to global change: The last 145 million years. Cambridge University Press, Cambridge.

Ross, A.J., Mellish, C., York, P. & Crighton, B. 2010. Burmese amber. Pp. 208–235 in: Penney, D. (Ed.) Biodiversity of fossils in amber from the major world deposits. Siri Scientific Press, Manchester.

Roth, L.M. 2003. Systematics and phylogeny of cockroaches (Dictyoptera: Blattaria). Oriental Insects, 37: 1–186.

Rozefelds, A.C. 1988. Insect leaf mines from the Eocene Anglesea locality, Victoria, Australia. Alcheringa, 12: 1–6.

Rozefelds, A.C. & Baar, M.D. 1991. Silicified Kalotermitidae (Isoptera) frass in conifer wood from a mid–Tertiary rainforest in central Queensland, Australia. Lethaia, 24: 439–442.

Rust, J. 1999. Fossil insects from the Fur and Olst Formations ("mo-clay") of Denmark (upper Palaeocene/lowermost Eocene). Proceedings of the First Palaeoentomological Conference, Moscow 1998. Bratislava: Amba Projects, 135–139.

Rust, J. 2000. Fossil record of mass moth migration. Nature, 405: 530–531.

Rust, J., Stumpner, A. & Gottwald, J. 1999. Singing and hearing in a Tertiary bushcricket. Nature, 399: 650.

Rust, J., Singh, H., Rana, R.S., McCann, T., Singh, L., Anderson, K., Sarkar, N., Nascimbene, P.C., Stebner, F., Thomas, J.C., Solórzano Kraemer, M., Williams, J.C., Engel, M.S., Sahni, A. & Grimaldi, D. 2010. Biogeographic and evolutionary implications of a diverse paleobiota in amber from the early Eocene of India. PNAS, 107: 18360–18365.

Sánchez, M.V., Genise, J.F., Bellosi, E.S., Román-Carrión, J.L. & Cantil, L.F. 2013. Dung beetle brood balls from Pleistocene highland palaeosols of Andean Ecuador: A reassessment of Sauer's Coprinisphaera and their palaeoenvironments. Palaeogeography, Palaeoclimatology, Palaeoecology, 386: 257–274.

Saneyoshi, M., Watabe, M., Suzuki, S. & Tsogtbaatar, K. 2011. Trace fossils on dinosaur bones from Upper Cretaceous eolian deposits in Mongolia: Taphonomic interpretation of paleoecosystems in ancient desert environments. Palaeogeography, Palaeoclimatology, Palaeoecology, 311: 38–47.

Sarzetti, L.C., Dinghi, P.A., Genise, J.F., Bedatou, E. & Verde, M. 2014. Curved fossil bee cells as tools for reconstructing the evolutionary history and palaeogeographical distribution of Diphaglossinae (Apoidea: Colletidae). Palaeontology, 57: 447–455.

Schlüter, T. 1981. Fossile Insekten aus dem Jura/Kreide-Grenzbereich Südwest-Ägyptens (Beiträge zur Paläontologie Ägyptens, Nr. 2). Berliner geowissenschaftliche Abhandlungen, A32: 33–61.

Schlüter, T. 2003. Fossil insects in Gondwana—localities and diversity trends. Acta Zoological Cracoviensia, 46(suppl.–Fossil Insects): 345–371.

Schlüter, T., Kohring, R. & Gregor, H.-J. 2003. Dragonflies preserved in transparent gypsum crystals from the Messinian (Upper Miocene) of Alba, northern Italy. Acta Zoological Cracoviensia, 46(suppl.–Fossil Insects): 373–379.

Schmidt, A.R., Perrichot, V., Svojtka, M., Anderson, K.B., Belete, K.H., Bussert, R., Dörfelt, H., Jancke, S., Mohr, B., Mohrmann, E., Nascimbene, P.C., Nel, A., Nel, E.P., Ragazzi, E., Roghi, G., Saupe, E.E., Schmidt, K., Schneider, H., Selden, P.A. & Vávra, N. 2010. Cretaceous African life captured in amber. PNAS early ed. www.pnas.org/cgi/doi/10.1073/pnas.1000948107.

Schmidt, A.R., Jancke, S., Lindquist, E.E., Ragazzi, E., Roghi, G., Nascimbene, P.C., Schmidt, K., Wappler, T. & Grimaldi, D.A. 2012. Arthropods in amber from the Triassic Period. PNAS, early ed. www.pnas.org/cgi/doi/10.1073/pnas.1208464109.

Schmidt, H. 1967. Die Bockkäfer (Cerambycidae) von Willershausen. Berichte Naturhistorischen Gesellschaft zu Hannover, 111: 113–120.

Schmied, H., Schwermann, A.H., van de Kamp, T., dos Santos Rolo, T. & Baumbach, T. 2013. Inside the clown. Synchrotron X-ray microtomography reveals extraordinary details of internal and genital structures of 30 million [year] old beetles. P. 145 in: Reitner et al. (Eds.) Palaeobiology and geobiology of fossil Lagerstätten through Earth history. (talk abstract)

Schoville, S.D. 2014. Current status of the systematics and evolutionary biology of Grylloblattidae (Grylloblattodea). Systematic Entomology, 39: 197–204.

Scott, A.C. & Taylor, T.N. 1983. Interactions of plants and animals during the Carboniferous. Bioscience, 33: 488–493.

Scudder, S.H. 1890. The Tertiary insects of North America. Government Printing Office, Washington.

Seilacher, A. 1953. Studien zur paläontologie: 1. Über die methoden der palichnologie. Neues Jahrbuch für Geologie und Paläontologie, Abhandlungen, 96: 421–452.

Selden, P.A. 2003. A new tool for fossil preparation. Geological Curator, 7: 337–339.

Selden, P.A. 2010. A theridiosomatid spider from the Early Cretaceous of Russia. Bulletin of the British Arachnological Society, 15: 61–69.

Selden, P.A. & Beattie, R.G. 2013. A spider fossil from the Jurassic Talbragar Fossil Fish Bed of New South Wales. Alcheringa, 37: 203–208.

Selden, P.A. & Edwards, D. 1989. Colonisation of the land. Pp. 122–152 in: Allen, K.C. & Briggs D.E.G. (Eds.) Evolution and the Fossil Record. Belahven Press, London.

Shabica, C.W. & Hay, A.A. (Eds.) 1997. Richardson's guide to the fossil fauna of Mazon Creek. Northeastern Illinois University Press, Chicago.

Sharov, A.G. 1973. Morphological features and habit of palaeodictyopterans. Pp. 49–63 in: Narchuk, E.P. (Ed.) Problems of insect palaeontology. Lectures on the XXIV annual readings in memory of N.A. Kholodkovsky (1–2 April, 1971). Nauka, Leningrad.

Sharpton, V.L. & Ward, P.D. (Eds.) 1990. Global catastrophes in Earth history; an interdisciplinary conference on impacts, volcanism, and mass mortality. Geological Society of America, Colorado.

Shcherbakov, D.E. 2007. Mesozoic spider mimics - Cretaceous Mimarachnidae fam.n. (Homoptera: Fulgoroidea). Russian Entomological Journal, 16: 259–264.

Shcherbakov, D.E. 2013. Permian ancestors of Hymenoptera and Raphidioptera. ZooKeys, 358: 45–67.

Shelford, R. 1911. The British Museum collection of Blattidae enclosed in amber. Journal of the Linnean Society, Zoology, 32: 59–69.

Shi, G., Grimaldi, D.A., Harlow, G.E., Wang, Jing, Wang, Jun, Yang, M., Lei, W., Li, Q. & Li, X. 2012. Age constraint on Burmese amber based on U–Pb dating of zircons. Cretaceous Research, 37: 155–163.

Sidorchuk, E.A. 2013. A new technique for the preparation of small-sized amber samples with application to mites. Pp. 189–201 in: Azar, D. et al. (Eds.) Insect evolution in an amberiferous and stone alphabet: Proceedings of the 6th International Congress on Fossil Insects, Arthropods and Amber. Brill, Leiden.

Sinitshenkova, N.D. 2002. Superorder Dictyoneuridea Handlirsch, 1906 (=Palaeodictyopteroidea). Pp. 115–124 in: Rasnitsyn, A.P. & Quicke, D.L.J. (Eds.) History of insects. Kluwer Academic Publishers, Dordrecht.

Slipinski, S.A., Leschen, R.A.B. & Lawrence, J.F. 2011. Order Coleoptera Linnaeus, 1758. In: Zhang, Z.-Q. (Ed.) Animal biodiversity: An outline of higher-level classification and survey of taxonomic richness. Zootaxa, 3148: 203–208.

Smith, D.M. 2000. Beetle taphonomy in a recent ephemeral lake, southeastern Arizona. Palaios, 15: 152–160.

Smith, D.M. & Moe-Hoffman, A.P. 2007. Taphonomy of Diptera in lacustrine environments: A case study from Florissant Fossil Beds, Colorado. Palaios, 22: 623–629.

Sohn, J.-C., Labandeira, C., Davis D. & Mitter, C. 2012. An annotated catalog of fossil and subfossil Lepidoptera (Insecta: Holometabola) of the world. Zootaxa, 3286: 1–132.

Solórzano Kraemer, M.M. 2007. Systematic, palaeoecology, and palaeobiogeography of the insect fauna from the Mexican amber. Palaeontographica Abteilung A, 282: 1–133.

Solórzano Kraemer, M. 2010. Mexican amber. Pp. 42–56 in: Penney, D. (Ed.) Biodiversity of fossils in amber from the major world deposits. Siri Scientific Press, Manchester.

Soriano, C. & Delclòs, X. 2006. New cupedid beetles from the Lower Cretaceous of Spain and the palaeogeography of the family. Acta Palaeontologica Polonica, 51: 185–200.

Soriano, C., Archer, M., Azar, D., Creaser, Ph., Delclòs, X., Godthelp, H., Hand, S., Jones, A., Nel, A., Néraudeau, D., Ortega-Blanco, J., Pérez de la Fuente, R., Perrichot, V., Saupe, E., Solórzano-Kraemer, M. & Tafforeau, P. 2010. Synchrotron X-ray imaging of inclusions in amber. Comptes Rendus Palevol, 9: 361–368.

Srivastava, A.K. & Agnihotri, D. 2011. Insect traces on Early Permian plants of India. Paleontological Journal, 45: 200–206.

Staniczek, A.H., Bechly, G. & Godunko, R.J. 2011. Coxoplectoptera, a new fossil order of Palaeoptera (Arthropoda: Insecta), with comments on the phylogeny of the stem group of mayflies (Ephemeroptera). Insect Systematics & Evolution, 42: 101–138.

Staniczek, A.H., Sroka, P. & Bechly, G. 2014. Neither silverfish nor fowl: the enigmatic Carboniferous *Carbotriplura kukalovae* Kluge, 1996 (Insecta: Carbotriplurida) is the putative fossil sister group of winged insects (Insecta: Pterygota). Systematc Entomology (earlyview), DOI: 10.1111/syen.12076.

Steinbach, G. & Schmidt, H. 1967. Zur Hymenopteren-Fauna des Pliozäns von Willershausen/Westharz. Berichte Naturhistorischen Gesellschaft zu Hannover, 111: 95–102.

Stockey, R.A. 1978. Reproduction biology of Cerro Cuadrado fossil conifers: Ontogeny and reproductive strategies in *Araucaria mirabilis* (Spegazzini) Windhausen. Palaeontographica B, 166: 1–15.

Stroiński, A. & Szwedo, J. 2011. *Yuripopoverus africanus* gen. et sp. n. from East African copal (Hemiptera: Fulgoromorpha: Ricaniidae). Polskie Pismo Entomologiczne, 80: 679–688.

Stull, G.W., Labandeira, C.C., Dimichele, W.A. & Chaney, D.S. 2013. The "seeds" on *Padgettia readi* are insect galls: Reassignment of the plant to *Odontopteris*, the gall to *Ovofoligallites* n. gen., and the evolutionary implications thereof. Journal of Paleontology, 87: 217–231.

Sukatsheva, I.D. 1982. Historical development of the Trichoptera. Transactions of the Paleontological Institute, USSR Academy of Sciences, 197: 1–111.

Sukatsheva, I.D. 1985. Jurassic cadisflies of South Siberia. In: Rasnitsyn, A.P. (Ed.) Jurassic insects of Siberia and Mongolia. Trudy Paleontologicheskogo Instituta Akademii Nauk SSSR, Moscow, 211: 115–119.

Sukatsheva, I.D. 1989. Cainozoic caddisflies from the Primor'ye Province. Pp. 151–160 in: Krassilov, V.A. & Klimova, R.S. (Eds.) The Cainozoic of the Far East. Biologo–Pochvenny Inst. Dal'nevostochnogo Otdeleniya Akademii Nauk SSSR, Vladivostok.

Sukatsheva, I.D. 1990. Caddisflies. Phryganeina. In: Rasnitsyn, A.P. (Ed.). Late Mesozoic insects of eastern Transbaikalia. Trudy Paleontologicheskogo Instituta Akademii Nauk SSSR, Moscow, 239: 94–122.

Sukatsheva, I.D. 1991. Cases of the Early Jurassic caddisflies (Insecta: Trichoptera) from Mongolia. Paleontological Journal, 28: 99–113.

Sukatsheva, I.D. 1994. Cases of Jurassic caddisflies (Insecta: Trichoptera) of Mongolia. Paleontological Journal, 28: 74–85.

Sukatsheva, I.D. 1999. The Lower Cretaceous caddisfly (Trichoptera) case assemblages. Proceedings of the First Palaeoentomological Conference, Moscow, 1998. Bratislava: Amba Projects, 163–165.

Sukatsheva, I.D. & Jarzembowski, E.A. 2001. Fossil caddisflies (Insecta: Trichoptera) from the Early Cretaceous of southern England II. Cretaceous Research, 22: 685–694.

Sutton, M., Rahman, I. & Garwood, R. 2014. Techniques for virtual paleontology (analytical methods in Earth and environmental science). Wiley-Blackwell/John Wiley & Sons.

Svenson, G.J. & Whiting, M.F. 2009. Reconstructing the origins of praying mantises (Dictyoptera: Mantodea): The roles of Gondwanan vicariance and morphological convergence. Cladistics, 25: 468–514.

Szwedo, J. & Ansorge, J. 2014. The first Mimarachnidae (Hemiptera: Fulgoromorpha) from Lower Cretaceous lithographic limestones of the Sierra del Montsec in Spain. Cretaceous Researc, http://dx.doi.org/10.1016/j.cretres.2014.03.001.

Szwedo, J. & Sontag, E. 2013. The flies (Diptera) say that amber from the Gulf of Gdańsk, Bitterfeld and Rovno is the same Baltic amber. Polskie Pismo Entomologiczne, 82: 379–388.

Szwedo, J., Bourgoin, T. & Lefebvre, F. 2004. Fossil planthoppers (Hemiptera: Fulgoromorpha) of the world. An annotated catalogue with notes on Hemiptera classification. Studio 1, Warsaw.

Tapanila, L. & Roberts, E.M. 2012. The earliest evidence of holometabolan insect pupation in conifer wood. PLoS ONE, 7(2): e31668.

Thackray, G.D. 1994. Fossil nest of sweat bees (Halictinae) from a Miocene paleosol, Rusinga Island, western Kenya. Journal of Paleontology, 68: 795–800.

Théobald, N. 1937. Les insectes fossiles des terrains Oligocènes de France. Mémoires de la Société Sciences, Nancy, N.S., 1: 1–437.

Theone Henning, J., Smith, D.M., Nufio, C.R. & Meyer, H.W. 2012. Depositional setting and fossil insect preservation: A study of the Late Eocene Florissant Formation, Colorado. Palaios, 27: 481–488.

Thienemann, A. 1933. Mückenlarven bilder Gestein. Natur und Museum, 63: 370–378.

Tilgner, E. 2000. The fossil record of Phasmida (Insecta: Neoptera). Insect Systematics & Evolution, 31: 473–480.

Tilley, D.B., Barrows, T.T. & Zimmerman, E.C. 1997. Bauxitic insect pupal cases of northern Australia. Alcheringa, 21: 157–160.

Tillyard, R.J. 1918. A fossil insect-wing from the roof of the coal-seam in the Sydney Harbour Colliery. Proceedings of the Linnean Society of New South Wales, 43: 260–264.

Tillyard, R.J. 1928. Some remarks on the Devonian fossil insects from the Rhynie Chert Beds Old Red Sandstone. Transactions of the Royal Entomological Society of London, 76: 65–71.

Tillyard, R.J. 1935. Upper Permian insects of New South Wales, Part 4. The order Odonata. Proceedings of the Linnean Society of New South Wales, 60: 374–384.

Tillyard, R.J. 1937. The ancestors of the Diptera. Nature, 139: 66–67.

Tindale, N.B. 1946. Triassic insects of Queensland, I. *Eoses*, a probable lepidopterous insect from the Triassic beds of Mt. Crosby, Queensland. Proceedings of the Royal Society of Queensland, 56: 37–46.

Toms, R.B. 2007. Rooting the phylogenetic tree for winged insects: Independent adaptations to terrestrial life. African Invertebrates, 48: 203–211.

Trautwein, M.D., Wiegmann, B.M., Beutel, R., Kjer, K.M. & Yeates, D.K. 2012. Advances in insect phylogeny at the dawn of the postgenomic era. Annual Review of Entomology, 57: 449–468.

Tripp, J.A., Higham, T.F.G. & Hedges, R.E.M. 2004. A pretreatment procedure for the AMS radiocarbon dating of sub-fossil insect remains. Radiocarbon, 46: 147–154.

Tshernova, O.A. 1977. Distinctive new mayfly nymphs (Ephemeroptera: Palingeniidae, Behingiidae) from the Jurassic of Transbaikalia. Paleontological Journal, 11: 221–226.

Upchurch, P., McGowan, A.J. & Slater, C.S.C. (Eds.) 2011. Palaeogeography and palaeobiogeography: Biodiversity in space and time. Systematics Association Special Volumes, CRC Press.

Van Dijk D.E. 1997. Insect faunas of South Africa from the Upper Permian and the Permian/Triassic Boundary. Palaeontologia Africana, 34: 43–48.

Van Dijk, D.E. & Geertsema, H. 1999. Permian insects from the Beaufort Group of Natal, South Africa. Annals of the Natal Museum, 40: 137–171.

Vasilenko, D.V. & Rasnitsyn, A.P. 2007. Fossil ovipositions of dragonflies: Review and interpretation. Paleontological Journal, 41: 1–4.

Vavra, N. 2009. Amber, fossil resins, and copal – Contributions to the terminology of fossil plant resins. Denisia, 26: 213–222.

Vialov, O.S. 1966. The traces of the vital activity of organisms and their paleontological significance. Naukova Dumka.

Vialov, O.S. 1968. Materials to classification of trace fossils and traces of activity of organisms. Paleontologichesky Sbornik, 5: 125–129.

Vialov, O.S. 1975. The fossil traces of insect feeding. Paleontologichesky Sbornik, 12: 147–155.

Vickery, V.R. & Poinar, G.O. Jr. 1994. Crickets (Grylloptera: Grylloidea) in Dominican amber. The Canadian Entomologist, 126: 13–22.

Vršanský, P., Ren, D. & Shih, C. 2010. Nakridletia ord. n. – Enigmatic insect parasites support sociality and endothermy of pterosaurs. Amba Projekty, 8: 1–16.

Vršanský, P., van de Kamp, T., Azar, D., Prokin, A., Vidlička, L. & Vagovič, P. 2013. Cockroaches probably cleaned up after dinosaurs. PLoS ONE, 8(12): e80560.

Wahlberg, N., Wheat, C.W. & Peña, C. 2013. Timing and patterns in the taxonomic diversification of Lepidoptera (butterflies and moths). PLoS ONE, 8(11): e80875.

Walter, H. 1983. Zur Taxonomie, Ökologie und Biostratigraphie der Ichnia Limnischer–terrestrischer Arthropoden des mitteleuropaischen Jungpaläozoikums. Freiberger Forschungsheft, 382: 146–193.

Wang, B., Zhang, H., Jarzembowski, E.A., Fang, Y. & Zheng, D. 2013. Taphonomic variability of fossil insects: A biostratinomic study of Paleontinidae and Tettigarctidae (Insecta: Hemiptera) from the Jurassic Daohugou Lagerstätte. Palaios, 28: 233–242.

Wang, M., Béthoux, O., Bradler, S., Jacques, F.M.B., Cui, Y. & Ren, D. 2014. Under cover at pre-angiosperm times: A cloaked phasmatodean insect from the Early Cretaceous Jehol Biota. PLoS ONE, 9(3): e91290.

Wang, Y., Liu, Z., Wang, X., Shih, C., Xhao, Y., Engel, M.S., Ren, D. 2010. Ancient pinnate leaf mimesis among lacewings. PNAS, 107: 16212–16215.

Wang, Y., Labandeira, C.C., Shih, C., Ding, Q., Wang, C., Zhao, Y. & Ren, D. 2012. Jurassic mimicry between a hangingfly and a ginkgo from China. PNAS, 109: 205147–20519.

Wappler, T. 2003. Die Insekten aus dem Mittel-Eozän des Eckfelder Maares, Vulkaneifel. Mainzer Naturwissenschaftliches Archiv, 27: 1–234, 18 pls.

Wappler, T., Smith, V.S. & Dalgleish, R.C. 2004. Scratching an ancient itch: An Eocene bird louse fossil. Proceedings of the Royal Society of London B (Supplement 5: Biology Letters), 271: 5255–5258.

Wappler, T., Hinsken, S., Brocks, J.J., Wetzel, A. & Meyer, C.A. 2005. A fossil sawfly of the genus *Athalia* (Hymenoptera: Tenthredinidae) from the Eocene–Oligocene boundary of Altkirch, France. Comptes Rendus Palevol, 4: 7–16.

Wappler, T., Garrouste, R., Engel, M.S. & Nel, A. 2013. Wasp mimicry among Palaeocene reduviid bugs from Svalbard. Acta Palaeontologica Polonica, 58: 883–887.

Wappler, T., Grímsson, F., Wang, B., Nel, A., Ólafsson, E., Kotov, A.A., Davis, S.R. & Engel, M.S. 2014. Before the 'Big Chill': A preliminary overview of arthropods from the middle Miocene of Iceland (Insecta, Crustacea). Palaeogeography, Palaeoclimatology, Palaeoecology (available online March 2014).

Wedmann, S. 2000. Die Insekten der oberoligozänen Fossillagerstätte Enspel (Westerwald, Deutschland): Systematik, Biostratinomie und Paläoökologie. Mainzer Naturwissenschaftliches Archiv, Beiheft, 23: 1–153.

Wedmann, S. 2010. A brief review of the fossil history of plant masquerade by insects. Palaeontographica Abteilung B-Palaophytologie, 283 (special issue): 175–182.

Wedmann, S., Bradler, S. & Rust, J. 2007. The first fossil leaf insect: 47 million years of specialized cryptic morphology and behavior. PNAS, 104: 565–569.

Wedmann, S., Poschmann, M. & Hörnschemeyer, T. 2010. Fossil insects from the Late Oligocene Enspel Lagerstätte and their palaeobiogeographic and palaeoclimatic significance. Palaeobiodiversity and Palaeoenvironments, 90: 49–58.

Weitschat, W. 2009. Jäger, Gejate, Parasiten und Blinde Passagiere – Momentaufnahmen aus dem Bernsteinwald. Denisia, 26: 243–256.

Weitschat, W. & Wichard, W. 2002. Atlas of plants and animals in Baltic amber. Verlag Dr Friedrich Pfiel, Munich.

Weitschat, W. & Wichard, W. 2010. Baltic amber. Pp. 80–115 in: Penney, D. (Ed.) Biodiversity of fossils in amber from the major world deposits. Siri Scientific Press, Manchester.

Wenzel, J.W. 1990. A social wasp's nest from the Cretaceous period, Utah, USA, and its biogeographical significance. Psyche, 97: 21–29.

Whalley, P.E.S. 1985. The systematics and palaeogeography of the Lower Jurassic insects of Dorset, England. Bulletin of the British Museum of Natural History (Geology), 39: 107–189.

Whalley, P. & Jarzembowski, E.A. 1981. A new assessment of *Rhyniella*, the earliest known insect, from the Devonian of Rhynie, Scotland. Nature, 291: 317.

Whiting, M.F. 2002. Mecoptera is paraphyletic: Multiple genes and phylogeny of Mecoptera and Siphonaptera. Zoologica Scripta, 31: 93–104.

Whiting, M.F., Whiting, A.S., Hastriter, M.W. & Dittmar, K. 2008. A molecular phylogeny of fleas (Insecta: Siphonaptera): Origins and host associations. Cladistics, 24: 677–707.

Wichard, W. 2007. Overview and descriptions of caddisflies (Insecta: Trichoptera) in Dominican amber (Miocene). Stuttgarter Beiträge fur Naturkunde (B), 366: 1–51.

Wichard, W. 2013. Overview and descriptions of Trichoptera in Baltic amber. Verlag Kessel, Remagen-Oberwinter.

Wichard, W., Gras, A., Gras, H. & Dreesmann, D. 2005. Antireflexbelag und Schillerfarben auf den Augen von Kocherfliegen im Bernstein (Trichoptera). Entomologia Generalis, 27: 223–238.

Wichard, W., Gröhn, C. & Seredszus, F. 2009. Aquatic insects in Baltic amber. Verlag Kessel, Remagen-Oberwinter.

Wiegmann, B.M., Kim, J. & Trautwein, M.D. 2009. Holometabolous insects (Holometabola). Pp. 260–263 in: Hedges, S.B. & Kumar, S. (Eds.) The timetree of life. Oxford University Press, Oxford.

Wilf, P. & Labandeira, C.C. 1999. Response of plant–insect associations to Paleocene–Eocene warming. Science, 284: 2153–2156.

Willmann, R. 1989. Rediscovered: *Permotipula patricia*, the oldest known fly. Naturwissenschaften, 76: 375–377.

Wilson, E.O. 1985. Invasion and extinction in the West Indian ant fauna, evidence from Dominican amber. Science, 229: 265–267.

Wilson, E.O. & Taylor, R.W. 1964. A fossil ant colony: New evidence of social antiquity. Psyche, 71: 93–103.

Wilson, H.M. & Martill, D.M. 2001. A new japygid dipluran from the Lower Cretaceous of Brazil. Palaeontology, 44: 1025–1031.

Winkler, I.S., Labandeira, C.C., Wappler, T. & Wilf, P. 2010. Distinguishing Agromyzidae (Diptera) leaf mines in the fossil record: New taxa from the Paleogene of North America and Germany and their evolutionary implications. Journal of Paleontology, 84: 935–954.

Wipfler, B., Pohl, H. & Predel, R. 2012. Two new genera and two new species of Mantophasmatodea (Insecta: Polyneoptera) from Namibia. ZooKeys, 166: 75–98.

Wipfler, B., Klug, R., Ge, S.-Q., Bai, M., Göbbels, J., Yang, X.-K. & Hörnschemeyer, T. 2014. The thorax of Mantophasmatodea, the morphology of flightlessness, and the evolution of the neopteran insects. Cladistics. doi: 10.1111/cla.12068.

Wittry, J. 2012. The Mazon Creek fossil fauna. Earth Science Club of Northern Illinois.

Wood, H.M., Matzke, N.J., Gillespie, R.G. & Griswold, C.E. 2012. Treating fossils as terminal taxa in divergence time estimation reveals ancient vicariance patterns in the palpimanoid spiders. Systematic Biology, 62: 264–284.

Wunderlich, J. 1986. Spinnenfauna Gestern und Heute. Fossil spinnen in Bernstein und ihre lebenden Verwandten. Erich Bauer Verlag, Wiesbaden.

Wunderlich, J. 2012. "Frozen behaviour" in "vampires" of spiders – fossil insect larvae of the family Mantispidae (Neuroptera) as parasites of sac spiders (Araneae: Clubionidae) in Eocene Baltic amber. Beiträge zur Araneologie, 7: 150–156.

Xing, L., Roberts, E.M., Harris, J.D., Gingras, M.K., Ran, H., Zhang, J., Xu, X., Burns, M.E. & Dong, Z. 2013. Novel insect traces on a dinosaur skeleton from the Lower Jurassic Lufeng Formation of China. Palaeogeography, Palaeoclimatology, Palaeoecology, 388: 58–68.

Yang, Q., Makarkin, V.N., Winterton, S.L., Khramov, A.V. & Ren, D. 2012. A remarkable new family of Jurassic insects (Neuroptera) with primitive wing venation and its phylogenetic position in Neuropterida. PLoS ONE, 7(9): e44762.

Yeates, D.K., Cameron, S.L. & Trautwein, M. 2012. A view from the edge of the forest: recent progress in understanding the relationships of the insect orders. Australian Journal of Entomology, 51: 79–87.

Zablocki, J. 1960. Pinus króli, nowy gatunek sosny trzeciorzędowej z pokładów soli kamiennej w Wieliczce. Studia Societatis Scientiarum Torunensis. Sectio D. Botanica, 4: 43–48.

Zakharov, P.B. 2013. Nomosystematics: A closer look at the theoretical foundation of biological classification. Siri Scientific Press, Manchester.

Žalohar, J. & Hitij, T. 2014. Fossil seahorses and other biota from the Tunjice Hills Konservat-Lagerstätte, slovenia. Monograph Series, Volume 6, Siri Scientific Press, Manchester.

Zhang, H.C., Zheng, D.R., Wang, B., Fang, Y. & Jarzembowski, E.A. 2013. The largest known odonate in China: *Hsiufua chaoi* Zhang et Wang, gen. et sp. nov. from the Middle Jurassic of Inner Mongolia. Chinese Science Bulletin, 58: 1579–1584.

Zhang, J. 1989. Fossil insects from Shanwang, Shandong, China. Shandong Science and Technology Publishing House.

Zhang, J., Sun, B. & Zhang, X. 1994. Miocene insects and spiders from Shangwang, Shandong. Huayu Nature Book Trade Co. Ltd.

Zhang, W., Shih, C., Labandeira, C.C., Sohn, J.-C., Davis, D.R., Santiago-Blay, J.A., Flint, O. & Ren, D. 2013. New fossil Lepidoptera (Insecta: Amphiesmenoptera) from the Middle Jurassic Jiulongshan Formation of northeastern China. PLoS ONE, 8(11): e79500.

Zhang, X.W., Ren, D., Pang, H. & Shih, C.K. 2009. Late Mesozoic chresmodids with forewing from Inner Mongolia, China (Polyneoptera: Archaeorthoptera). Acta Geologica Sinica, 84: 38–46.

Zhang, Z., Schneider, J.W. & Hong, Y. 2013. The most ancient roach (Blattodea): A new genus and species from the earliest Late Carboniferous (Namurian) of China, with a discussion of the phylomorphogeny of early blattids, Journal of Systematic Palaeontology, 11: 27–40.

Zhang, Z.-Q. 2011. Phylum Arthropoda von Siebold, 1848 In: Zhang, Z.-Q. (Ed.) Animal biodiversity: An outline of higher-level classification and survey of taxonomic richness. Zootaxa, 3148: 99–103.

Zhao, J., Zhao, Y., Shih, C., Ren, D. & Wang, Y. 2010. Transitional fossil earwigs – A missing link in Dermaptera evolution. BMC Evolutionary Biology, 10: 344.

Zherikhin, V.V. 2002a. Pattern of insect burial and conservation. Pp. 17–63 in: Rasnitsyn, A.P. & Quicke, D.L.J. (Eds.) History of insects, Kluwer Academic Publishers, Dordrecht.

Zherikhin, V.V. 2002b. Insect trace fossils. Pp. 303–324 in: Rasnitsyn, A.P. & Quicke, D.L.J. (Eds.) History of insects, Kluwer Academic Publishers, Dordrecht.

Zherikhin, V.V. 2003. Insect trace fossils, their diversity, classification and scientific importance. Acta Zoological Cracoviensia, 46(suppl.–Fossil Insects): 59–66.

Zherikhin, V.V. & Eskov, K.Yu. 1999. Mesozoic and Lower Tertiary resins in former USSR. Estudios Museo Ciencias Naturales de Alava, 14(Num. Espec. 2): 119–131.

Zherikhin, V.V., Mostovski, M.B., Vrsansky, P., Blagoderov, V.A. & Lukashevich, E.D. 1999. The unique Lower Cretaceous locality of Baissa and other contemporaneous insect-bearing sites in North and West Transbaikalia. Proceedings of the First Palaeoentomological Conference, Moscow, 1998. Bratislava: Amba Projects, 185–192.

Zhou, Z. & Zhang, B. 1989. A sideritic *Protocupressinoxylon* with insect borings and frass from the Middle Jurassic, Henan, China. Review of Paleobotany and Palynology, 59: 133–143.

Żyła, D., Wegierek, P., Owocki, K. & Niedźwiedzki, G. 2013. Insects and crustaceans from the latest Early–early Middle Triassic of Poland. Palaeogeography, Palaeoclimatology, Palaeoecology, 371: 136–144.

Internet resources

http://fossilinsects.net
Home page of the International Palaeoentomological Society.
http://fossilinsects.colorado.edu/
This Fossil Insect Collaborative will make available all the major collections of fossil insect specimens in the United States by creating electronic specimen records consisting of digital images and associated collection data.
http://edna.palass-hosting.org/
EDNA, the fossil insect database, is designed to hold details of the holotypes of all the fossil insects in the world. The data come from an exhaustive literature search and the 2013 edition contains 26,200 species names [including synonyms] extracted from 5018 references. The data are held in 38 fields, all of which are searchable, independently or in combination, and the output can contain any one or more as required.
http://fossilworks.org/?page=paleodb
The gateway to the Paleobiology Database

Index to genera cited in the text

Some related titles from *Siri Scientific Press*

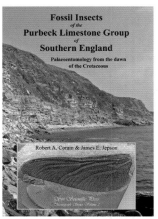

Coram, R.A. & Jepson, J.E. 2012. *Fossil Insects of the Purbeck Limestone Group of Southern England: Palaeoentomology from the Dawn of the Cretaceous*. Hard cover, 144 pages, 230 illustrations. ISBN 978-0-9567795-3-3.

REVIEWS: *PalAss Newsl.* (2012: 81): "Drs Rob Coram and James Jepson provide a unique perspective, as viewed through compound eyes, based on two decades of study and revealing an inordinate fondness for insects. This easy to read and well illustrated mini-monograph is an essential palaeontological guide to the semi-arid Jurassic-Cretaceous transition and its immediate aftermath on a basinal and regional scale."

Antenna – Bulletin of the Royal Entomological Society (2012): "Drs Rob Coram and James Jepson bring us right up to date with the entomology and ecology of a lost world examined in the light of modern knowledge and new techniques."

Dunlop, J.A. & Penney, D. 2012. *Fossil Arachnids*. Hard cover, 192 pages, 144 illustrations/photographs. ISBN 978-0-9567795-4-0.

REVIEWS: *ZooKeys* (2012): "... absolutely unique within the arachnological literature to date. There is barely any overlap with previously published books, which usually only briefly touch on the fossil record. It will fill a long-standing void on the shelves of arachnological libraries, and will be of interest to palaeontologists and neontologists alike, both as a source of reference or merely to browse through the stunning images it contains."

PalAss Newsl. (2013: 89–90): "This book, written by two of the world's foremost experts on fossil arachnids, is a comprehensive yet accessible account of a diverse group of arthropods, and represents the first thorough overview since Petrunkevitch's 1955 *Treatise*. The book is very well written and is a very thorough and up-to-date treatment of this subject area. It would be a worthwhile addition to any palaeontologist's library. It would also be useful to arachnologists who want an overview of the fossil record."

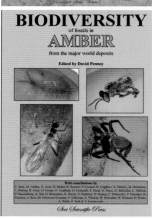

Penney, D. (editor) 2010. *Biodiversity of Fossils in Amber from the Major World Deposits*. Hard cover, 304 pages, full colour throughout. ISBN 978-0-9558636-4-6.

REVIEWS: *Antenna – Bulletin of the Royal Entomological Society* (2011): "This impressive book constitutes a reliable source of information on the palaeodiversity of amber arthropods, it will beyond doubt become a reference handbook for all amber students and general entomologists. It is a must have for all entomological libraries, recommended to both amateur and professional entomologists alike. The audience of this book is potentially very broad and will include not only palaeontologists and entomologists, but also students and all amber enthusiasts."

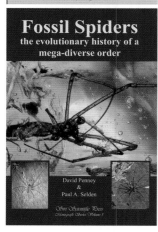

Penney, D. & Selden, P.A. 2011. *Fossil Spiders: The evolutionary history of a mega-diverse order*. Hard cover, 128 pages, 87 photos. ISBN 978-0-9558636-5-3.

REVIEWS: *ZooKeys* (2011): "...an absolutely unique book in the spider literature to date. It is authoritatively written by two of the leading researchers in this field and provides broad coverage of their combined 50 years experience and expert knowledge. The book is hard back and presented on high quality glossy paper. It is richly illustrated thoughout by numerous high quality photographs of fossil spiders. In conclusion, this book deserves a place on the shelves of the libraries of all professional and amateur arachnologists alike, in addition to those of invertebrate palaeontologists."

TO ORDER THESE BOOKS & SIMILAR TITLES
visit our online shop at http://www.siriscientificpress.co.uk
email: books@siriscientificpress.co.uk

We are always happy to hear from new potential authors